STUDENT'S SOLUTION MANUAL

Gary P. Egan

Monroe Community College

Aimee L. Calhoun

Monroe Community College

to accompany

A Survey of Mathematics with Applications

Sixth Edition and Expanded Sixth Edition

Allen R. Angel

Stuart R. Porter

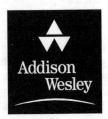

Addison Wesley

Boston San Francisco New York
London Toronto Sydney Tokyo Singapore Madrid
Mexico City Munich Paris Cape Town Hong Kong Montreal

ACKNOWLEDGMENTS

We would like to thank Allen Angel, Christine Dunn, and Dennis Runde, the authors of *A Survey of Mathematics with Applications*, for their support and encouragement; Julie Vincelli from Julmar Secretarial Service for her assistance; and Rachel Reeve from Addison Wesley Longman.

Gary Egan
Aimee Calhoun

I would like to thank my loving wife Claudia and my daughters Kelsey and Emily for their incredible patience during the preparation of this manual.

Gary Egan

Special thanks to my husband, Justin, for his help and believing in me. The sacrifices he made mean so much.

Aimee Calhoun

Reproduced by Addison Wesley Longman Publishing Company Inc. from camera-ready copy supplied by the authors.

Copyright © 2001 Addison Wesley Longman.

ISBN   0-201-61323-9

2 3 4 5 6 7 8 9 10 VG 03 02 01

Table of Contents

CHAPTER ONE

CRITICAL THINKING SKILLS

<u>**Exercise Set 1.1**</u>

1. a) 1, 2, 3, 4, 5, ...
    b) counting numbers

3. When a scientist or mathematician makes a prediction based on specific observations it is called a conjecture.
5. Deductive reasoning is the process of reasoning to a specific conclusion from a general statement.
7. Inductive reasoning: a general conclusion from observation of specific cases.

9. 1 5(1+ 4) 10(4+6) 10(6+4) 5(4+1) 1

11. 1 + 2 + 3 + 4 + 5 + 6 = 21

13. $\triangle$

15.

17. 13, 15, 17 (Add 2 to previous number)

19. -1, 1, -1 (Alternate -1 and 1)

21. $\frac{1}{16}$, $\frac{1}{32}$, $\frac{1}{64}$ (Multiply previous number by $\frac{1}{2}$)

23. 36, 49, 64 (The numbers in the sequence are the squares of the counting numbers.)

25. 34, 55, 89 (Each number in the sequence is the sum of the previous two numbers.)

27. a) Answers will vary.
    b) The sum of the digits is 9.
    c) The sum of the digits in the product when a one or two digit number is multiplied by 9 is 9.

29. a) 36, 49, 64
    b) Square the numbers 6, 7, 8, 9 and 10
    c) 8 x 8 = 64   9 x 9 = 81
    72 is not a square number since it falls between the two square numbers 64 and 81.

31. blue: 1, 5, 7, 10, 12   purple: 2, 4, 6, 9, 11   yellow: 3, 8

33. a) 8% because 6.5% + 1.5% = 8%
    b) A general conclusion was made based on observations of specific cases. (1.5% was gained in each of the two previous years.)

35.

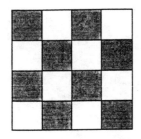

37. a) You should obtain the original number.
   b) You should obtain the original number.
   c) Conjecture: The result is always the original number.
   d) n, $3n$, $3n+6$, $\dfrac{3n+6}{3} = \dfrac{3n}{3} + \dfrac{6}{3} = n+2$, $n+2-2 = n$

39. a) You should obtain the number 5.
   b) You should obtain the number 5.
   c) Conjecture: No matter what number is chosen, the result is always the number 5.
   d) n, $n+1$, $n+n+1 = 2n+1$, $2n+1+9 = 2n+10$, $\dfrac{2n+10}{2} = \dfrac{2n}{2} + \dfrac{10}{2} = n+5$, $n+5-n = 5$

41. 50 x 50 = 2500 is one example.

43. 7 is a counting number. The sum of 7 and 3 is 10. 10 divided by 2 is 5, which is not even.

45. The product of 5 multiplied by itself is 25, which is not even.

47 a) The sum of the measures of the angles should be $180°$.
   b) Yes, the sum of the measures of the angles should be $180°$.
   c) The sum of the measures of the interior angles of a triangle is $180°$.

49. 129, the numbers in positions are found as follows: a   b
                                                                 c   a + b + c

Exercise Set 1.2

(Note: Answers in this section will vary depending on how you round your numbers. The answers may differ from the answers in the back of the textbook. All answers are approximate.)

1. 333 + 296.4 + 93.5 + 20.4 + 315.9
   → 333 + 296 + 94 + 20 + 316 = 1059

3. 297,700 x 4087 → 300,000 x 4000
   = 1,200,000,000

5. $\dfrac{405}{0.049} \to \dfrac{400}{0.05} = 8000$

7. 0.048 x 1964 → 0.05 x 2000 = 100

9. 31,640 x 79,264 → 32,000 x 79,000
   = 2,528,000,000

11. 592 x 2070 x 992.62 → 600 x 2000 x 1000
   = 1,200,000,000

13. 12.1 miles per week x 52 weeks →
   12 miles per week x 52 weeks = 624 miles

15. $\dfrac{\$68.90}{29} \to \dfrac{\$70}{30} \approx \$2.33$

17. 42.8 hours x $7.95 per hour
   → 43 hours x $8 per hour = $344

19. 167 + 203 + 137 → 170 + 200 + 140 = 510 lbs.

21. $\dfrac{1}{4}$ of $102,272 → $\dfrac{1}{4} \times \$102,000 = \$25,500$

23. $\dfrac{24,300}{8} \to \dfrac{24,000}{8} = 3000$ lbs.

25. 1690 x 2 (round trip) x 2 (round trips per month)
   x 12 (months) → 1700 x 2 x 2 x 12
   = 81,600 miles

27. Team A: 189 + 172 + 191 → 190 + 170 + 190
   = 550
   Team B: 183 + 229 + 167 → 180 + 230 + 170
   = 580, 580 – 550 = 30 lbs.

29. 3.8 x (60 ft. x 80.2 ft.) → 4 x (60 x 80)
   = 19,200 grubs

31. a) ≈ 2.5 miles
   b) ≈ 4 kilometers

33. a) 24% of \$41,105 → 24% of \$41,000
    = 0.24 x \$41,000 = \$9840
    b) 39% of \$41,105 → 39% of \$41,000
    = 0.39 x \$41,000 = \$15,990
37. a) luxury cars, minivans, large cars
    b) 30% of \$18,209 → 30% of \$18,200
    = 0.30 x \$18,200 = \$5460
    c) 43% of \$27,937 → 40% of \$30,000
    = 0.40 x \$30,000 = \$12,000
41. ≈ 90
45. ≈ 10%
49. ≈ 45 ft.

35. a) ≈ 4 million
    b) ≈ 98 million
    c) ≈ 98 - 39 = 59 million
    d) ≈ 20 + 80 + 80 + 60 + 40 = 280 million
39. about 20

43. ≈ 150°
47. ≈ 9 square units

Exercise Set 1.3

1. $\dfrac{1\ in.}{4.5\ ft.} = \dfrac{7.5\ in.}{x\ ft.}$

   $1x = 7.5(4.5)$

   $x = 33.75\ ft.$

3. $\dfrac{3\ ft.}{1.2\ ft.} = \dfrac{48.4\ ft.}{x\ ft.}$

   $3x = 48.4(1.2)$

   $\dfrac{3x}{3} = \dfrac{58.08}{3}$

   $x = 19.36\ ft.$

5. $\$1.70 + \$.15\left(5 - \dfrac{1}{8}\right)(8)$

   $= \$1.70 + \$.15\left(4\dfrac{7}{8}\right)(8)$

   $= \$1.70 + \$.15\left(\dfrac{39}{8}\right)(8)$

   $= \$1.70 + \$.15(39) = \$1.70 + \$5.85 = \$7.55$

7. a) ≈ 38 cents per pound
   b) $22,000(\$.55) = \$12,100$
   $22,000(\$.38) = \$8360$ break-even point
   $\$12,100 - \$8360 = \$3740$
   c) $22,000(\$.10) = \$2200$
   $22,000(\$.38) = \$8360$ break-even point
   $\$2200 - \$8360 = -\$6160$ or loss of $6160

9. $\dfrac{(mach)3}{2310\ mph} = \dfrac{(mach)1}{x\ mph}$

   $3x = 1(2310)$

   $\dfrac{3x}{3} = \dfrac{2310}{3}$

   $x = 770\ mph$

11. a) weekly rate: \$70
    daily rate: \$18(5) = \$90
    savings: \$90 - \$70 = \$20
    b) weekly rate: \$50
    daily rate: \$12(5) = \$60
    The weekly rate is cheaper by \$60 - \$50 = \$10.
    c) \$4 for first hour + \$2 (6 remaining hours)
    = \$4 + \$12 = \$16

13. $\$3.75 + (21-3)(\$0.50) = \$3.75 + 18(\$0.50)$
    $= \$3.75 + \$9 = \$12.75$

15. $\dfrac{\$23,000,000}{32} = \$718,750$

17. a) $\dfrac{460}{50} = 9.2$ min.

    b) $\dfrac{1550}{25} = 62$ min.

    c) $\dfrac{1400}{35} = 40$ min.

    d) $\dfrac{1550}{25} + \dfrac{2200}{25} = \dfrac{3750}{25} = 150$ min.

19. a) 11% of 273,300,000

    $= 0.11(273,300,000) = 30,063,000$

    b) 10% of 970,000 $= 0.10(970,000) = 97,000$

    c) 3% of 970,000 $= 0.03(970,000) = 29,100$

21. by mail: $(\$52.80 + \$5.60 + \$8.56) \times 4 = \$267.84$

    tire store:

    $\$324 + \$324(.08) = \$324 + \$25.92 = \$349.92$

    savings: $\$349.92 - \$267.84 = \$82.08$

23. a) $\$620(.12) = \$74.40$

    b) $\$1200(.22) = \$264$

    c) $\$1200 - \$1000 = \$200$ loss

    profit $= \$264 - \$200 = \$64$

25. Let $x = $ the amount above $\$42,350$

    $\$10,200 - \$6,352.50 = \$3847.50$

    $\dfrac{.28x}{.28} = \dfrac{\$3847.50}{.28}$

    $x \approx \$13,741.07$

    $\$42,350 + \$13,741.07 = \$56,091.07$

27. a) 2 day service: $\$11.75 \times 52 = \$611$

    priority overnight: $\$28 \times 52 = \$1456$

    savings: $\$1456 - \$611 = \$845$

    b) express mail: $\$17.25 \times 52 = \$897$

    next day air: $\$25.75 \times 52 = \$1339$

    savings: $\$1339 - \$897 = \$442$

29. a) $\$150 + \$75 + \$40 (12$ months$)$

    $= \$150 + \$75 + \$480 = \$705$

    b) $\$150 + \$125 + \$40 (12$ months$)$

    $= \$150 + \$125 + \$480 = \$755$

    c) 50 (5 compared to 0.1)

31. cost after 1 year: $\$450 + \$450(.06)$

    $= \$450 + \$27 = \$477$

    cost after 2 years: $\$477 + \$477(.06)$

    $= \$477 + \$28.62 = \$505.62$

33. a) $\dfrac{\$200}{\$41} \approx 4.9$ The maximum number of 10-packs is 4.

    $\$200 - (4 \times \$41) = \$200 - \$164 = \$36$, $\dfrac{\$36}{\$17} \approx 2.1$ Deirdre can also buy two 4-packs.

10-packs	4-packs	Number of rolls	Cost
4	2	48	$198
3	4	46	$191
2	6	44	$184
1	9	46	$194
0	11	44	$187

Maximum number of rolls of film is 48.

b) $198 when she purchases four 10-packs and two 4-packs.

35. a) water/milk: $3(1) = 3$ cups   salt: $3\left(\dfrac{1}{8}\right) = \dfrac{3}{8}$ tsp.

cream: $3(3) = 9$ tbsp. $= \dfrac{9}{16}$ cup (because 16 tbsp. = 1 cup)

b) water/milk: $\dfrac{2+3.75}{2} = \dfrac{5.75}{2} = 2.875$ cups $= 2\dfrac{7}{8}$ cups

salt: $\dfrac{.25+.5}{2} = \dfrac{.75}{2} = .375$ tsp. $= \dfrac{3}{8}$ tsp.   cream: $\dfrac{.5+.75}{2} = \dfrac{1.25}{2} = .625$ cups $= \dfrac{5}{8}$ cup

c) water/milk: $3\dfrac{3}{4} - 1 = \dfrac{15}{4} - \dfrac{4}{4} = \dfrac{11}{4} = 2\dfrac{3}{4}$ cups

salt: $\dfrac{1}{2} - \dfrac{1}{8} = \dfrac{4}{8} - \dfrac{1}{8} = \dfrac{3}{8}$ tsp.   cream: $\dfrac{3}{4} - \dfrac{3}{16} = \dfrac{12}{16} - \dfrac{3}{16} = \dfrac{9}{16}$ cup = 9 tbsp.

d) Differences exist in water/milk because the amount for 4 servings is not twice that for 2 servings. Differences also exist in Cream of Wheat because $\dfrac{1}{2}$ cup is not twice 3 tbsp.

37. $1\ ft.^2$ would be $12\ in.$ by $12\ in.$ Thus,

$1\,ft.^2 = 12\ in. \times 12\ in. = 144\ in.^2$

39. Area of original rectangle = lw

Area of new rectangle = $(2l)(2w) = 4lw$

Thus, if the length and width of a rectangle are doubled, the area is 4 times as large.

41. $7 + 7 - (7 \div 7) = 13$

43. $\dfrac{60}{4} = 15$

Zebras	Number of Zebra Feet	Cranes	Number of Crane Feet	Number of Heads
15	60	0	0	15
14	56	2	4	16
13	52	4	8	17
12	48	6	12	18

Therefore, there are 12 zebras and 6 cranes.

45. a) $(4 \times 4) + (3 \times 3) + (2 \times 2) + (1 \times 1)$

$= 16 + 9 + 4 + 1 = 30$

b) $(7 \times 7) + (6 \times 6) + (5 \times 5) + 30$

$= 49 + 36 + 25 + 30 = 140$

47. a) Place the object, 1 g., and 3 g. on one side and 9 g. on the other side.

b) Place the object, 9 g., and 3 g. on one side and 27 g. and 1 g. on the other side.

49.

15	1	11
5	9	13
7	17	3

51. $21, 12, 33$ Multiply the number in the center of the middle row by 3.

53. $3 \times 2 \times 1 = 6$ ways

55. $35 - 15 = 20$

57.

	7	
3	1	4
5	8	6
	2	

Other answers are possible, but 1 and
8 must appear in the center.

59.

1	2	3	4	5
2	3	4	5	1
3	4	5	1	2
4	5	1	2	3
5	1	2	3	4

Other answers are possible.

61.   Mary is the skier.

63.   Areas of the colored regions are:
$1 \times 1, 1 \times 1, 2 \times 2, 3 \times 3, 5 \times 5, 8 \times 8, 13 \times 13,$

21×21; $1 + 1 + 4 + 9 + 25 + 64 + 169 + 441$
$= 714$ square units

Review Exercises

1. 23, 28, 33 (Add 5 to previous number)
2. 25, 36, 49 (Next three perfect squares)
3. 64, -128, 256 (Multiply previous number by –2)
4. 25, 32, 40 (19 + 6 = 25, 25 + 7 = 32,
    32 + 8 = 40)
5. 10, 4, - 3 (15 - 5 = 10, 10 - 6 = 4, 4 - 7 = -3)
6. $\dfrac{3}{8}, \dfrac{3}{16}, \dfrac{3}{32}$ (Multiply previous number by $\dfrac{1}{2}$)

7.

8.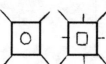

9. a) The original number and the final number are the same.
    b) The original number and the final number are the same.
    c) Conjecture: The final number is the same as the original number.
    d) $n, 2n, 2n+10, \dfrac{2n+10}{2} = \dfrac{2n}{2} + \dfrac{10}{2} = n+5, n+5-5 = n$

10. This process will always result in an answer of 3. $n, n+5, 6(n+5) = 6n+30, 6n+30-12$

    $= 6n+18, \dfrac{6n+18}{2} = \dfrac{6n}{2} + \dfrac{18}{2} = 3n+9, \dfrac{3n+9}{3} = \dfrac{3n}{3} + \dfrac{9}{3} = n+3, n+3-n = 3$

11. $6^2 - 4^2 = 36 - 16 = 20$, 20 is an even number.
    (Note: Answers for Ex. 12 - 25 will vary depending on how you round your numbers. The answers may differ from the answers in the back of the textbook. All answers are approximate.)

12. 204,600 x 1963 → 205,000 x 2000
    = 410,000,000

13. $\dfrac{19,254.5}{524.3} \rightarrow \dfrac{19,000}{500} = 38$

14. 346 .2 + 96.402 + 1.04 + 897 + 821 →
    350 + 100 + 1 + 900 + 800 = 2151

15. 21% of 1012 → 20% of 1000
    = .20 x 1000 = 200

16. Answers will vary.

17. 8 x $12.99 → 8 x $13 = $104

18. 6% of $202 → 6% of 200 = .06 x 200 = $12

19. $\dfrac{1.1\ mi.}{22\ min.} \rightarrow \dfrac{1\ mi.}{20\ min.} = \dfrac{3\ mi.}{60\ min.} = 3\ mph$

20. $2.49 + $0.79 + $1.89 + $0.10 + $2.19 + $6.75
    → $2 + $1 + $2 + $0 + $2 + $7 = $14.00

21. $5\,in. = \dfrac{20}{4}\,in. = 20\left(\dfrac{1}{4}\right)in. = 20(0.1)mi. = 2mi.$

22. 80 − 12 = 68

23. 5300 + 570 + 80 = 5950

24. 13 square units

25. length = 1.75 in. , 1.75(12.5) ≈ 22 ft.
    height = .625 in. , .625(12.5) ≈ 8 ft.

26. dialed direct: $1.20 + 14($0.30)
    = $1.20 + $4.20 = $5.40
    savings: $7.50 - $5.40 = $2.10

27. $2 + 7($0.90) = $2 + $6.30 = $8.30
    change: $10 - $8.30 = $1.70

28. 4($3.45) = $13.80 for four six-packs
    savings: $13.80 - $12.60 = $1.20

29. Eurich's: $2\ hr. = 120\ min., \dfrac{120}{15} = 8$, $8 \times \$10 = \$80$

    Starr's: $2\ hr. = 120\ min., \dfrac{120}{30} = 4$, $4 \times \$25 = \$100$

    Eurich's is better by $20 .

30. $\$1.35 + \left[\left(10 - \dfrac{1}{5}\right)(5)\right]\$.20$

    $= \$1.35 + \left[\left(\dfrac{50}{5} - \dfrac{1}{5}\right)(5)\right]\$.20$

    $= \$1.35 + \left[\dfrac{49}{5}(5)\right]\$.20$

    $= \$1.35 + 49 \times \$.20 = \$1.35 + \$9.80$

    $= \$11.15$

31. 10% of $530 = 0.10 x $530 = $53
    $53 x 7 = $371
    savings: $371 - $60 = $311

32. $\dfrac{1.5\ mg.}{10\ lbs.} = \dfrac{x\ mg.}{47\ lbs.}$

    $10x = 47(1.5)$

    $\dfrac{10x}{10} = \dfrac{70.5}{10}$

    $x = 7.05\ mg.$

33. $3800 - 0.30($3800) = $3800 - $1140
    = $2660 take-home
    25% of $2660 = .25 x $2660 = $665

34. 9 a.m. Eastern is 6 a.m. Pacific, from 6 a.m. Pacific to 1:35 p.m. Pacific is 7 hr. 35 min. , 7 hr. 35 min. - 50 min. stop = 6 hr. 45 min.

35. 3 p.m. - 4 hr. = 11 a.m.
July 26, 11 a.m.

36. a) $1 \, in. \times 1 \, in. = 2.54 \, cm. \times 2.54 \, cm.$

$= 6.4516 \, cm.^2 \approx 6.45 \, cm.^2$

b) $1 \, in. \times 1 \, in. \times 1 \, in. = 2.54 \, cm. \times 2.54 \, cm.$

$\times 2.54 \, cm. = 16.387064 \, cm.^3 \approx 16.39 \, cm.^3$

c)

$$\frac{1 \, in.}{2.54 \, cm.} = \frac{x \, in.}{1 \, cm.}$$

$$2.54x = 1(1)$$

$$\frac{2.54x}{2.54} = \frac{1}{2.54}$$

$$x \approx .39 \, in.$$

37. Each figure has an additional two dots. To get the hundredth figure, 97 more figures must be drawn, 97(2) = 194 dots added to the third figure. Thus, 194 + 7 = 201.

38.

21	7	8	18
10	16	15	13
14	12	11	17
9	19	20	6

39.

23	25	15
13	21	29
27	17	19

40. 59 min., 59 sec. Since it doubles every second, the jar was half full 1 second earlier than 1 hour.

41. 6

42. Nothing. Each friend paid $9 for a total of $27; $25 to the hotel, $2 to the clerk.
$25 for the room + $3 for each friend + $2 for the clerk = $30

43. Let $x =$ total weight of the four women

$\frac{x}{4} = 130$, $x = 520$, $\frac{520 + 180}{5} = \frac{700}{5} = 140 \, lbs.$

44. Yes, 3 quarters and 4 dimes, or 1 half dollar, 1 quarter and 4 dimes, or 1 quarter and 9 dimes. Other answers are possible.

45. $6 \, cm. \times 6 \, cm. \times 6 \, cm. = 216 \, cm.^3$

46. Place six coins in each pan with one coin off to the side. If it balances, the heavier coin is the one on the side. If the pan does not balance, take the six coins on the heavier side and split them into two groups of three. Select the three heavier coins and weigh two coins. If the pan balances, it is the third coin. If the pan does not balance, you can identify the heavier coin.

47. $\frac{n(n+1)}{2} = \frac{500(501)}{2} = \frac{250,500}{2} = 125,250$

48. 16 blue: 4 green → 8 blue, 2 yellow → 5 blue, 2 white → 3 blue

49. 90: 101, 111, 121, 131, 141, 151, 161, 171, 181, 191,...

50. The fifth figure will be an octagon with equal sides. Inside the octagon will be a 7-sided figure with each side of equal length. The figure will have one antenna. The nth figure will have n + 3 sides of equal length. Inside the figure will be a figure of n + 2 sides of equal length. If n is an odd number, it will have one antenna. If n is an even number, it will have 2 antennas.

51. 61: The sixth figure will have 6 rows of 6 tiles and 5 rows of 5 tiles (6 x 6 + 5 x 5 = 36 + 25 = 61)

52. Some possible answers are given below. There are other possibilities.

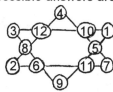 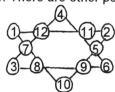 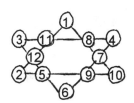

53. a) 2

   b) There are 3 choices for the first spot. Once that person is standing, there are 2 choices for the second spot and 1 for the third. Thus, 3 x 2 x 1 = 6.

   c) 4 x 3 x 2 x 1 = 24

   d) 5 x 4 x 3 x 2 x 1 = 120

   e) n x (n - 1) x (n - 2) x (n - 3) x ... x 2 x 1 = n! where n is the number of people in line.

Chapter Test

1. 18, 21, 24   (Add 3 to previous number)

2. $\dfrac{1}{81}, \dfrac{1}{243}, \dfrac{1}{729}$ (Multiply previous number by $\dfrac{1}{3}$)

3. a) The result is the original number plus 1.

   b) The result is the original number plus 1.

   c) Conjecture: The result will always be the original number plus 1.

   d) $n, 5n, 5n+10, \dfrac{5n+10}{5} = \dfrac{5n}{5} + \dfrac{10}{5} = n+2, n+2-1 = n+1$

(Note: Answers for Ex. 4 - 7 will vary depending on how you round your numbers. The answers may differ from the answers in the back of the textbook. All answers are approximate.)

4. 0.00417 x 990,000 →
   0.004 x 1,000,000 = 4000

5. $\dfrac{91,000}{0.00302} \rightarrow \dfrac{90,000}{0.003} = 30,000,000$

6. 7 square units

7. a) 25% - 7% = 18%
   b) 25% - 9% = 16%

8. Let $x =$ number of therms used

$$7.42 + .62(x-3) = 100.42$$
$$7.42 + .62x - 1.86 = 100.42$$
$$5.56 + .62x = 100.42$$
$$\underline{-5.56 \qquad\qquad -5.56}$$
$$\dfrac{.62x}{.62} = \dfrac{94.86}{.62}$$
$$x = 153 \text{ therms}$$

9. $\dfrac{\$15}{\$3.60} \approx 4.167$ The maximum number of 6-packs is 4.

   $\$15 - (4 \times \$3.60) = \$15 - \$14.40 = \$.60$

   Thus, no individual cans can be purchased.

6-packs	Indiv. Cans	Number of cans
4	0	24
3	4	22
2	8	20
1	12	18
0	16	16

   Maximum number of cans is 24.

10. 1 cut yields 2 equal pieces. Cut each of these 2 equal pieces to get 4 equal pieces.
    3 cuts → 3(2.5 min.) = 7.5 min.

11. 2.5 in. by 1.8 in. → 2.5 x 12 by 1.8 x 12
    = 30 in. by 21.6 in. ≈ 30 in. by 22 in.

12. $12.75 x 40 = $510
     $12.75 x 1.5 x 10 = $191.25
     $510 + $191.25 = $701.25
     $701.25 - $652.25 = $49

13.

40	15	20
5	25	45
30	35	10

14.   Christine drove the first 15 miles at 60 mph which took $\frac{15}{60} = \frac{1}{4}$ hr., and the second 15 miles at 30 mph which took $\frac{15}{30} = \frac{1}{2}$ hr. for a total time of $\frac{3}{4}$ hr. If she drove the entire 30 miles at 45 mph, the trip would take $\frac{30}{45} = \frac{2}{3}$ hr. (40 min.) which is less than $\frac{3}{4}$ hr. (45 min.).

15.   2 x 6 x 8 x 9 x 13 = 11,232; 11 does not divide 11,232

16.   243: 260 - 17 = 243, 234 + 9 =243, 274 - 31 = 243

17.   a) 3 x $3.99 = $11.97
      b) 9($1.75 x .75) ≈ $11.81
      c) $11.97 - $11.81 = $0.16   Using the coupon is least expensive by $0.16.

18.   8: $ → on   * → off
      $$$$, $$$*, $$*$, $*$$, *$$$, *$*$, *$$*, $*$*

CHAPTER TWO

SETS

Exercise Set 2.1

1. A **set** is a collection of objects.
3. Description: The set of even counting numbers less than 7.
   Roster form: {2, 4, 6}
   Set-builder notation: $\{x | x \in N \text{ and } x < 7\}$
5. A set is **finite** if it either contains no elements or the number of elements in the set is a natural number.
7. Two sets are **equivalent** if they contain the same number of elements.
9. $N = \{1, 2, 3, 4, 5, ...\}$
11. A **universal set**, symbolized by U, is a set that contains all the elements for any specific discussion.

13. Not well defined, "best" is interpreted differently by different people.

15. Well defined, contents can be clearly determined.

17. Well defined, contents can be clearly determined.
19. Infinite, number of elements in the set is not a natural number.
21. Finite, number of elements in the set is a natural number.
23. Infinite, number of elements in the set is not a natural number.
25. {Nebraska, Nevada, New Hampshire, New Jersey, New Mexico, New York, North Carolina, North Dakota}

27. {11, 12, 13, 14, ..., 177}

29. $C = \{4\}$

31. { } or $\varnothing$

33. $E = \{6, 7, 8, 9, ..., 71\}$

35. $A = \{x \mid x \in N \text{ and } x < 10\}$
    or $A = \{x | x \in N \text{ and } x \leq 9\}$

37. $C = \{x \mid x \in N \text{ and } x \text{ is a multiple of } 3\}$

39. $E = \{x \mid x \in N \text{ and } x \text{ is odd}\}$

41. $C = \{x \mid x \text{ is one of the three manufacturers of calculators with the greatest sales in the United States}\}$

43. A is the set of natural numbers less than or equal to 7.

45. L is the set of Great Lakes in the U.S.

47. B is the set of the five tallest buildings in the U.S.

49. E is the set of natural numbers greater than 5 and less than or equal to 12.

51. False, {b} is a set and not an element of the set

53. False, h is not an element of the set.

55. False, 3 is an element of the set.

57. True, Titanic is an element of the set.

59. $n(A) = 4$

61. $n(C) = 0$

63. Both, A and B contain exactly the same elements.
65. Neither, the sets have a different number of elements.
67. Equivalent, both sets contain the same number of elements, 3.
69. a) A is the set of natural numbers greater than 2. B is the set of all numbers greater than 2.
    b) Set A contains only natural numbers, while set B contains other types of numbers, including fractions and decimal numbers.
    c) A = {3, 4, 5, 6, ...}
    d) No, set B cannot be written in roster form since we cannot list all the elements in set B.
71. Cardinal, 19 tells how many.

73. Ordinal, sixteenth tells Lincoln's relative position.

75. Answers will vary.

77. Answers will vary.

Exercise Set 2.2

1. Set A is a **subset** of set B, symbolized by $A \subseteq B$, if and only if all the elements of set A are also elements of set B.
3. If $A \subseteq B$, then every element of set A is also an element of set B. If $A \subset B$, then every element of set A is also an element of set B and set A ≠ set B.
5. $2^n - 1$
7. False, English is an element, not a subset.

9. True, { } is a subset of every set.

11. True, 5 is not an element of {2, 4, 6}.

13. False, the set {∅} contains the element ∅.

15. True, { } and ∅ each represent the empty set.

17. False, the set {0} contains the element 0.

19. False, {5} is a subset, not an element.

21. False, no set is a proper subset of itself.

23. True, {apple, orange, plum} is a subset of {plum, orange, apple}.

25. $B \subseteq A, B \subset A$

27. $A \subseteq B, A \subset B$

29. $B \subseteq A, B \subset A$

31. $A = B, A \subseteq B, B \subseteq A$

33. { } is the only subset.

35. { }, {car}, {boat}, {car, boat}

37. a) { }, {a}, {b}, {c}, {d}, {a, b}, {a, c}, {a, d}, {b, c}, {b, d}, {c, d}, {a, b, c}, {a, b, d}, {a, c, d}, {b, c, d}, {a, b, c, d}
    b) All the sets in part a) are proper subsets of A except {a, b, c, d}.

39. True, every proper subset is a subset.

41. False, no set is a proper subset of itself.

43. True, ∅ is a proper subset of every set except itself.

45. True, every set is a subset of the universal set.

47. True, ∅ is a proper subset of every set except itself and U ≠ ∅.

49. True, ∅ is a subset of every set.

51. The number of options is equal to the number of subsets of {RAM, modem, video card, hard drive, processor, sound card}, which is $2^6 = 2 \times 2 \times 2 \times 2 \times 2 \times 2 = 64$.
53. The number of variations is equal to the number of subsets of the set, which is
    $2^7 = 2 \times 2 \times 2 \times 2 \times 2 \times 2 \times 2 = 128$.
55. E = F since they are both subsets of each other.

57.   a) Yes, because a is a member of set D.
       b) No, c is an element of set D.
       c) Yes, each element of {a, b} is an element of set D.

Exercise Set 2.3

1.

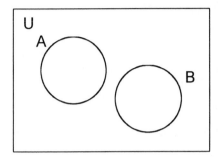

3.

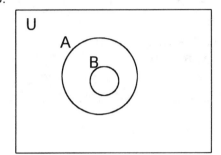

5.

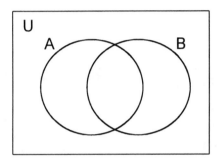

7. Combine the elements from set A and set B into one set. List any element that is contained in both sets only once.

9. a) Or is generally interpreted to mean union.
    b) And is generally interpreted to mean intersection.

11. Region II, the intersection of the two sets.

13.

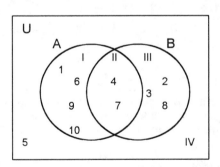

15.

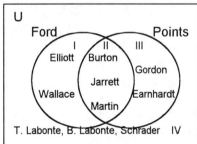

17. The set of U.S. senators who did not vote in favor of the Hartley-Domingo bill.

19. The set of universities in the U.S. that do not have the word State in their name.

21. The set of universities in the U.S. that have the word State or the word South in their name.

23. The set of universities in the U.S. that have the word State in their name and do not have the word South in their name.

25. The set of U.S. corporations whose headquarters are in the state of New York and whose chief executive officer is a woman.

27. The set of U.S. corporations whose chief executive officer is a woman and who do not employ at least 100 people.

29. The set of U.S. corporations whose headquarters are in the state of New York and whose chief executive officer is a woman and who employs at least 100 people.

31. B = {a, f, g, h, r}

33. U = {a, b, c, f, g, h, m, p, r, t, w, z}

35. A $\cup$ B = {a, b, c, h, t, w} $\cup$ {a, f, g, h, r} = {a, b, c, f, g, h, r, t, w}

37. (A $\cap$ B)' From #34, A $\cap$ B = {a, h}. (A $\cap$ B)' = {a, h}' = {b, c, f, g, m, p, r, t, w, z}

39. A = {L, Δ, @, *, $}

41. U = {L, Δ, @, *, $, R, $\square$, ∞, Σ, Z}

43. A $\cap$ B = {L, Δ, @, *, $} $\cap$ {*, $, R, $\square$} = {*, $}

45. A' $\cap$ B = {L, Δ, @, *, $}' $\cap$ {*, $, R, $\square$} = {R, $\square$, ∞, Σ, Z} $\cap$ {*, $, R, $\square$} = {R, $\square$}

47. A $\cup$ B = {1, 2, 4, 5, 8} $\cup$ {2, 3, 4, 6} = {1, 2, 3, 4, 5, 6, 8}

49. B' = {2, 3, 4, 6}' = {1, 5, 7, 8}

51. (A $\cup$ B)' From #47, A $\cup$ B = {1, 2, 3, 4, 5, 6, 8}. (A $\cup$ B)' = {1, 2, 3, 4, 5, 6, 8}' = {7}

53. (A $\cup$ B)' $\cap$ B From #51, (A $\cup$ B)' = {7}. (A $\cup$ B)' $\cap$ B = {7} $\cap$ {2, 3, 4, 6} = { }

55. (B $\cup$ A)' $\cap$ (B' $\cup$ A') From #51, (A $\cup$ B)' = (B $\cup$ A)' = {7}.
    (B $\cup$ A)' $\cap$ (B' $\cup$ A') = {7} $\cap$ ({2, 3, 4, 6}' $\cup$ {1, 2, 4, 5, 8}') = {7} $\cap$ ({1, 5, 7, 8} $\cup$ {3, 6, 7})
    = {7} $\cap$ {1, 3, 5, 6, 7, 8} = {7}

57. A' = {a, c, d, f, g, i}' = {b, e, h, j, k}

59. A $\cap$ C = {a, c, d, f, g, i} $\cap$ {a, b, f, i, j} = {a, f, i}

61. (A $\cup$ C)' From #59, A $\cap$ C = {a, f, i}. (A $\cap$ C)' = {a, f, i}' = {b, c, d, e, g, h, j, k}

63. A $\cup$ (C $\cap$ B)' = {a, c, d, f, g, i} $\cup$ ({a, b, f, i, j} $\cap$ {b, c, d, f, g})' = {a, c, d, f, g, i} $\cup$ {b, f}'
    = {a, c, d, f, g, i} $\cup$ {a, c, d, e, g, h, i, j, k} = {a, c, d, e, f, g, h, i, j, k}

65. A' $\cap$ (B $\cap$ C) From #63, B $\cap$ C = {b, f}. A' $\cap$ (B $\cap$ C) = {a, c, d, f, g, i}' $\cap$ {b, f}
    = {b, e, h, j, k} $\cap$ {b, f} = {b}

67. A $\cap$ B = {1, 3, 5, 7, 9} $\cap$ {2, 4, 6, 8} = { }

69. A' $\cup$ B = {1, 3, 5, 7, 9}' $\cup$ {2, 4, 6, 8} = {2, 4, 6, 8} $\cup$ {2, 4, 6, 8} = {2, 4, 6, 8} = B

71. A $\cap$ C' = {1, 3, 5, 7, 9} $\cap$ {1, 2, 3, 4, 5}' = {1, 3, 5, 7, 9} $\cap$ {6, 7, 8, 9} = {7, 9}

73. (B $\cap$ C)' = ({2, 4, 6, 8} $\cap$ {1, 2, 3, 4, 5})' = {2, 4}' = {1, 3, 5, 6, 7, 8, 9}

75. (C $\cap$ B) $\cup$ A From #73, C $\cap$ B = {2, 4}. (C $\cap$ B) $\cup$ A = {2, 4} $\cup$ {1, 3, 5, 7, 9} = {1, 2, 3, 4, 5, 7, 9}

77. (A' $\cup$ C) $\cap$ B = ({1, 3, 5, 7, 9}' $\cup$ {1, 2, 3, 4, 5}) $\cap$ {2, 4, 6, 8} = ({2, 4, 6, 8} $\cup$ {1, 2, 3, 4, 5}) $\cap$ {2, 4, 6, 8}
    = {1, 2, 3, 4, 5, 6, 8} $\cap$ {2, 4, 6, 8} = {2, 4, 6, 8} = B

79. (A $\cup$ B)' $\cap$ C From #68, A $\cup$ B = {1, 2, 3, 4, 5, 6, 7, 8, 9}.
    (A $\cup$ B)' $\cap$ C = {1, 2, 3, 4, 5, 6, 7, 8, 9}' $\cap$ {1, 2, 3, 4, 5} = { } $\cap$ {1, 2, 3, 4, 5} = { }

81. A set and its complement will always be disjoint since the complement of a set is all of the elements in the universal set that are not in the set. Therefore, a set and its complement will have no elements in common. For example, if U = {1, 2, 3, 4, 5, 6} and A = {1, 2, 5}, then A' = {3, 4, 6}.
    A $\cap$ A' = {1, 2, 5} $\cap$ {3, 4, 6} = { }

83. Let A = {students on the baseball team} and B = {students on the football team}.
    n(A $\cup$ B) = n(A) + n(B) - n(A $\cap$ B) = 16 + 35 - 7 = 44

85. a) A $\cup$ B = {a, b, c, d} $\cup$ {b, d, e, f, g, h} = {a, b, c, d, e, f, g, h}, n(A $\cup$ B) = 8,
    A $\cap$ B = (a, b, c, d} $\cap$ {b, d, e, f, g, h} = {b, d}, n(A $\cap$ B) = 2.
    n(A) + n(B) - n(A $\cap$ B) = 4 + 6 - 2 = 8
    Therefore, n(A $\cup$ B) = n(A) + n(B) - n(A $\cap$ B).
    b) Answers will vary.
    c) Elements in the intersection of A and B are counted twice in n(A) + n(B).

87. A $\cup$ B = {1, 2, 3, 4, ...} $\cup$ {4, 8, 12, 16, ...} = {1, 2, 3, 4, ...} = A

89. B $\cap$ C = {4, 8, 12, 16, ...} $\cap$ {2, 4, 6, 8, ...} = {4, 8, 12, 16, ...} = B

91. A $\cap$ C = {1, 2, 3, 4, ...} $\cap$ {2, 4, 6, 8, ...} = {2, 4, 6, 8, ...} = C

93. B' ∩ C = {4, 8, 12, 16, ...}' ∩ {2, 4, 6, 8, ...} = {0, 1, 2, 3, 5, 6, 7, 9, 10, 11, 13, 14, 15, ...} ∩ {2, 4, 6, 8, ...}
      = {2, 6, 10, 14, 18, ...}

95. (A ∩ C) ∩ B' From #91, A ∩ C = C. (A ∩ C) ∩ B' = C ∩ B'.
      From #93, B' ∩ C = C ∩ B' = {2, 6, 10, 14, 18, ...}

97. A ∪ A' = U

99. A ∪ ∅ = A

101. A ∩ ∅ = ∅

103. A ∩ U = A

105. If A ∩ B = B, then B ⊆ A.

107. If A ∩ B = ∅, then A and B are disjoint sets.

109. If A ∩ B = A, then A ⊆ B.

111. A - B = {b, c, e, f, g, h} - {a, b, c, g, i} = {e, f, h}

113. A' - B = {b, c, e, f, g, h}' - {a, b, c, g, i}
        = {a, d, i, j, k} - {a, b, c, g, i} = {d, j, k}

115. A - B = {2, 4, 5, 7, 9, 11, 13} - {1, 2, 4, 5, 6, 7, 8, 9, 11} = {13}

117. (A - B)' From # 115, A - B = {13}.
        (A - B)' = {13}'
        = {1, 2, 3, 4, 5, 6, 7, 8, 9, 10, 11, 12, 14, 15}

119. (B - A)' From #116, B - A = {1, 6, 8}.
        (B - A)' = {1, 6, 8}' = {2, 3, 4, 5, 7, 9, 10, 11, 12, 13, 14, 15}

Exercise Set 2.4

1. Region V, the intersection of all three sets.

3. A ∩ B is represented by regions II and V. If A ∩ B contains 10 elements and region V contains 6 elements, then region II contains 10 - 6 = 4 elements.

5. (A ∪ B)' = A' ∩ B', (A ∩ B)' = A' ∪ B'

7.

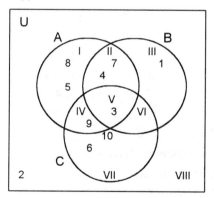

9.

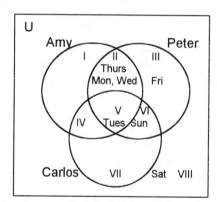

11.

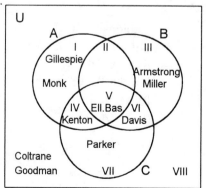

13.

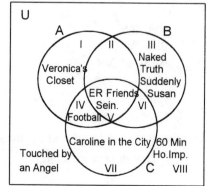

15. Levis, V
17. Nike, VI
19. Fruit of the Loom, IV
21. Victoria's Secret, VII
23. L.L. Bean, VI
25. Levis, V
27. VI
29. IV
31. I
33. V
35. II
37. VII
39. I
41. VIII
43. VI
45. A = {1, 2, 3, 4, 5, 6}
47. C = {4, 5, 6, 7, 8, 10}
49. A ∩ B = {3, 4, 5}
51. (B ∩ C)' = {1, 2, 3, 6, 9, 10, 11, 12}
53. A ∪ B = {1, 2, 3, 4, 5, 6, 7, 8, 9, 12}
55. (A ∪ C)' = {9, 11, 12}
57. A' = {7, 8, 9, 10, 11, 12}

59. (A ∪ B)'   A' ∩ B'

Set	Regions	Set	Regions
A	I, II	A	I, II
B	II, III	A'	III, IV
A ∪ B	I, II, III	B	II, III
(A ∪ B)'	IV	B'	I, IV
		A' ∩ B'	IV

Both statements are represented by the same region, IV, of the Venn diagram. Therefore, (A ∪ B)' = A' ∩ B' for all sets A and B.

61. A' ∪ B'   A ∩ B

Set	Regions	Set	Regions
A	I, II	A	I, II
A'	III, IV	B	II, III
B	II, III	A ∩ B	II
B'	I, IV		
A' ∪ B'	I, III, IV		

Since the two statements are not represented by the same regions, A' ∪ B' ≠ A ∩ B for all sets A and B.

63. A' ∪ B'   (A ∪ B)'

Set	Regions	Set	Regions
A	I, II	A	I, II
A'	III, IV	B	II, III
B	II, III	A ∪ B	I, II, III
B'	I, IV	(A ∪ B)'	IV
A' ∪ B'	I, III, IV		

Since the two statements are not represented by the same regions, A' ∪ B' ≠ (A ∪ B)' for all sets A and B.

65. (A ∩ B')'   A' ∪ B

Set	Regions	Set	Regions
A	I, II	A	I, II
B	II, III	A'	III, IV
B'	I, IV	B	II, III
A ∩ B'	I	A' ∪ B	II, III, IV
(A ∩ B')'	II, III, IV		

Both statements are represented by the same regions, II, III, IV, of the Venn diagram. Therefore, (A ∩ B')' = A' ∪ B for all sets A and B.

67.   A ∪ (B ∩ C)

Set	Regions
B	II, III, V, VI
C	IV, V, VI, VII
B ∩ C	V, VI
A	I, II, IV, V
A ∪ (B ∩ C)	I, II, IV, V, VI

(A ∪ B) ∩ C

Set	Regions
A	I, II, IV, V
B	II, III, V, VI
A ∪ B	I, II, III, IV, V, VI
C	IV, V, VI, VII
(A ∪ B) ∩ C	IV, V, VI

Since the two statements are not represented by the same regions, A ∪ (B ∩ C) ≠ (A ∪ B) ∩ C for all sets A, B, and C.

69.   A ∩ (B ∪ C)   (B ∪ C) ∩ A

Set	Regions	Set	Regions
B	II, III, V, VI	B	II, III, V, VI
C	IV , V, VI, VII	C	IV, V, VI, VII
B ∪ C	II, III, IV, V, VI, VII	B ∪ C	II, III, IV, V, VI, VII
A	I, II, IV, V	A	I, II, IV, V
A ∩ (B ∪ C)	II, IV, V	(B ∪ C) ∩ A	II, IV, V

Both statements are represented by the same regions, II, IV, V, of the Venn
diagram. Therefore, A ∩ (B ∪ C) = (B ∪ C) ∩ A for all sets A, B, and C

71.   A ∩ (B ∪ C)   (A ∩ B) ∪ (A ∩ C)

Set	Regions	Set	Regions
B	II, III, V, VI	A	I, II, IV, V
C	IV, V, VI, VII	B	II, III, V, VI
B ∪ C	II, III, IV, V, VI, VII	A ∩ B	II, V
A	I, II, IV, V	C	IV, V, VI, VII
A ∩ (B ∪ C)	II, IV, V	A ∩ C	IV, V
		(A ∩ B) ∪ (A ∩ C)	II, IV, V

Both statements are represented by the same regions, II, IV, V, of the Venn
diagram. Therefore, A ∩ (B ∪ C) = (A ∩ B) ∪ (A ∩ C) for all sets A, B, and C.

73.   A ∩ (B ∪ C)'   A ∩ (B' ∩ C')

Set	Regions	Set	Regions
B	II, III, V, VI	B	II, III, V, VI
C	IV, V, VI, VII	B'	I, IV, VII, VIII
B ∪ C	II, III, IV, V, VI, VII	C	IV, V, VI, VII
(B ∪ C)'	I, VIII	C'	I, II, III, VIII
A	I, II, IV, V	B' ∩ C'	I, VIII
A ∩ (B ∪ C)'	I	A	I, II, IV, V
		A ∩ (B' ∩ C')	I

Both statements are represented by the same region, I, of the Venn diagram.
Therefore, A ∩ (B ∪ C)' = A ∩ (B' ∩ C') for all sets A, B, and C.

75.   (A ∪ B)' ∩ C   (A' ∪ C) ∩ (B' ∪ C)

Set	Regions	Set	Regions
A	I, II, IV, V	A	I, II, IV, V
B	II, III, V, VI	A'	III, VI, VII, VIII
A ∪ B	I, II, III, IV, V, VI	C	IV, V, VI, VII
(A ∪ B)'	VII, VIII	A' ∪ C	III, IV, V, VI, VII, VIII
C	IV, V, VI, VII	B	II, III, V, VI
(A ∪ B)' ∩ C	VII	B'	I, IV, VII, VIII
		B' ∪ C	I, IV, V, VI, VII, VIII
		(A' ∪ C) ∩ (B' ∪ C)	IV, V, VI, VII, VIII

Since the two statements are not represented by the same regions, (A ∪ B)' ∩ C ≠ (A' ∪ C) ∩ (B' ∪ C)
for all sets A, B, and C.

77. a) $(A \cup B) \cap C = (\{1, 2, 3, 4\} \cup \{3, 6, 7\}) \cap \{6, 7, 9\} = \{1, 2, 3, 4, 6, 7\} \cap \{6, 7, 9\} = \{6, 7\}$
$(A \cap C) \cup (B \cap C) = (\{1, 2, 3, 4\} \cap \{6, 7, 9\}) \cup (\{3, 6, 7\} \cap \{6, 7, 9\}) = \varnothing \cup \{6, 7\} = \{6, 7\}$
Therefore for the specific sets, $(A \cup B) \cap C = (A \cap C) \cup (B \cap C)$.
b) Answers will vary.
c) $(A \cup B) \cap C$ $(A \cap C) \cup (B \cap C)$

Set	Regions		Set	Regions
A	I, II, IV, V		A	I, II, IV, V
B	II, III, V, VI		C	IV, V, VI, VII
$A \cup B$	I, II, III, IV, V, VI		$A \cap C$	IV, V
C	IV, V, VI, VII		B	II, III, V, VI
$(A \cup B) \cap C$	IV, V, VI		$B \cap C$	V, VI
			$(A \cap C) \cup (B \cap C)$	IV, V, VI

Both statements are represented by the same regions, IV, V, VI, of the Venn diagram.
Therefore, $(A \cup B) \cap C = (A \cap C) \cup (B \cap C)$ for all sets A, B, and C.

79.

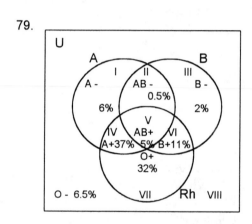

81.a)   A: Male, B: College degree, C: Greater than $30,000

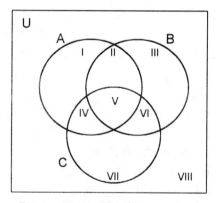

b)   Region V; $A \cap B \cap C$
c)   Region VI; $A' \cap B \cap C$
d)   Region I; $A \cap B' \cap C'$

83. $n(A \cup B \cup C) = n(A) + n(B) + n(C) - 2n(A \cap B \cap C) - n(A \cap B \cap C') - n(A \cap B' \cap C)$
     $- n(A' \cap B \cap C)$

Exercise Set 2.5

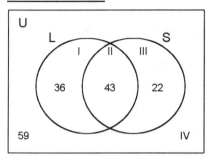

1. a) 36, Region I
    b) 22, Region III
    c) 59, Region IV

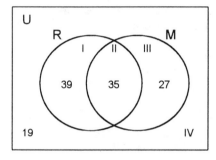

3. a) 39, Region I
    b) 27, Region III
    c) 101, the sum of the numbers in Regions I, II, III

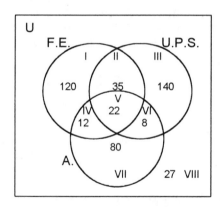

5. a) 27, Region VIII
    b) 80, Region VII
    c) 340, the sum of the numbers in Regions I, III, VII
    d) 55, the sum of the numbers in Regions II, IV, VI
    e) 337, the sum of the numbers in Regions I, II, III, IV, V, VI

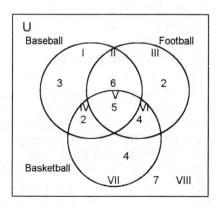

7. a) 2, Region III
    b) 6, Region II
    c) 22, the sum of the numbers in Regions I, II, III, IV, V, VI
    d) 11, the sum of the numbers in Regions I, II, III
    e) 12, the sum of the numbers in Regions II, IV, VI

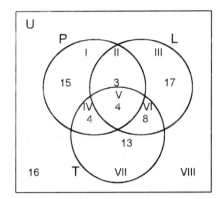

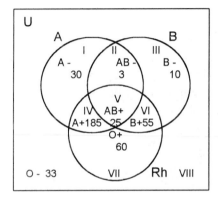

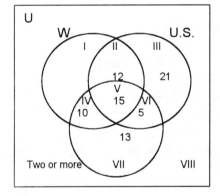

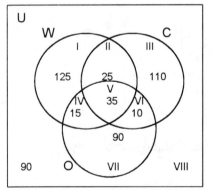

9. a) 13, Region VII
    b) 45, the sum of the numbers in
    Regions I, III, VII
    c) 64, the sum of the numbers in
    Regions I through VII
    d) 15, the sum of the numbers in
    Regions II, IV, VI
    e) 16, Region VIII

11. a) 185, Region IV
     b) 10, Region III
     c) 25, Region V
     d) 401, the sum of the numbers in
     Regions I through VIII

13. The Venn diagram shows the number of cars
     driven by women is 37, the sum of the
     numbers in Regions II, IV, V. This exceeds
     the 35 women the agent claims to have
     surveyed.

15. a) 410, the sum of the numbers in
     Regions I through VII
     b) 35, Region V
     c) 90, Region VIII
     d) 50, the sum of the numbers in
     Regions II, IV, VI.
     The number of farmers growing wheat only,
     Region I, is 125. The number growing corn
     only, Region III, is 110. The number growing
     oats only, Region VII, is 90. 60 farmers grew
     wheat and corn, Regions II and V. 200
     farmers grew wheat. Therefore, the sum of
     the numbers in Regions I, II, IV, V must
     equal 200. 125 + 60 + number in Region IV
     = 200. Thus, the number in Region IV is 15.

Exercise Set 2.6

1. An **infinite set** is a set that can be placed in a one-to-one correspondence with a proper subset of itself.

3. $\{4, 5, 6, 7, 8, ..., n + 3, ...\}$
   $\downarrow\downarrow\downarrow\downarrow\ \downarrow\qquad\downarrow$
   $\{5, 6, 7, 8, 9, ..., n + 4, ...\}$

5. $\{6, 8, 10, 12, 14, ..., 2n + 4, ...\}$
   $\downarrow\ \downarrow\ \downarrow\ \downarrow\ \downarrow\qquad\downarrow$
   $\{8, 10, 12, 14, 16, ..., 2n + 6, ...\}$

7. $\{4, 7, 10, 13, 16, ..., 3n + 1, ...\}$
   $\downarrow\ \downarrow\ \downarrow\ \downarrow\ \downarrow\qquad\downarrow$
   $\{7, 10, 13, 16, 19, ..., 3n + 4, ...\}$

9. $\{6, 11, 16, 21, 26, ..., 5n + 1, ...\}$
   $\downarrow\ \downarrow\ \downarrow\ \downarrow\ \downarrow\qquad\downarrow$
   $\{11, 16, 21, 26, 31, ..., 5n + 6, ...\}$

11. $\{1, \dfrac{1}{3}, \dfrac{1}{5}, \dfrac{1}{7}, \dfrac{1}{9}, ..., \dfrac{1}{2n - 1}, ...\}$
   $\downarrow\ \downarrow\ \downarrow\ \downarrow\ \downarrow\qquad\downarrow$
   $\{\dfrac{1}{3}, \dfrac{1}{5}, \dfrac{1}{7}, \dfrac{1}{9}, \dfrac{1}{11}, ..., \dfrac{1}{2n + 1}, ...\}$

13. $\{1, 2, 3, 4, 5, ..., n, ...\}$
   $\downarrow\downarrow\downarrow\downarrow\downarrow\qquad\downarrow$
   $\{3, 6, 9, 12, 15, ..., 3n, ...\}$

15. $\{1, 2, 3, 4, 5, ..., n, ...\}$
   $\downarrow\ \downarrow\downarrow\downarrow\ \downarrow\qquad\downarrow$
   $\{4, 6, 8, 10, 12, ..., 2n + 2, ...\}$

17. $\{1, 2, 3, 4, 5, ..., n, ...\}$
   $\downarrow\downarrow\downarrow\downarrow\ \downarrow\qquad\downarrow$
   $\{2, 5, 8, 11, 14, ..., 3n - 1, ...\}$

19. $\{1, 2, 3, 4, 5, ..., n, ...\}$
   $\downarrow\ \downarrow\ \downarrow\ \downarrow\ \downarrow\qquad\downarrow$
   $\{5, 8, 11, 14, 17, ..., 3n + 2, ...\}$

21. $\{1, 2, 3, 4, 5, ..., n, ...\}$
   $\downarrow\ \downarrow\ \downarrow\ \downarrow\ \downarrow\qquad\downarrow$
   $\{\dfrac{1}{3}, \dfrac{1}{4}, \dfrac{1}{5}, \dfrac{1}{6}, \dfrac{1}{7}, ..., \dfrac{1}{n + 2}, ...\}$

23. $\{1, 2, 3, 4, 5, ..., n, ...\}$
   $\downarrow\ \downarrow\ \downarrow\ \downarrow\ \downarrow\qquad\downarrow$
   $\{1, 4, 9, 16, 25, ..., n^2, ...\}$

25. $\{1, 2, 3, 4, 5, ..., n, ...\}$
   $\downarrow\ \downarrow\ \downarrow\ \downarrow\ \downarrow\qquad\downarrow$
   $\{3, 9, 27, 81, 243, ..., 3^n, ...\}$

Review Exercises

1. True

2. False, the word best makes the statement not well defined.

3. True

4. False, no set is a proper subset of itself.

5. False, 6, 12, 18, 24, ... are members of both sets.

6. True

7. False, both sets do not contain exactly the same elements.

8. True

9. True

10. True

11. True

12. True

13. True

14. True

15. $A = \{7, 9, 11, 13, 15\}$

16. $B = \{TX, NM, CO, KS, MO, AR\}$

17. $C = \{1, 2, 3, 4, ..., 296\}$

18. $D = \{9, 10, 11, 12, ..., 96\}$

19. $A = \{x \mid x \in N \text{ and } 72 < x < 100\}$

20. $B = \{x \mid x \in N \text{ and } x > 85\}$

21. $C = \{x \mid x \in N \text{ and } x < 3\}$

22. $D = \{x \mid x \in N \text{ and } 23 \le x \le 41\}$

23. A is the set of capital letters in the English alphabet from E through M, inclusive.

24. B is the set of U.S. coins with a value of less than one dollar.

25. C is the set of the last three lowercase letters in the English alphabet.

26. D is the set of numbers greater than or equal to 3 and less than 9.

27. $A \cap B = \{1, 3, 5, 7\} \cap \{5, 7, 9, 13\} = \{5, 7\}$

28. $A \cup B' = \{1, 3, 5, 7\} \cup \{5, 7, 9, 13\}' = \{1, 3, 5, 7\} \cup \{1, 3, 11, 15\} = \{1, 3, 5, 7, 11, 15\}$

29. $A' \cap B = \{1, 3, 5, 7\}' \cap \{5, 7, 9, 13\} = \{9, 11, 13, 15\} \cap \{5, 7, 9, 13\} = \{9, 13\}$

30. $(A \cup B)' \cup C = (\{1, 3, 5, 7\} \cup \{5, 7, 9, 13\})' \cup \{1, 7, 13\} = \{1, 3, 5, 7, 9, 13\}' \cup \{1, 7, 13\}$
    $= \{11, 15\} \cup \{1, 7, 13\} = \{1, 7, 11, 13, 15\}$

31. $2^4 = 2 \times 2 \times 2 \times 2 = 16$

32. $2^4 - 1 = (2 \times 2 \times 2 \times 2) - 1 = 16 - 1 = 15$

33.

34. $A \cup B = \{a, c, d, e, f, g, i, k\}$

35. $A \cap B' = \{d, i\}$

36. $A \cup B \cup C = \{a, b, c, d, e, f, g, i, k\}$

37. $A \cap B \cap C = \{e\}$

38. $(A \cup B) \cap C = \{a, c, d, e, f, g, i, k\} \cap \{a, b, d, e\} = \{a, d, e\}$

39. $(A \cap B) \cup C = \{e, f, g\} \cup \{a, b, d, e\} = \{a, b, d, e, f, g\}$

40. $(A' \cup B')'$ $A \cap B$

Set	Regions	Set	Regions
A	I, II	A	I, II
A'	III, IV	B	II, III
B	II, III	$A \cap B$	II
B'	I, IV		
$A' \cup B'$	I, III, IV		
$(A' \cup B')'$	II		

The two statements are represented by the same region, II, of the Venn diagram. Therefore,

$(A' \cup B')' = A \cap B$ for all sets A and B.

41. $(A \cup B') \cup (A \cup C')$

Set	Regions
A	I, II, IV, V
B	II, III, V, VI
B'	I, IV, VII, VIII
$A \cup B'$	I, II, IV, V, VII, VIII
C	IV, V, VI, VII
C'	I, II, III, VIII
$A \cup C'$	I, II, III, IV, V, VIII
$(A \cup B') \cup (A \cup C')$	I, II, III, IV, V, VII, VIII

$A \cup (B \cap C)'$

Set	Regions
B	II, III, V, VI
C	IV, V, VI, VII
$B \cap C$	V, VI
$(B \cap C)'$	I, II, III, IV, VII, VIII
A	I, II, IV, V
$A \cup (B \cap C)'$	I, II, III, IV, V, VII, VIII

The two statements are represented by the same regions, I, II, III, IV, V, VII, VIII, of the Venn diagram. Therefore, $(A \cup B') \cup (A \cup C') = A \cup (B \cap C)'$ for all sets A, B, and C.

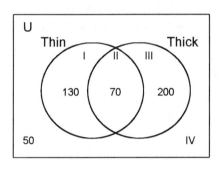

42.   The company paid $450 since the sum of the numbers in Regions I through IV is 450.

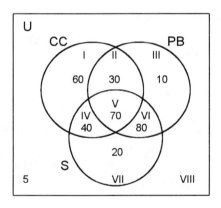

43. a) 315, the sum of the numbers in Regions I through VIII
b) 10, Region III
c) 30, Region II
d) 110, the sum of the numbers in Regions III, VI, VII

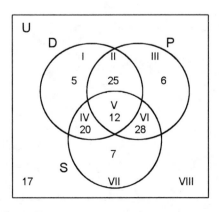

44. a)   5, Region I
b)   18, the sum of the numbers in Regions I, III, VII
c)   73, the sum of the numbers in Regions II, IV, VI
d)   28, Region VI
e)   41, the sum of the numbers in Regions III, VI, VII

45. {2, 4, 6, 8, 10, ..., 2n, ...}
    ↓ ↓ ↓ ↓ ↓   ↓
    {4, 6, 8, 10, 12, ..., 2n + 2, ...}

46. {3, 5, 7, 9, 11, ..., 2n + 1, ...}
    ↓ ↓ ↓ ↓ ↓   ↓
    {5, 7, 9, 11, 13, ..., 2n + 3, ...}

47. {1, 2, 3, 4, 5, ..., n, ...}
    ↓ ↓ ↓ ↓ ↓   ↓
    {5, 8, 11, 14, 17, ..., 3n + 2, ...}

48. {1, 2, 3, 4, 5, ..., n, ...}
    ↓ ↓ ↓ ↓ ↓   ↓
    {4, 9, 14, 19, 24, ..., 5n - 1, ...}

Chapter Test

1. True

2. False, the sets do not contain exactly the same elements.

3. True

4. False, the second set has no subset that contains the element 7.

5. False, the empty set is a proper subset of every set except itself.

6. False, the set has 2^3 = 2 x 2 x 2 = 8 subsets.

7. True

8. False, $A \cup A'$ = U.

9. True

10. A = {1, 2, 3, 4, 5, 6, 7}

11. Set A is the set of natural numbers less than 8.

12. $A \cap B$ = {3, 5, 7, 9} $\cap$ {7, 9, 11, 13} = {7, 9}

13. $A \cup C'$ = {3, 5, 7, 9} $\cup$ {3, 11, 15}' = {3, 5, 7, 9} $\cup$ {5, 7, 9, 13} = {3, 5, 7, 9, 13}

14. $A \cap (B \cap C)'$ = {3, 5, 7, 9} $\cap$ ({7, 9, 11, 13} $\cap$ {3, 11, 15})'
    = {3, 5, 7, 9} $\cap$ {11}' = {3, 5, 7, 9} $\cap$ {3, 5, 7, 9, 13, 15} = {3, 5, 7, 9} = A

15. n(A $\cap$ B') = n({3, 5, 7, 9} $\cap$ {7, 9, 11, 13}') = n({3, 5, 7, 9} $\cap$ {3, 5, 15}) = n({3, 5}) = 2

16.

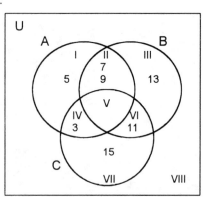

17. $A \cap (B \cup C')$ $(A \cap B) \cup (A \cap C')$

Set	Regions	Set	Regions
B	II, III, V, VI	A	I, II, IV, V
C	IV, V, VI, VII	B	II, III, V, VI
C'	I, II, III, VIII	$A \cap B$	II, V
$B \cup C'$	I, II, III, V, VI, VIII	C	IV, V, VI, VII
A	I, II, IV, V	C'	I, II, III, VIII
$A \cap (B \cap C')$	I, II, V	$A \cap C'$	I, II
		$(A \cap B) \cup (A \cap C')$	I, II, V

The two statements are represented by the same regions, I, II, V, of the Venn diagram.

Therefore, $A \cap (B \cup C') = (A \cap B) \cup (A \cap C')$ for all sets A, B, and C.

18. a)

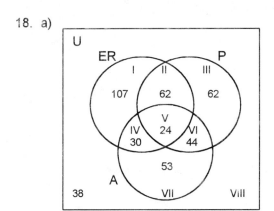

b) 222, the sum of the numbers in Regions I, III, VII.

c) 38, Region VIII

d) 136, the sum of the numbers in Regions II, IV, VI

e) 160, the sum of the numbers in Regions II, IV, V, VI

f) 231, the sum of the numbers in Regions I, II, III

g) 62, Region II

19. $\{7, 8, 9, 10, 11, ..., n + 6, ...\}$
    $\downarrow \downarrow \downarrow \downarrow \downarrow \qquad \downarrow$
    $\{8, 9, 10, 11, 12, ..., n + 7, ...\}$

20. $\{1, 2, 3, 4, 5, ..., n, ...\}$
    $\downarrow \downarrow \downarrow \downarrow \downarrow \qquad \downarrow$
    $\{1, 3, 5, 7, 9, ..., 2n - 1, ...\}$

CHAPTER THREE

LOGIC

Exercise Set 3.1

1. A simple statement is a sentence that conveys one idea and can be identified as either true or false.

3. a) Some are   b) All are
   c) Some are not   d) None are

5. Let p: The ink is purple.
   The symbolic form is ~ p. The negation symbol, ~ , represents the word <u>not</u>.

7. When a compound statement contains more than one connective a comma can be used to indicate which simple statements are to be grouped together. When writing a statement symbolically, the simple statements on the same side of the comma are to be grouped together within parentheses.

9. compound; conjunction, $\wedge$

11. compound; biconditional, $\leftrightarrow$

13. compound; disjunction, $\vee$

15. simple statement

17. compound; negation, ~

19. compound; conjunction, $\wedge$

21. compound; negation, ~

23. No flowers are yellow.

25. Some fish do not swim.

27. All dogs have fleas

29. Some books are round.

31. All rain forests are being destroyed.

33. No students maintain an A average.

35. ~ p

37. ~ q $\vee$ ~ p

39. ~ p $\rightarrow$ ~ q

41. ~ q $\leftrightarrow$ ~ p

43. ~ p $\wedge$ ~ q

45. ~ (q $\rightarrow$ ~ p)

47. Firemen do not wear red suspenders.

49. Firemen wear red suspenders or firemen work hard.

51. If firemen do not work hard, then firemen wear red suspenders.

53. It is false that firemen wear red suspenders or firemen work hard.

55. Firemen do not work hard and firemen do not wear red suspenders.

57. (p $\wedge$ q) $\vee$ r

59. (r $\leftrightarrow$ ~ p) $\vee$ ~ q

61. (r $\wedge$ q) $\rightarrow$ p

63. (r $\leftrightarrow$ q) $\wedge$ p

65. q $\rightarrow$ (p $\leftrightarrow$ r)

67. The water is 70° and the sun is shinning, or we will go swimming.

69. If the sun is shinning then the water is 70°, or we will go swimming.

71. If we do not go swimming, then the sun is shinning and the water is 70°.

73. If the sun is shinning then we go swimming, and the water is 70°.

75. The sun is shinning if and only if the water is 70°, and we go swimming.

77. Not permissible. In the list of choices, the connective "or" is the exclusive or, thus one can order either the soup or the salad but not both items.

79. Not permissible. Potatoes and pasta cannot be ordered together.

81. a) $(\sim p) \to q$ b) conditional   83. a) $(\sim q) \wedge (\sim r)$ b) conjunction

85. a) $(p \vee q) \to r$ b) conditional   87. a) $r \to (p \vee q)$ b) conditional

89. a) $(\sim p) \leftrightarrow (\sim q \to r)$ b) biconditional   91. a) $(r \wedge \sim q) \to (q \wedge \sim p)$ b) conditional

93. a) $\sim [(p \wedge q) \leftrightarrow (p \vee r)]$ b) negation

95. c: Carol Britz visited Nancy Hart.
    d: Carol Britz did drive to Maine.
    a) $c \vee \sim d$ b) disjunction

97. p: You pay your taxes.
    a: You will get audited.
    s: The sun is shinning.
    a) $\sim (p \to \sim a)$ b) negation

99. f: The fruit is red.
    v: The vegetables are carrots.
    e: You will eat well.
    a) $(f \vee v) \to e$ b) conditional

101. o: The store is open.
     s: Today is Sunday.
     f: It is before 5 PM.
     a) $o \leftrightarrow (\sim s \vee f)$ b) biconditional

103. e: The store is empty.
     s: Today is Sunday.
     f: It is after 5 PM.
     a) $(e \leftrightarrow s) \vee f$ b) disjunction

105. $[(\sim q) \to (r \vee p)] \leftrightarrow [(\sim r) \wedge q]$, biconditional

107. a) The conjunction and disjunction have the same dominance.

   c) If we evaluate the truth table for $p \vee q \wedge r$ using the order $(p \vee q) \wedge r$ we get a different solution than if we used the order $p \vee (q \wedge r)$. Therefore, unless we are told where the parentheses belong, we do not know which solution is correct.

Exercise Set 3.2

1. a) $2^2 = 2 \times 2 = 4$ distinct cases
   b)

	p	q
case 1:	T	T
case 2	T	F
case 3:	F	T
case 4:	F	F

3. a)

p	q	p	$\wedge$	q
T	T	T	T	T
T	F	T	F	F
F	T	F	F	T
F	F	F	F	F
		1	3	2

   b) Only in case 1, when both simple statements are true.

5.

p	p	$\wedge$	$\sim p$
T	T	F	F
F	F	F	T
	1	3	2

7.

p	q	q	$\vee$	$\sim p$
T	T	T	T	F
T	F	F	F	F
F	T	T	T	T
F	F	F	T	T
		1	3	2

9.

p	q	$\sim p$	$\vee$	$\sim q$
T	T	F	F	F
T	F	F	T	T
F	T	T	T	F
F	F	T	T	T
		1	3	2

11.

p	q	~	(p	∧	~q)
T	T	T	T	F	F
T	F	F	T	T	T
F	T	T	F	F	F
F	F	T	F	F	T
		4	1	3	2

13.

p	q	r	(p	∧	r)	∨	~q)
T	T	T	T		T	F	
T	T	F	F		F	F	
T	F	T	T		T	T	
T	F	F	F		T	T	
F	T	T	F		F	F	
F	T	F	F		F	F	
F	F	T	F		T	T	
F	F	F	F		T	T	
			1		3	2	

15.

p	q	R	r	∨	(p	∧	~q)
T	T	T	T	T	T	F	F
T	T	F	F	F	T	F	F
T	F	T	T	T	T	T	T
T	F		–	–	–	–	–
F	T						
F	T						
F	F						
F	F						

17.

p	q	r	~q	∧	(r	∨	~p)
T	T	T	F	F	T	T	F
T	T	F	F	F	F	F	F
T	F	T	T	T	T	T	F
T	F	F	T	F	F	F	F
F	T	T	F	F	T	T	T
F	T	F	F	F	F	T	T
F	F	T	T	T	T	T	T
F	F	F	T	T	F	T	T
			1	5	2	4	3

19.

p	q	r	(~q	∧	r)	∨	p
T	T	T	F	F	T	T	T
T	T	F	F	F	F	T	T
T	F	T	T	T	T	T	T
T	F	F	T	F	F	T	T
F	T	T	F	F	T	F	F
F	T	F	F	F	F	F	F
F	F	T	T	T	T	T	F
F	F	F	T	F	F	F	F
			1	3	2	5	4

21.   p: Driving is fun.
q: Walking is good exercise.
In symbolic form the statement is p ∧ q.

p	q	p∧q
T	T	T
T	F	F
F	T	F
F	F	F
		1

23.   p: The sock fits.
q: The shoe fits.
In symbolic form the statement is p ∧ ~ q.

p	q	p	∧	~q
T	T	T	F	F
T	F	T	T	T
F	T	F	F	F
F	F	F	F	T
		1	3	2

25.   p: Ricardo will take mathematics.
q: Ricardo will take history.
r : Ricardo will take psychology.
In symbolic form the statement is (p ∨ q) ∧ ~ r.

p	q	r	(p ∨ q)	∧	~r
T	T	T	T	F	F
T	T	F	T	T	T
T	F	T	T	F	F
T	F	F	T	T	T
F	T	T	T	F	F
F	T	F	T	T	T
F	F	T	F	F	F
F	F	F	F	F	T
			1	3	2

27.   p: Karen uses American Online.
q: Karen uses Yahoo.
r : Karen uses Microsoft Explorer.
In symbolic form the statement is (p ∧ q) ∧ ~ r).

p	q	r	(p ∧ q)	∧	~r
T	T	T	T	F	F
T	T	F	T	T	T
T	F	T	F	F	F
T	F	F	F	F	T
F	T	T	F	F	F
F	T	F	F	F	T
F	F	T	F	F	F
F	F	F	F	F	T
			1	3	2

29. p: The password is pistachio.
     q: The gate is open.
     In symbolic form the statement is p ∧ (q ∨ ~ q).

p	q	p	∧	(q	∨	~q)
T	T	T	T	T	T	F
T	F	T	T	F	T	T
F	T	F	F	T	T	F
F	F	F	F	F	T	T
		1	5	2	4	3

31. ~p ∨ (q ∧ r)
      F ∨ (F ∧ T)
      F ∨   F
              F
     Therefore the statement is false.

33. (~q ∧ ~p) ∨ ~r
     (T   ∧ F) ∨ F
           F   ∨ F
                F
     Therefore the statement is false.

35. (p ∧ ~q) ∨ r
     (T ∧   T) ∨ T
          T   ∨ T
               T
     Therefore the statement is true.

37. (~r ∧ p) ∨ q
     (T   ∧ F) ∨ T
           F   ∨ T
                T
     Therefore the statement is true.

39. (~q ∨ ~p) ∧ r
     (F   ∨   T) ∧ F
           T   ∧ F
                F
     Therefore the statement is false.

41. (~p ∨ ~q) ∨ (~r ∨ q)
     (T   ∨ F) ∨ (T   ∨ T)
           T   ∨   T
                     T
     Therefore the statement is true.

43.   4 + 3 = 7 or 6 + 4 = 12
           T   ∨   F
                   T
     Therefore the statement is true.

45. p: Elvis Presley was born in Tupelo Mississippi.   p ∨ q
     q: The giraffe has only two legs.   T ∨ F
                                                                                 True

47. p: Algebra is a mathematics course.   (p ∧ q) ∧ ~ r
     q: Geometry is a mathematics course.   (T ∧ T) ∧ T
     r : Shakespearean literature is a mathematics course.   T   ∧ T
                                                                                  True

49. p: Marco Polo played football.   (p ∨ q) ∧ r
     q: John Glenn built houses.   (F ∨ F) ∧ T
     r : George Washington is on a US one dollar bill.   F   ∧ T
                                                                                 False

51. p: 28 pounds of cheese was consumed by the   p ∧ ~ q
        average American in 1909.   F ∧ ~ T
     q: The average American consumed 154 pounds   F ∧ F
        sweeteners in 1997.   False

53. p: 30% of Americans get 6 hours of sleep each night.
     q: 9% of Americans get 5 hours of sleep each night.

$\sim (p \wedge q)$
$\sim (F \wedge T)$
$\sim \quad F$
True

---

55. In symbolic form the statement is $\sim p \wedge q$.

p	q	~p	∧	q
T	T	F	F	T
T	F	F	F	F
F	T	T	T	T
F	F	T	F	F
		1	3	2

The statement is true in case 3.

---

57. In symbolic form the statement is $p \vee \sim q$.

p	q	p	∨	~q
T	T	T	T	F
T	F	T	T	T
F	T	F	F	F
F	F	F	T	T
		1	3	2

The statement is true in cases 1, 2, & 4.

---

59. In symbolic form the statement is $(p \wedge q) \vee r$.

p	q	r	(p	∧	q)	∨	r
T	T	T		T		T	T
T	T	F		T		T	F
T	F	T		F		T	T
T	F	F		F		F	F
F	T	T		F		T	T
F	T	F		F		F	F
F	F	T		F		T	T
F	F	F		F		F	F
				1		3	2

The statement is true in cases 1, 2, 3, 5, and 7.

---

61. In symbolic form the statement is $q \vee (p \wedge \sim r)$.

p	q	r	q	∨	(p	∧	~r)
T	T	T	T	T	T	F	F
T	T	F	T	T	T	T	T
T	F	T	F	F	T	F	F
T	F	F	F	T	T	T	T
F	T	T	T	T	F	F	F
F	T	F	T	T	F	F	T
F	F	T	F	F	F	F	F
F	F	F	F	F	F	F	T
			4	5	1	3	2

The statement is true in cases 1, 2, 4, 5, and 6.

63.a) Ms. Duncan qualifies for the loan. Mrs. Tuttle qualifies for the loan.

  b) The Furmans do not qualify since they are married and do not have a combined income of $46,000

65.a) Mike Bolinder qualifies for the special fare.
  b) Gina Vela does not qualify since she will return after April 1st. Laura Griffin Heller does not qualify since she is not returning on a Tuesday Wednesday, or Thursday. Christos G. does not qualify since he will not be staying over at least one Saturday. Alex Chang does not qualify since he is not returning on a Tuesday, Wednesday, or Thursdayz

---

67.

p	q	r	[(q	∧	~r)	∧	(~p	∨	~q)]	∨	(p	∨	~r)
T	T	T	T	F	F	F	F	F	F	T	T	T	F
T	T	F	T	T	T	F	F	F	F	T	T	T	T
T	F	T	F	F	F	F	F	T	T	T	T	T	F
T	F	F	F	F	T	F	F	T	T	T	T	T	T
F	T	T	T	F	F	F	T	T	F	F	F	F	F
F	T	F	T	T	T	T	T	T	F	T	F	T	T
F	F	T	F	F	F	F	T	T	T	F	F	F	F
F	F	F	F	F	T	F	T	T	T	T	F	T	T
			1	3	2	7	4	6	5	11	8	10	9

---

69. Yes. Each statement uses the exact same arrangement of connectives

Exercise Set 3.3

1.a)

p	q	p	→	q
T	T	T	T	T
T	F	T	F	F
F	T	F	T	T
F	F	F	T	F
		1	3	2

b) The conditional statement is false only in the case when antecedent is true and the consequent is false, otherwise it is true.

5. A tautology is a compound statement that is true in every case.

7.

p	q	p	→	~q
T	T	T	F	F
T	F	T	T	T
F	T	F	T	F
F	F	F	T	T
		1	3	2

11.

p	q	~q	↔	p
T	T	F	F	T
T	F	T	T	T
F	T	F	T	F
F	F	T	F	F
		1	3	2

15.

p	q	q	→	(p	→	~q)
T	T	T	F	T	F	F
T	F	F	T	T	T	T
F	T	T	T	F	T	F
F	F	F	T	F	T	T
		4	5	1	3	2

19.

p	q	r	q	↔	(r	∧	p)
T	T	T	T	T		T	
T	T	F	T	F		F	
T	F	T	F	F		T	
T	F	F	F	T		F	
F	T	T	T	F		F	
F	T	F	T	F		F	
F	F	T	F	T		F	
F	F	F	F	T		F	
			2	3		1	

3.a) Substitute the truth values for the simple statement. Then evaluate the compound statement for that specific case.

b)

$[(p \rightarrow q) \vee (\sim q \rightarrow r)] \rightarrow \sim r$
$[(T \rightarrow F) \vee (\sim F \rightarrow T)] \rightarrow \sim T$
$[\quad F \quad \vee (T \rightarrow T)] \rightarrow F$
$[\quad F \quad \vee \quad T \quad] \rightarrow F$
$\qquad\qquad T \qquad\qquad \rightarrow F$
$\qquad\qquad\qquad\qquad\qquad F$

In this specific case the statement is false.

9.

p	q	~	(p ↔ q)
T	T	F	T
T	F	T	F
F	T	T	F
F	F	F	T
		2	1

13.

p	q	p	↔	(q	∨	p)
T	T	T	T		T	
T	F	T	T		T	
F	T	F	F		T	
F	F	F	T		F	
		1	3		2	

17.

p	q	r	p	→	(q	∨	r)
T	T	T	T	T		T	
T	T	F	T	T		T	
T	F	T	T	T		T	
T	F	F	T	F		F	
F	T	T	F	T		T	
F	T	F	F	T		T	
F	F	T	F	T		T	
F	F	F	F	T		F	
			2	3		1	

21.

p	q	r	(q	∨	~r)	↔	~p
T	T	T	T	T	F	F	F
T	T	F	T	T	T	F	F
T	F	T	F	F	F	T	F
T	F	F	F	T	T	F	F
F	T	T	T	T	F	T	T
F	T	F	T	T	T	T	T
F	F	T	F	F	F	F	T
F	F	F	F	T	T	T	T
			1	3	2	5	4

23.

p	q	r	(~r	∨	~q)	→	p
T	T	T	F	F	F	T	T
T	T	F	T	T	F	T	T
T	F	T	F	T	T	T	T
T	F	F	T	T	T	T	T
F	T	T	F	F	F	T	F
F	T	F	T	T	F	F	F
F	F	T	F	T	T	F	F
F	F	F	T	T	T	F	F
			1	3	2	5	4

25.

p	q	r	(p	→	q)	↔	(~q	→	~r)
T	T	T		T		T	F	T	F
T	T	F		T		T	F	T	T
T	F	T		F		T	T	F	F
T	F	F		F		F	T	T	T
F	T	T		T		T	F	T	F
F	T	F		T		T	F	T	T
F	F	T		T		F	T	F	F
F	F	F		T		T	T	T	T
				1		5	2	4	3

27. p: I cut the grass.
q: I will need to rake.
r: I will need to bag the clippings

p	q	r	p	→	(q ∧ r)
T	T	T	T	T	T
T	T	F	T	F	F
T	F	T	T	F	F
T	F	F	T	F	F
F	T	T	F	T	T
F	T	F	F	T	F
F	F	T	F	T	F
F	F	F	F	T	F
			2	3	1

29. p: The cable is out.
q: We can watch T.V.
r: We will use the antenna.
In symbolic form the statement is
(p ↔ ~q) ∨ r.

p	q	r	(p	↔	~q)	∨	r
T	T	T	T	F	F	T	T
T	T	F	T	F	F	F	F
T	F	T	T	T	T	T	T
T	F	F	T	T	T	T	F
F	T	T	F	T	F	T	T
F	T	F	F	T	F	T	F
F	F	T	F	F	T	T	T
F	F	F	F	F	T	F	F
			2	3	1	5	4

31. p: The computer is being used.
q: We can use the telephone.
r: We can use the fax machine.
In symbolic form the statement is
(~p → q) ∨ r.

p	q	r	(~p	→	q)	∨	r
T	T	T	F	T	T	T	T
T	T	F	F	T	T	T	F
T	F	T	F	T	F	T	T
T	F	F	F	T	F	T	F
F	T	T	T	T	T	T	T
F	T	F	T	T	T	T	F
F	F	T	T	F	F	T	T
F	F	F	T	F	F	F	F
			1	3	2	5	4

33.

p	q	~q	→	p
T	T	F	T	T
T	F	T	T	T
F	T	F	T	F
F	F	T	F	F
		1	3	2

Neither

35.

p	Q	~q	∧	(q ∧ p)
T	T	F	F	T
T	F	T	F	F
F	T	F	F	F
F	F	T	F	F
		1	3	2

Self-contradiction

37.

p	q	(~p	→	q)	∨	~p
T	T	F	T	T	T	F
T	F	F	T	F	T	F
F	T	T	T	T	T	T
F	F	T	F	F	T	T
		1	3	2	5	4

Tautology

39.

p	q	(p ∨ q)	→	(q ∧ p)
T	T	T	T	T
T	F	T	F	F
F	T	T	F	F
F	F	F	T	F
		1	3	2

Not an implication

41.

p	q	(q ∧ p) → (p ∧ q)		
T	T	T	T	T
T	F	F	T	F
F	T	F	T	F
F	F	F	T	F
		1	3	2

Implication

43.

p	q	[(p → q) ∧ (q → p)] → (p ↔ q)				
T	T	T	T	T	T	T
T	F	F	F	T	T	F
F	T	T	F	F	T	F
F	F	T	T	T	T	T
		1	3	2	5	4

Implication

45. ~ p → (q ∧ ~ r)
    F   → (F ∧ F)
    F   →   F
        T

47. (q ∧ ~ p) ↔ ~ r
   (F ∧ F) ↔ F
     F   ↔ F
        T

49. (~ p ∧ ~ q) ∨ ~ r
   (F ∧ T) ∨ F
       F   ∨ F
         F

51. (p ∧ r) ↔ (p ∨ ~ q)
    T ↔ (T ∨ T)
    T ↔   T
       T

53. (~ p ↔ r) ∨ (~ q ↔ r)
  (F ↔ T) ∨ (T ↔ T)
     F   ∨   T
       T

55. ~ [(p ∨ q) ↔ (p → ~ r)]
  ~ [(T ∨ F) ↔ (T → F)]
  ~ [T   ↔   F]
  ~ [F   ]
  T

57. p: 2 + 3 = 5. (T)   p → q
   q: 4 + 2 = 6. (T)   T → T
                     T

59. p: 2 + 3 = 6. (F)   (p ∨ q) ∧ r
   q: 4 + 5 = 8. (F)   F   ∧ T
   r : 2 = 1 + 1. (T)   F

61. p: A pound contains 16 ounces. (T)   p ↔ (q ∨ r)
   q: A foot is equal to 15 inches. (F)   T ↔   T
   r : A yard is equal to 3 feet. (T)   True

63. p: July 4th is Independence Day. (T)   (p ∨ q) ∧ r
   q: Two dimes have the same value as 1 quarter. (F)   T ∧ T
   r : One dollar has the same value as 100 pennies. (T)   True

65. d: Io has a diameter of 1000-3161 miles. (T)   (d ∨ w) ∧ a
   w: Thebe may have water. (F)   (T ∨ F) ∧ T
   a: Io may have atmosphere. (T)   T ∧ T
                             True

67. d: Phoebe has a larger diameter than Rhea. (F)   (d ↔ w) ∧ c
   w: Callisto may have water. (T)   (F ↔ T) ∧ T
   c: Calypso has a diameter of 6 – 49 miles. (T)   F ∧ T
                             False

69. f: The most common cosmetic surgery for females is liposuction. (T)   (f ∨ m) ∧ n
   m: The most common procedure for males is eyelid surgery. (F)   (T ∨ F) ∧ F
   n: 20% of male cosmetic surgery is nose reshaping. (F)   T ∧ F
                              False

71. p → q
   T → T
     T

73. ~ p → q
   F → T
     T

75. q ↔ p
   T ↔ T
     T

77. No. Your father does not say what he will do if he does not get the raise. He may decide to buy the car even if he does not get the raise.

79.

p	q	r	[(p ∨ q)	→	~r]	↔	(p	∧	~q)
T	T	T	T	F	F	T	T	F	F
T	T	F	T	T	T	F	T	F	F
T	F	T	T	F	F	F	T	T	T
T	F	F	T	T	T	T	T	T	T
F	T	T	T	F	F	T	F	F	F
F	T	F	T	T	T	F	F	F	F
F	F	T	F	T	F	F	F	F	T
F	F	F	F	T	T	F	F	F	T
			1	3	2	7	4	6	5

81. Let p: Heads I win. If we assume that you losing means that I win, then this statement is of the form p ∨ ~ p which is a tautology.

83.

	Tiger	Boots	Sam	Sue
bowl:	blue	yellow	red	green
food:	Nine Lives	Whiskas	Friskies	Meow Mix

Exercise Set 3.4

1. ⇔

3. Construct a truth table for each statement and then compare the answer columns. If they are identical, then the statements are equivalent. If the answer columns are not identical, then the statements are not equivalent.

5. ~ (p ∧ q) ⇔ ~ p ∨ ~ q
   ~ (p ∨ q) ⇔ ~ p ∧ ~ q

7. converse ⇔ inverse;   conditional ⇔ contrapositive

9. Using DeMorgan's Laws on the statement ~ (p ∨ q), we get the following: (1) p ∨ q, (2) ~ p ∨ ~ q,
   (3) ~ p ∧ ~ q. Therefore ~ (p ∨ q) ⇔ ~ p ∧ ~ q.

11. Using DeMorgan's Laws on the statement ~ (p ∧ q), we get the following: (1) p ∧ q, (2) ~ p ∧ ~ q,
    (3) ~ p ∨ ~ q. Therefore ~ (p ∧ q) is not equivalent to ~ p ∧ q.

13. Using DeMorgan's Laws on the statement p ∧ q, we get the following: (1) ~ (p ∧ q), (2) ~ (~ p ∧ ~ q),
    (3) ~ (~ p ∨ ~ q). Therefore p ∧ q ⇔ ~ (~ p ∨ ~ q).

15. Using DeMorgan's Laws on the statement ~ (p ∧ ~ q), we get the following: (1) p ∧ ~ q, (2) ~ p ∧ q,
    (3) ~ p ∨ q. Therefore ~ (p ∧ ~ q) ⇔ ~ p ∨ q.

17. Using DeMorgan's Laws on the statement (~ p ∨ ~ q) → r, we get the following:
    (1) ~ (~ p ∨ ~ q) → r, (2) ~ (p ∨ q) → r, (3) ~ (p ∧ q) → r. Therefore (~ p ∨ ~ q) → r ⇔ ~ (p ∧ q) → r

19.

p	q	~p → q	p ∧ q
T	T	F T T	T
T	F	F T F	F
F	T	T T T	F
F	F	T F F	F
		1 3 2	1

The statements are not equivalent.

21.

p	q	p → q	~ q → ~ p
T	T	T	F T F
T	F	F	T F F
F	T	T	F T T
F	F	T	T T T
		1	1 3 2

The statements are equivalent.

23.

p	q	r	(p ∨ q) ∨ r	p ∨ (q ∨ r)
T	T	T	T T T	T T T
T	T	F	T T F	T T T
T	F	T	T T T	T T T
T	F	F	T T F	T T F
F	T	T	T T T	F T T
F	T	F	T T F	F T T
F	F	T	F T T	F T T
F	F	F	F F F	F F F
			1 3 2	2 3 1

The statements are equivalent.

25.

p	q	r	q ↔ (p ∧ ~r)	q → (p ∨ r)
T	T	T	T F T F F	T T T
T	T	F	T T T T T	T T T
T	F	T	F T T F F	F T T
T	F	F	F F T T T	F T T
F	T	T	T F F F F	T T T
F	T	F	T F F F T	T F F
F	F	T	F T F F F	F T T
F	F	F	F T F F T	F T F
			1 5 3 4 2	1 3 2

The statements are not equivalent.

27.

p	q	r	(p → q) ∧ (q → r)	(p → q) → r
T	T	T	T T T T T	T T T
T	T	F	T F F F F	T F F
T	F	T	F F F T T	F T T
T	F	F	F F F T T	F T F
F	T	T	T T T T T	T T T
F	T	F	T F F F F	T F F
F	F	T	T T T T T	T T T
F	F	F	T T T T T	T F F
			1 3 2	1 3 2

The statements are not equivalent.

29.

p	q	(p → q) ∧ (q → p)	p ↔ q
T	T	T T T T T	T
T	F	F F T T F	F
F	T	T F F F T	F
F	F	T T T T T	T
		1 3 2	1

The statements are equivalent.

31. p: The boat is at the dock.
q: The boat will depart.
In symbolic form the statement is ~ (p ∨ q). Applying DeMorgan's Laws we get:
(1) p ∨ q, (2) ~ p ∨ ~ q, (3) ~ p ∧ ~ q. The boat is not at the dock and the boat will not depart.
(1) p ∧ q, (2) ~ p ∧ ~ q, (3) ~ p ∨ ~ q. The ink is not red or the pen does not have a ball point.

33. p: The house has one phone line.
q: The house has two phone lines.
In symbolic form the statement is ~ p ∨ ~ q. Applying DeMorgan's Laws we get: (1) ~ (~ p ∨ ~ q),
(2) ~ (p ∨ q), (3) ~ (p ∧ q). It is false that the house has one phone line and the house has two phone lines.

35. p: The novel is written by Dinya Floyd.
q: It is well illustrated.
In symbolic form the statement is ~ p ∧ ~ q. Applying DeMorgan's Laws we get: (1) ~ (~ p ∧ ~ q),
(2) ~ (p ∧ q), (3) ~ (p ∨ q). It is false that the novel is written by Dinya Floyd or it is well illustrated.

37. p: We go to Cozemel.
q: We will go snorkeling.
r : We will go to Senior Frogs.
In symbolic form the statement is p → (q ∨ ~ r). Applying DeMorgan's Laws we get: (1) p → ~ (q ∨ ~ r),
(2) p → ~ (~ q ∨ r), (3) p → ~ (~ q ∧ r). If we go to Cozemel, then it is false that we will not go snorkeling and we will go to Senior Frogs.

39. p: You drink milk.
q: Your bones will be strong.
In symbolic form the statement is p → q. p → q ⇔ ~ p ∨ q. You do not drink milk or your bones will be strong.

41. p: John painted the picture.
q: Ada purchased the picture.
In symbolic form the statement is p ∨ ~ q. p ∨ ~ q ⇔ ~ p → ~ q. If John did not paint the picture, then Ada did not purchase the picture.

43. p: The noise is too loud.

q: The police will come.

In symbolic form the statement is $\sim p \to \sim q$. $\sim p \to \sim q \Leftrightarrow p \lor \sim q$. The noise is too loud or the police will not come.

45. p: You are 18 years old.

q: You are eligible to vote.

In symbolic form the statement is $(p \to q) \land (q \to p)$.

$(p \to q) \land (q \to p) \Leftrightarrow p \leftrightarrow q$. You are 18 years old if and only if you are eligible to vote.

47. p: An animal is a mammal.

q: An animal is warm blooded.

In symbolic form the statement is $p \leftrightarrow q$.

$p \leftrightarrow q \Leftrightarrow (p \to q) \land (q \to p)$. If an animal is a mammal then it is warm blooded, and if an animal is warm blooded then it is a mammal.

49. p: The fish are biting.

q: We will go fishing.

In symbolic form the statement is $p \to q$.

converse: $q \to p$; If we go fishing, then the fish are biting.

inverse: $\sim p \to \sim q$; If the fish are not biting, then we will not go fishing.

contrapositive: $\sim q \to \sim p$; If we do not go fishing, then the fish are not biting.

51. p: The phone bill is large.

q: You will have to give up your phone.

In symbolic form the statement is $p \to q$.

converse: $q \to p$; If you have to give up your phone, then the phone bill is large.

inverse: $\sim p \to \sim q$; If the phone bill is not large, then you will not have to give up your phone.

contrapositive: $\sim q \to \sim p$; If you do not have to give up your phone, then the phone bill is not large

53. p: The dog is friendly.

q: I will get out of the car.

In symbolic form the statement is $\sim p \to \sim q$.

converse: $\sim q \to \sim p$; If I do not get out of the car, then the dog is not friendly.

inverse: $p \to q$; If the dog is friendly, then I will get out of the car.

contrapositive: $q \to p$; If I get out of the car, then the dog is friendly.

55. p: The sun is shining.

q: We will go down to the marina.

r: We will take out the sailboat.

In symbolic form the statement is $p \to (q \land r)$.

converse: $(q \land r) \to p$; If we go down to the marina and we take out the sail boat, then the sun is shining.

inverse: $\sim p \to \sim (q \land r)$; Applying DeMorgan's Laws the statement becomes $\sim p \to (\sim q \lor \sim r)$. If the sun is not shining, then we will not go down to the marina or we will not take out the sail boat.

contrapositive: $\sim (q \land r) \to \sim p$; Applying DeMorgan's Laws the statement becomes $(\sim q \lor \sim r) \to p$. If we do not go down to the marina or we do not take out the sail boat, then the sun is not shining.

57. If two angles of the triangle are equal, then the triangle is isosceles. The statement is true.

59. If 2 divides the units digit of the counting number, then 2 divides the counting number. The statement is true.

61. If two lines are not parallel, then the two lines intersect in at least one point. The statement is true.

63. If the polygon is a quadrilateral, then the sum of the interior angles of the polygon measure 360^0. The statement is true.

65. p: Maria has retired.
    q: Maria is still working.
    In symbolic form the statements are: a) ~ p ∨ q, b) q → ~ p, c) p → ~ q
    Statement (c) is the contrapositive of statement (b). Therefore, statements (b) and (c) are equivalent.

		a) ~p ∨ q	b) q → ~ p
p	q		
T	T	F T T	T F F
T	F	F F F	F T F
F	T	T T T	T T T
F	F	T T F	F T T
		1 3 2	1 3 2

Since the truth tables for (a) and (b) are different we conclude that only statements (b) and (c) are equivalent.

67. p: The car is reliable.
    q: The car is noisy.
    In symbolic form the statements are: a) ~ p ∧ q, b) ~ p → ~ q, c) ~ (p ∨ ~ q.
    If we use DeMorgan's Laws on statement (a), we get statement (c). Therefore, statements (a) and (c) are equivalent. If we look at the truth tables for statements (a), (b), and (c) we see that only statements (a) and (c) are equivalent.

		a) ~ p ∧ q	b) ~ p → ~ q	c) ~ (p ∨ ~ q)
p	q			
T	T	F F T	F T F	F TT F
T	F	F F F	F T T	F TT T
F	T	T T T	T F F	T FF F
F	F	T F F	T T T	F FT T
		1 3 2	1 3 2	4 13 2

69. p: The house is made of wood.
    q: The shed is made of wood.
    In symbolic form the statements are: a) ~ p ∨ ~ q, b) p → ~ q, c) ~ (q ∧ ~ p).
    Using the fact that p → q ⇔ ~ p ∨ q to rewrite statement (b), we get ~ p ∨ ~ q. Therefore, statements (a) and (b) are equivalent. Looking at the truth tables for all three, it can be determined that only statements (a) and (b) are equivalent.

		a) ~ p ∨ ~ q	b) p → ~ q	c) ~ (q ∧ ~ p)
p	q			
T	T	F F F	T F F	T T F F
T	F	F T T	T T T	T F F F
F	T	T T F	F T F	F T T T
F	F	T T T	F T T	T F F T
		1 3 2	1 3 2	4 1 3 2

71. p: You will get a speeding ticket.

q: You speed.

In symbolic form the statements are: a) $\sim p \leftrightarrow \sim q$, b) $\sim (p \leftrightarrow \sim q)$, c) $p \to q$.

Looking at the truth tables for statements (a), (b), and (c) it can be determined that only statements (a) and (b) are equivalent.

p	q	a) $\sim p \leftrightarrow \sim q$			b) $\sim (p \leftrightarrow \sim q)$				c) $p \to q$
T	T	F	T	F	T	T	F	F	T
T	F	F	F	T	F	T	T	T	F
F	T	T	F	F	F	F	T	F	T
F	F	T	T	T	T	F	F	T	T
		1	3	2	4	1	3	2	1

73. p: You are fishing at 1 PM.

q: You are driving a car at 1 PM.

In symbolic form the statements are: a) $p \to q$, b) $\sim p \lor q$, c) $\sim (p \land \sim q)$.

Using the fact that $p \to q \Leftrightarrow \sim p \lor q$, we see that (a) and (b) are equivalent statements.

If we use DeMorgan's Laws on statement (b) we get statement (c). Therefore all three statements are equivalent.

75. p: The pay is good.

q: Today is Monday.

r : I will take the job.

Looking at the truth tables for statements (a), (b), and (c), we can determine that none of these statements are equivalent.

p	q	r	a) $(p \land q) \to r$			b) $\sim r \to \sim (p \lor q)$				c) $(p \land q) \lor r$		
T	T	T	T	T	T	F	T	F	T	T	T	T
T	T	F	T	F	F	T	F	F	T	T	T	F
T	F	T	F	T	T	F	T	F	T	F	T	T
T	F	F	F	T	F	T	F	F	T	F	F	F
F	T	T	F	T	T	F	T	F	T	F	T	T
F	T	F	F	T	F	T	F	F	T	F	F	F
F	F	T	F	T	T	F	T	T	F	F	T	T
F	F	F	F	T	F	T	T	T	F	F	F	F
			1	3	2	1	4	3	2	1	3	2

77. p: The package was sent by Federal Express.

q: The package was sent by United Parcel Service.

r : The package arrived on time.

Using the fact that $p \to q \Leftrightarrow \sim p \lor q$, to rewrite statement (c) we get $p \lor (\sim q \land r)$. Therefore, statements (a) and (c) are equivalent. Looking at the truth table for statements (a) and (b), we can conclude that only statements (a) and (c) are equivalent.

p	q	r	a) $p \lor (\sim q \land r)$					b) $r \leftrightarrow (p \lor \sim q)$				
T	T	T	T	T	F	F	T	T	T	T	T	F
T	T	F	T	T	F	F	F	F	F	T	T	F
T	F	T	T	T	T	T	T	T	T	T	T	T
T	F	F	T	T	T	F	F	F	F	T	T	T
F	T	T	F	F	F	F	T	T	F	F	F	F
F	T	F	F	F	F	F	F	F	T	F	F	F
F	F	T	F	T	T	T	T	T	T	F	T	T
F	F	F	F	F	T	F	F	F	F	F	T	T
			1	5	2		4 3	1	5	2	4	3

79. p: The car needs oil.
    q: The car needs gas.
    r : The car is new.
    In symbolic form the statements are: a) $p \wedge (q \vee r)$, b) $p \wedge \sim (\sim q \wedge \sim r)$, c) $p \to (q \vee \sim r)$. If we use DeMorgan's Laws on the disjunction in statement (a), we obtain $p \wedge \sim (\sim q \wedge \sim r)$. Therefore, statements (a) and (b) are equivalent. If we compare the truth tables for (a) and (c) we see that they are not equivalent. Therefore, only statements (a) and (b) are equivalent.

p	q	r	$p \wedge (q \vee r)$			$p \to (q \vee \sim r)$			
T	T	T	T	T	T	T	T	T T	F
T	T	F	T	T	T	T	T	T T	T
T	F	T	T	T	T	T	F	F F	F
T	F	F	T	F	F	T	T	F T	T
F	T	T	F	F	T	F	T	T T	F
F	T	F	F	F	T	F	T	T T	T
F	F	T	F	F	T	F	T	F F	F
F	F	F	F	F	F	F	T	F T	T
			1	3	2	1	5	2 4	3

81. Yes.   conditional: If it is a bird, then it can fly. (False)
              converse: If it can fly, then it is a bird. (False)
83. Yes.   conditional: If 2 + 5 = 7, then 5 + 1 = 4. (False)
              contrapositive: If 5 + 1 ≠ 4, then 2 + 5 ≠ 7. (False)
85. If we use DeMorgan's Laws to rewrite $\sim p \vee q$ we get $\sim (p \wedge \sim q)$. Since $\sim p \vee q \Leftrightarrow \sim (p \wedge \sim q)$ and $p \to q \Leftrightarrow \sim p \vee q$, we can conclude that $p \to q \Leftrightarrow \sim (p \wedge \sim q)$. Other answers are possible.
87. Research problem.

Exercise Set 3.5

1. An argument is valid when its conclusion necessarily follows from the given set of premises.
3. Yes. If the conclusion does not follow from the set of premises, then the argument is invalid.
5. (1) Write the argument in symbolic form.
   (2) Compare the form of the argument with forms that are known to be valid or invalid. If there are no known form to compare then go on to step 3.
   (3) Write a conditional statement of the form. $(p_1 \wedge p_2) \to c$.
   (4) Construct a truth table for the statement in step 3.
   (5) If the truth table is a tautology, then the argument is valid. If the truth table is not a tautology, then the argument is invalid.

7. a) $p \to q$ b)   If the sky is clear, then I will go to the game.
          $\underline{p}$ $\underline{\text{The sky is clear.}}$
          $\therefore q$ ∴ I will go to the game.

9. a) $p \to q$ b)   If the soil is dry, then the grass needs water.
          $\underline{\sim q}$ $\underline{\text{The grass does not need water.}}$
          $\therefore \sim p$ ∴ The soil is not dry.

11. a) $p \to q$ b)   If you wash my car, then I will give you $5.
          $\underline{q}$ $\underline{\text{I will give you \$5.}}$
          $\therefore p$ ∴ You washed my car.

13.

$[(p \rightarrow q) \wedge \sim p] \rightarrow q$

p	q	(p→q)	∧	~p	→	q
T	T	T	F	F	T	T
T	F	F	F	F	T	F
F	T	T	T	T	T	T
F	F	T	T	T	F	F
		1	3	2	5	4

The argument is invalid.

15. This argument is the law of detachment and therefore it is valid.

17.

$[\sim p \wedge (p \vee q)] \rightarrow \sim q$

p	q	~p	∧	(p∨q)	→	~q
T	T	F	F	T	T	F
T	F	F	F	T	T	T
F	T	T	T	T	F	F
F	F	T	F	F	T	T
		1	3	2	5	4

The argument is a fallacy.

19. This argument is the fallacy of the inverse. Therefore it is not valid.

21.

$[(\sim p \rightarrow q) \wedge \sim q] \rightarrow \sim p$

p	q	~p	→	q	∧	~q	→	~p
T	T	F	T	T	F	F	T	F
T	F	F	T	F	T	T	F	F
F	T	T	T	T	F	F	T	T
F	F	T	F	F	F	T	T	T
		1	3	2	5	4	7	6

The argument is invalid.

23. This argument is the law of syllogism and therefore it is valid.

25.

$[(p \leftrightarrow q) \wedge (q \wedge r)] \rightarrow (p \vee r)$

p	q	r	(p↔q)	∧	(q∧r)	→	(p∨r)
T	T	T	T	T	T	T	T
T	T	F	T	F	F	T	T
T	F	T	F	F	F	T	T
T	F	F	F	F	F	T	T
F	T	T	F	F	T	T	T
F	T	F	F	F	F	T	F
F	F	T	T	F	F	T	T
F	F	F	T	F	F	T	F
			1	3	2	5	4

The argument is valid.

27.

$[(r \leftrightarrow p) \wedge (\sim p \wedge q)] \rightarrow (p \wedge r)$

p	q	r	(r↔p)	∧	~p	∧	q	→	(p∧r)
T	T	T	T	F	F	F	T	T	T
T	T	F	F	F	F	F	T	T	F
T	F	T	T	F	F	F	F	T	T
T	F	F	F	F	F	F	F	T	F
F	T	T	F	F	T	T	T	T	F
F	T	F	T	T	T	T	T	F	F
F	F	T	F	F	T	F	F	T	F
F	F	F	T	F	T	F	F	T	F
			1	5	2	4	3	7	6

The argument is invalid.

29.

$[(p \rightarrow q) \wedge (q \vee r) \wedge (r \vee p)] \rightarrow p$

p	q	r	(p→q)	∧	(q∨r)	∧	(r∨p)	→	p
T	T	T	T	T	T	T	T	T	T
T	T	F	T	T	T	T	T	T	T
T	F	T	F	F	T	F	T	T	T
T	F	F	F	F	F	F	T	T	T
F	T	T	T	T	T	T	T	F	F
F	T	F	T	T	T	F	F	T	F
F	F	T	T	T	T	T	T	F	F
F	F	F	T	F	F	F	F	T	F
			1	3	2	5	4	7	6

The argument is invalid.

31.

$[(p \rightarrow q) \wedge (r \rightarrow \sim p) \wedge (p \vee r)] \rightarrow (q \vee \sim p)$

p	q	r	(p→q)	∧	(r→~p)	~p	∧	(p∨r)	→	(q∨~p)
T	T	T	T	F	T	F	F	F	T	T T F
T	T	F	T	T	F	T	F	T	T	T T F
T	F	T	F	F	T	F	F	F	T	T F F
T	F	F	F	F	F	T	F	T	T	T F F
F	T	T	T	T	T	T	T	T	T	T T T
F	T	F	T	T	F	T	T	F	F	T T T
F	F	T	T	T	T	T	T	T	T	T F T
F	F	F	T	T	F	T	T	F	F	T F T
			1	5	2	4	3	7	6	11 9 10 8

The argument is valid.

33. t: Today is Tuesday. $t \rightarrow b$
    b: We will play bingo. $\underline{t}$
                             $\therefore b$

This argument is the law of detachment and therefore it is valid.

35. w: The sweater is white. $w \vee r$
    r: The sweater is red. $\underline{\sim r}$
                              $\therefore w$

w	r	[(w ∨ r) ∧ ~ r] → w
T	T	T F F T T
T	F	T T T T T
F	T	T F F T F
F	F	F F T T F
		1 3 2 5 4

The argument is valid.

37. r: The painting is a Rembrandt.
    p: The painting is a Picasso.
    $r \vee p$
    $p \rightarrow \sim r$
    $\therefore \sim p$

r	p	[(r ∨ p) ∧ (p → ~ r)] → ~ p
T	T	T F T F F T F
T	F	T T F T F T T
F	T	T T T T T F F
F	F	F F F T T T T
		1 5 2 4 3 7 6

The argument is invalid.

39. t: The package is more than 2 pounds.
    m: We can mail the package.
    $\sim t$
    $t \rightarrow m$
    $\therefore m$

t	m	[~ t ∧ (t → m)] → m
T	T	F F T T T
T	F	F F F T F
F	T	T T T T T
F	F	T T T F F
		2 3 1 5 4

The argument is invalid.

41. g: The garden has vegetables.
    f: The garden has flowers.
    $g \vee f$
    $\sim f \rightarrow g$
    $\therefore f \vee g$

g	f	[(g ∨ f) ∧ (~ f → g)] → (f ∨ g)
T	T	T T F T T T T
T	F	T T T T T T T
F	T	T T F T F T T
F	F	F F T F F T F
		1 5 2 4 3 7 6

The argument is valid.

43. c: The children are young. $c \rightarrow d$
    d: We will get a dog. $d \leftrightarrow \sim w$
    w: We will get a white carpet. $\therefore c \rightarrow \sim w$

c	d	w	[(c → d) ∧ (d ↔ ~ w)] → (c → ~ w)
T	T	T	T F T F F T T F F
T	T	F	T T T T T T T T T
T	F	T	F F F T F T T F F
T	F	F	F F F F T T T T T
F	T	T	T F T F F T F T F
F	T	F	T T T T T T F T T
F	F	T	T T F T F T F T F
F	F	F	T F F F T T F T T
			1 5 2 4 3 9 6 8 7

The argument is valid.

45. c: The cat is in the room. $c \rightarrow m$
    m: The mice are hiding. $\underline{\sim m}$
                                 $\therefore \sim c$

This argument is the law of contraposition and therefore it is valid.

47. b: Bonnie passed the bar exam. $b \rightarrow p$
    p: Bonnie will practice law. $\underline{\sim p}$
                                    $\therefore \sim b$

This argument is the law of contraposition and therefore it is valid

49.   c: The baby is crying.   c ∧ ~ h
h: The baby is hungry.   h → c
∴ h

c	h	[(c ∧ ~ h) ∧ (h → c)] → h
T	T	T F F F T T T
T	F	T T T T T F F
F	T	F F F F F T T
F	F	F F T F T T F
		1 3 2 5 4 7 6

The argument is invalid

51.   f: The football team wins the game.
d: Dave played quarterback.
s: The team is in second place.
f → d
d → ~ s
∴ f → s
Using the law of syllogism, this argument is invalid.

53.   l: The lights are on.
p: We can play ball.
u: The umpires are present.
l → p
u → p
∴ l → u

55.   h: You do your homework everyday.
a: You will get an A.
h → a
h
∴ a   (the law of detachment)
Therefore, you will get an A.

57. p: John reads the history assignment.
q: John fixes the car.
p ∨ q
~ p
∴ p   (the law of disjunctive syllogism)
Therefore, John fixes the car.

59. d: You close the deal.
c: You will get a commission.
d → c
~ c
∴ ~ d   (the law of contraposition)
Therefore, you did not close the deal.

61. c: You pay off your credit card bill.   ~ c → p
p: You will have to pay interest.   p → m
m: The bank makes money.   ∴ ~ c → m   (the law of syllogism)
Therefore, if you do not pay off your credit card bill, then the bank makes money.

63. No. An argument is <u>invalid</u> only when the conjunction of the premises are true and the conclusion is false.

Exercise Set 3.6

1. A syllogism
3. The conclusion necessarily follows from the given set of premises.
5. Yes. If the conjunction of the premises is false in all cases, then the argument is valid regardless of the truth value of the conclusion.

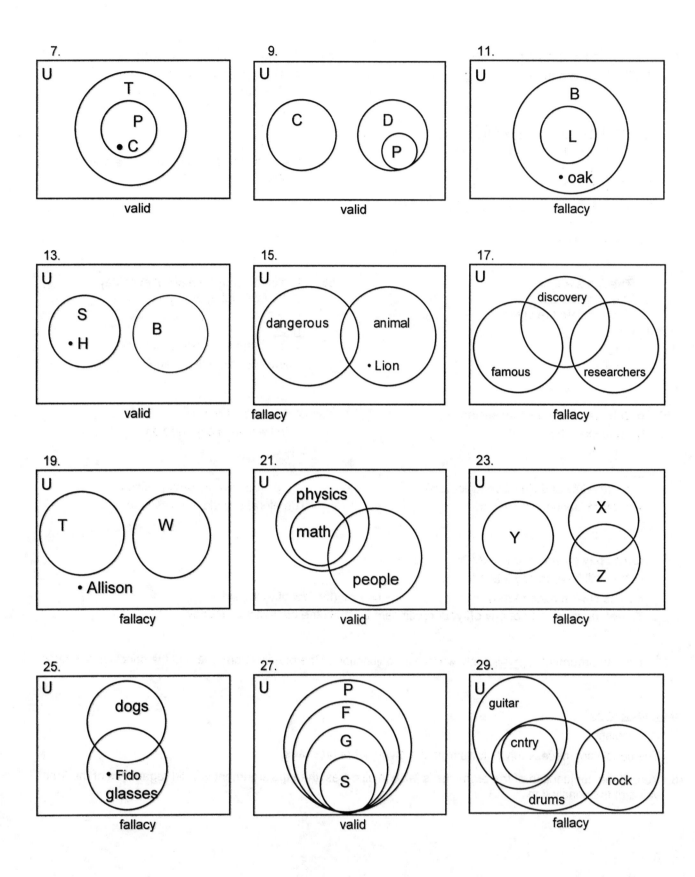

7.
U
T
P
• C
valid

9.
U
C
D
P
valid

11.
U
B
L
• oak
fallacy

13.
U
S
• H
B
valid

15.
U
dangerous
animal
• Lion
fallacy

17.
U
discovery
famous
researchers
fallacy

19.
U
T
W
• Allison
fallacy

21.
U
physics
math
people
valid

23.
U
Y
X
Z
fallacy

25.
U
dogs
• Fido
glasses
fallacy

27.
U
P
F
G
S
valid

29.
U
guitar
cntry
rock
drums
fallacy

31. $[(P \rightarrow Q) \land (P \lor Q)] \rightarrow \sim P$ can be expressed as a set statement by $[(P' \cup Q) \cap (P \cup Q)] \subseteq P'$. If this statement is true, then the argument is valid; otherwise, the argument is invalid.

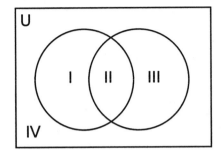

Set	Regions
$P' \cup Q$	II, III, IV
$P \cup Q$	I, II, III
$(P' \cup Q) \cap (P \cup Q)$	II, III
P'	III, IV

Since $(P' \cup Q) \cap (P \cup Q)$ is not a subset of P', the argument is invalid.

Review Exercises

1. No people drink milk.
2. All dogs have fleas.
3. Some butterflies bite.
4. No locks are keyless.
5. Some pens do not use ink.
6. Some rabbits wear glasses.
7. The coffee is Maxwell House or the coffee is hot.
8. The coffee is not hot and the coffee is strong.
9. The coffee is Maxwell House if and only if the coffee is not strong.
10. If the coffee is hot, then the coffee is strong and it is not Maxwell House.
11. The coffee is Maxwell House or the coffee is not hot, and the coffee is not strong.
12. The coffee is not Maxwell House, if and only if the coffee is strong and the coffee is not hot.
13. $p \rightarrow r$
14. $r \land q$
15. $(r \rightarrow q) \lor \sim p$
16. $(q \leftrightarrow p) \land \sim r$
17. $(r \land q) \lor \sim p$
18. $\sim (r \land q)$

19.

p	q	$(p$	$\lor$	$q)$	$\land$	$\sim p$
T	T		T		F	F
T	F		T		F	F
F	T		T		T	T
F	F		F		F	T
			1		3	2

20.

p	q	q	$\leftrightarrow$	$(p$	$\lor$	$\sim q)$
T	T	T	T	T	T	F
T	F	F	F	T	T	T
F	T	T	F	F	F	F
F	F	F	F	F	T	T
		1	5	2	4	3

21.

p	q	r	p	$\land$	$(\sim q$	$\lor$	$r)$
T	T	T	T	T	F	T	T
T	T	F	T	F	F	F	F
T	F	T	T	T	T	T	T
T	F	F	T	T	T	T	F
F	T	T	F	F	F	T	T
F	T	F	F	F	F	F	F
F	F	T	F	F	T	T	T
F	F	F	F	F	T	T	F
			4	5	1	3	2

22.

p	q	r	p	$\rightarrow$	$(q$	$\land$	$\sim r)$
T	T	T	T	F	T	F	F
T	T	F	T	T	T	T	T
T	F	T	T	F	F	F	F
T	F	F	T	F	F	F	T
F	T	T	F	T	T	F	F
F	T	F	F	T	T	T	T
F	F	T	F	T	F	F	F
F	F	F	F	T	F	F	T
			4	5	1	3	2

23.

p	q	r	(p ∨ q)	↔	(p ∨ r)
T	T	T	T	T	T
T	T	F	T	T	T
T	F	T	T	T	T
T	F	F	T	T	T
F	T	T	T	T	T
F	T	F	T	F	F
F	F	T	F	F	T
F	F	F	F	T	F
			1	3	2

24.

p	q	r	(p ∧ q)	→	~r
T	T	T	T	F	F
T	T	F	T	T	T
T	F	T	F	T	F
T	F	F	F	T	T
F	T	T	F	T	F
F	T	F	F	T	T
F	F	T	F	T	F
F	F	F	F	T	T
			1	3	2

25. p: 4 − 1 = 3   p → q
      q: 2 + 2 = 3   T → F
                           F

26. p: The St. Louis arch is in   p ∨ q
         St. Louis.   T ∨ F
      q: Abraham Lincoln is buried   T
         in Grant's Tomb.

27. p: George Washington was the first president of the U.S.   (p ∨ q) → r
      q: All mushrooms are edible.   (T ∨ F) → F
      r: Florida is south of Central America.   T   → F
                                                           F

28. p: 3 + 7 = 11   (p ∨ q) ∧ r
      q: 6 + 5 = 11   (F ∨ T) ∧ T
      r: 7 × 6 = 42   T ∧ T
                             T

29. p: Michael Jordan averaged 33.4 points per game.   (p ↔ q) ∨ r
      q: Jerry West averaged 29.1 points per game.   (T ↔ T) ∨ F
      r: Wilt Chamberlain played for 10 years.   T ∨ F
                                     T

30. p: Magic Johnson played for 15 years.   p ∨ (q → r)
      q: Kareem Abdul-Jabbar scored 6000 points.   F ∨ (F → T)
      r: Elgin Baylor played for 12 years.   F ∨   T
                                       T

31. (p ∨ q) ↔ (~ r ∧ p)
     (T ∨ F) ↔ (T ∧ T)
       T   ↔   T
             T

32. (p → ~ r) ∨ (p ∧ q)
     (T → T) ∨ (T ∧ F)
        T   ∨   F
             T

33. ~ r ↔ [(p ∨ q) ↔ ~ p]
     T ↔ [(T ∨ F) ↔ F]
     T ↔ [T   ↔ F]
     T ↔   F
       F

34. ~ [(q ∧ r) → (~ p ∨ r)]
     ~ [(F ∧ F) → (F ∨ F)]
     ~ [F   →   F]
     ~   T
     F

35. Using the fact that (p → q) ⇔ (~ p ∨ q), we can conclude that ~ p → ~ q ⇔ p ∨ ~ q.

36.

p	q	~ p	∨	~ q	~ p	↔	q
T	T	F	F	F	F	F	T
T	F	F	T	T	F	T	F
F	T	T	T	F	T	T	T
F	F	T	T	T	T	F	F
		1	3	2	1	3	2

The statements are not equivalent.

37.

p	q	r	~p	v	(q ∧ r)		(~p	v	q)	∧	(~p	v	r)
T	T	T	F	T	T		F	T	T	T	F	T	T
T	T	F	F	F	F		F	T	T	F	F	F	F
T	F	T	F	F	F		F	F	F	F	F	T	T
T	F	F	F	F	F		F	F	F	F	F	F	F
F	T	T	T	T	T		T	T	T	T	T	T	T
F	T	F	T	T	F		T	T	T	T	T	T	F
F	F	T	T	T	F		T	T	F	T	T	T	T
F	F	F	T	T	F		T	T	F	T	T	T	F
			2	3	1		1	3	2	7	4	6	5

The statements are equivalent.

38.

p	q	(~q	→	p)	∧	p		~	(~p	↔	q)	v	p
T	T	F	T	T	T	T		T	F	F	T	T	T
T	F	T	T	T	T	T		F	F	T	F	T	T
F	T	F	T	F	F	F		F	T	T	T	F	F
F	F	T	F	F	F	F		T	T	F	F	T	F
		1	3	2	5	4		4	1	3	2	6	5

The statements are not equivalent.

39. p: The stapler is empty.

q: The stapler is jammed.

In symbolic form the statement is p ∨ q. Using the fact that p → q ⇔ ~p ∨ q, we can rewrite the given statement as ~p → q. If the stapler is not empty, then the stapler is jammed.

40. p: The boy sang bass.

q: The girl sang alto.

In symbolic form the statement is p ∧ q. Using DeMorgan's Laws we get p ∧ q ⇔ ~(~p ∨ ~q). It is false that the boy did not sing bass or the girl did not sing alto.

41. p: Newsweek is a comic book.

q: Time is an almanac.
The symbolic form is ~(p ∨ ~q).
Using DeMorgan's Laws we get

~(p ∨ ~q) ⇔ ~p ∧ q. Newsweek is not a comic book and Time is an almanac.

42. p: There is water in the vase.

q: The flowers will wilt.

In symbolic form the statement is ~p → q

Using the fact that p → q ⇔ ~p ∨ q, we get ~p → q ⇔ p ∨ q. There is water is in the vase or the flowers will wilt.

43. p: I went to the party.

q: I finished my special report.

Using DeMorgan's Laws we get
~p ∧ ~q ⇔ ~(p ∨ q). It is not true that I went to the party or I finished my special report.

44. If you do not have to stop, then the railroad crossing light is not flashing red.

45. If John's eyes do not need to be checked, then John is not having difficulty seeing.

46. If I am not at work, then today is a holiday.

47. If the carpet stains, then it is not Scotch-guarded or it is not properly cared for.

48. Converse: If I get a passing grade, then I studied.

Inverse: If I don't study, then I will not get a passing grade.

Contrapositive: If I don't get a passing grade, then I didn't study.

49. p: The temperature is over 80^0.

q: The air conditioner will come on.

In symbolic form the statements are: a) p → q, b) ~p ∨ q, c) ~(p ∧ ~q).

Using the fact that p → q ⇔ ~p ∨ q, statements (a) and (b) are equivalent. Using DeMorgan's Laws on statement (b) we get ~(p ∧ ~q). Therefore all three statements are equivalent.

50. p: The screwdriver is on the workbench.

q: The screwdriver is on the counter.

In symbolic form the statements are: a) p ↔ ~ q, b) ~ q → ~ p, c) ~ (q ∧ ~ p). Looking at the truth tables for statements (a), (b), and (c) we can conclude that none of the statements are equivalent.

		a)			b)			c)			
p	q	p ↔ ~q			~q → ~p			~ (q ∧ ~ p)			
T	T	T	F	F	F	T	F	T	T	F	F
T	F	T	T	T	T	F	F	T	F	F	F
F	T	F	T	F	F	T	T	F	T	T	T
F	F	F	F	T	T	T	T	T	F	F	T
		1	3	2	1	3	2	4	1	3	2

51. p: 2 + 3 = 6.

q: 3 + 1 = 5.

In symbolic form the statements are: a) p → q, b) p ↔ ~ q, c) ~ q → ~ p. Statement (c) is the contrapositive of statement (a). Therefore statements (a) and (c) are equivalent. Since the truth tables for statements (a) and (b) are different we can conclude that only statements (a) and (c) are equivalent.

p	q	p → q	p ↔ ~q		
T	T	T	T	F	F
T	F	F	T	T	T
F	T	T	F	T	F
F	F	T	F	F	T
		1	1	3	2

52. p: The sale is on Tuesday.

q: I have money.

r : I will go to the sale.

In symbolic form the statements are: a) (p ∧ q) → r, b) r → (p ∧ q), c) r ∨ (p ∧ q).

The truth table for statements (a), (b), and (c) shows that none of the statements are equivalent.

p	q	r	(p ∧ q) → r			r → (p ∧ q)			r ∨ (p ∧ q)		
T	T	T	T	T	T	T	T	T	T	T	T
T	T	F	T	F	F	F	T	T	F	T	T
T	F	T	F	T	T	T	F	F	T	T	F
T	F	F	F	T	F	F	T	F	F	F	F
F	T	T	F	T	T	T	F	F	T	T	F
F	T	F	F	T	F	F	T	F	F	F	F
F	F	T	F	T	T	T	F	F	T	T	F
F	F	F	F	T	F	F	T	F	F	F	F
			1	3	2	1	3	2	1	3	2

53.

p	q	[(p → q) ∧ ~ p] → q				
T	T	T	F	F	T	T
T	F	F	F	F	T	F
F	T	T	T	T	T	T
F	F	T	T	T	F	F
		1	3	2	5	4

The argument is invalid.

54.

p	q	r	[(p ∧ q)	∧	(q → r)]	→	(p → r)
T	T	T	T	T	T	T	T
T	T	F	T	F	F	T	F
T	F	T	F	F	T	T	T
T	F	F	F	F	T	T	F
F	T	T	F	F	T	T	T
F	T	F	F	F	F	T	T
F	F	T	F	F	T	T	T
F	F	F	F	F	T	T	T
			1	3	2	5	4

The argument is valid.

55. p: Nicole is in the hot tub.
q: Nicole is in the shower.

p ∨ q

p̲

∴ ~ q

p	q	[(p ∨ q)	∧	p]	→	~ q
T	T	T	T	T	F	F
T	F	T	T	T	T	T
F	T	T	F	F	T	F
F	F	F	F	F	T	T
		1	3	2	5	4

The argument is invalid.

56. p: The car has a sound system.
p: Rick will buy the car.
r : The price is less than $18,000.

p → q

~̲r̲ ̲→̲ ̲~̲q̲

∴ p → r

p	q	r	[(p → q)	∧	(~r → ~q)]	→	(p → r)
T	T	T	T	T	F	T	F	T	T
T	T	F	T	F	T	F	F	T	F
T	F	T	F	F	F	T	T	T	F
T	F	F	F	F	T	T	T	T	F
F	T	T	T	T	F	T	F	T	T
F	T	F	T	F	T	F	F	T	T
F	F	T	T	T	F	T	T	T	T
F	F	F	T	T	T	T	T	T	T
			1	5	2	4	3	7	6

The argument is valid.

57.

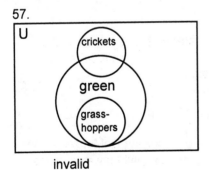

invalid

58.

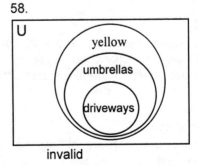

invalid

Chapter Test

1. (p ∧ r) ∨ ~ q

2. (r → q) ∨ ~ p

3. ~ (r ↔ ~ q)

4. It is false that if Celion is the president, then Ron is not the secretary.

5. Celion is the president, if and only if Sheldon is the vice president and Ron is the secretary.

6.

p	q	r	[~	(p → r)]	∧	q
T	T	T	F	T	F	T
T	T	F	T	F	T	T
T	F	T	F	T	F	F
T	F	F	T	F	F	F
F	T	T	F	T	F	T
F	T	F	F	T	F	T
F	F	T	F	T	F	F
F	F	F	F	T	F	F
			2	1	4	3

7.

p	q	r	(q	↔	~r)	∨	p
T	T	T	T	F	F	T	T
T	T	F	T	T	T	T	T
T	F	T	F	T	F	T	T
T	F	F	F	F	T	T	T
F	T	T	T	F	F	F	F
F	T	F	T	T	T	T	F
F	F	T	F	T	F	T	F
F	F	F	F	F	T	F	F
			1	3	2	5	4

8.　p: 2 + 6 = 8
　　q: 7 – 12 = 5
　　p ∨ q
　　T ∨ F
　　　T

9.　p: A scissors can cut paper.
　　q: A dime has the same value as 2 nickels.
　　r : Louisville is a city in Kentucky.
　　(p ∨ q) ↔ r
　　(T ∨ T) ↔ T
　　　　T　↔ T
　　　　　T

10.　[~(r → ~ p)] ∧ (q → p)
　　[~(T → F)] ∧ (F → T)
　　[~　F　] ∧　T
　　　T　　　∧　T
　　　　　　　T

11.　(r ∨ q) ↔ (p ∧ ~ q)
　　(T ∨ F) ↔ (T ∧　T)
　　　T　↔　　　T
　　　　　T

12.　Applying DeMorgan's Law to statement (a), we get:　(1) ~(~p ∨ q), (2) ~(p ∨ ~ q), and (3) ~(p ∧ ~ q).
Therefore, ~ p ∨ q ⟺ ~(p ∧ ~ q).

13.　p: The bird is red.
　　q: It is a cardinal.
In symbolic form the statements are: a) p → q,　b) ~ p ∨ q,　c) ~ p → ~ q.　Statement (c) is the inverse of statement (a) and thus they cannot be equivalent.　Using the fact that p → q ⟺ ~ p ∨ q, to rewrite statement (a) we get ~ p ∨ q.　Therefore statements (a) and (b) are equivalent.

14.　p:　The test is today.
　　q:　The concert is tonight.
In symbolic form the statements are: a)　~ (p ∨ q),　b)　~ p ∧ ~ q,　c) ~ p → ~ q.　Applying DeMorgan's Law to statement (a) we get: ~ p ∧ ~ q.　Therefore statements (a) and (b) are equivalent.　When we compare the truth tables for statements (a), (b), and (c) we see that only statements (a) and (b) are equivalent.

p	q	~	(p ∨ q)	~p	∧	~q	~p	→	~q
T	T	F	T	F	F	F	F	T	F
T	F	F	T	F	F	T	F	T	T
F	T	F	T	T	F	F	T	F	F
F	F	T	F	T	T	T	T	T	T
		2	1	1	3	2	1	3	2

Table headers: a) ~ (p ∨ q)　　b) ~ p ∧ ~ q　　c) ~ p → ~ q

15. s: The soccer team won the game.   s → f
     f: Sue played fullback.   f → p
     p: The team is in second place.   ∴ s → p
     This argument is the law of syllogism and therefore it is valid.

16.

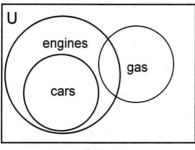

Fallacy

17. Some leopards are not spotted.

18. No people are funny.

19. Inverse: If the apple is not red, then it is not a delicious apple.
     Converse: If it is a delicious apple, then the apple is red.
     Contrapositive: If it is not a delicious apple, then the apple is not red.

20. Yes. An argument is valid when its conclusion necessarily follows from the given set of premises. It
     doesn't matter whether the conclusion is a true or false statement.

CHAPTER FOUR

SYSTEMS OF NUMERATION

<u>**Exercise Set 4.1**</u>

1. A **number** is a quantity, and it answers the question "How many?". A **numeral** is a symbol used to represent a number.

3. C, ρ, 9, 百

5. Hindu-Arabic numeration system

7. In a **multiplicative system** there are numerals for each number less than the base and for powers of the base. Each numeral less than the base is multiplied by a numeral for the power of the base and these products are added to obtain the number.

9. 100 + 100 + 10 + 10 + 10 + 1 + 1 = 232

11. 1000 + 1000 + 100 + 100 + 100 + 100 + 10 + 10 + 1 + 1 + 1 = 2423

13. 100,000 + 100,000 + 100,000 + 10,000 + 10,000 + 10,000 + 1000 + 1000 + 1000 + 1000 + 100 + 100 + 10 + 1 + 1 + 1 + 1 = 334,214

15. 9999 ∩∩∩ ||||||

17. ⚞⚞ ∩∩∩∩ |||||

19. ∝ 𝕍𝕍𝕍𝕍𝕍𝕍𝕍⚞⚞⚞ 99999999 ∩∩∩∩ |||||

21. 10 + (5 - 1) = 10 + 4 = 14

23. 500 + (50 - 10) + 5 + 1 + 1 = 547

25. 1000 + (500 - 100) + (100 - 10) + 1 + 1 = 1492

27. 1000 + (1000 - 100) + (50 - 10) + 5 = 1945

29. 10(1000) + 1000 + 1000 + 500 + 100 + 50 + 10 + 5 + 1 = 12,666

31. 9(1000) + (500 - 100) + 50 + 10 + (5 - 1) = 9464

33. XLVII

35. CLXIV

37. MM

39. MMMMDCCXCIII

41. $\overline{\text{IX}}$CMXCIX

43. $\overline{\text{XX}}$DCXLIV

45. 9(10) + 4 = 94

47. 4(1000) + 8(10) + 1 = 4081

49. 7(1000) + 6(100) + 5(10) = 7650

51. 四
    十
    七

53. 三
    百
    七
    十
    八

55. 三
    千
    五
    百
    七
    十

57. 200 + 60 + 4 = 264

59. 20(1000) + 2(1000) + 500 + 5 = 22,505

61. 9(1000) + 600 + 7 = 9607

63. $\mu \zeta$

65. $\psi \kappa \beta$

67. $\lambda' \varepsilon' \psi \delta$

69. Advantage: Numbers can be written in a compact form.
    Disadvantage: A ciphered system has many symbols to be memorized.

71. Advantage: Numbers can be written in a compact form.
    Disadvantage: A ciphered system has many symbols to be memorized.
    The Hindu-Arabic system has fewer symbols, more compact notation, the inclusion of zero, and the capability of expressing decimal numbers and fractions.

73. 1000 + (1000 - 100) + 10 + 10 + 10 + 5 + 1
    = 1936, ↑999999999∩∩∩IIIIII,
    $\alpha' \pi \lambda \varsigma$,
    一
    千
    九
    百
    三
    十
    六

75. 400 + 20 + 2 = 422, 9999∩∩II,
    CDXXII,
    四
    百
    二
    十
    二

77. $\pi' \varsigma' \theta' \pi \varsigma \theta$

Exercise Set 4.2

1. A base 10 place-value system

3. A true positional-value system requires a base and a set of symbols, including a symbol for zero and one for each counting number less than the base.

5. Write each numeral times its corresponding positional value.

7. $(10 + 1)(1) = 11$ and $(10 + 1)(60) = 660$

9. $1, 20, 18 \times 20, 18 \times 20^2, 18 \times 20^3$

11. $(5 \times 10) + (7 \times 1)$

13. $(3 \times 100) + (5 \times 10) + (9 \times 1)$

15. $(8 \times 100) + (9 \times 10) + (7 \times 1)$

17. $(5 \times 1000) + (2 \times 100) + (6 \times 10) + (2 \times 1)$

19. $(1 \times 10,000) + (0 \times 1000) + (7 \times 100) + (3 \times 10) + (2 \times 1)$

21. $(3 \times 100,000) + (4 \times 10,000) + (6 \times 1000) + (8 \times 100) + (6 \times 10) + (1 \times 1)$

23. $(10 + 10 + 1 + 1 + 1 + 1)(1) = 24$

25. $(10 + 1 + 1 + 1)(60) + (1 + 1 + 1 + 1)(1) = 13(60) + 4(1) = 780 + 4 = 784$

27. $1(60^2) + (10 + 10 + 1)(60) + (10 - (1 + 1))(1) = 3600 + 21(60) + (10 - 2)(1) = 3600 + 1260 + 8 = 4868$

29. 76 is 1 group of 60 and 16 units remaining

31. 121 is 2 groups of 60 and 1 unit remaining

33. 3685 is 1 group of 3600, 1 group of 60, and 25 units remaining

35. $2(20) + 11(1) = 40 + 11 = 51$

37. $12(18 \times 20) + 0(20) + 1(1) = 4320 + 0 + 1 = 4321$

39. $11(18 \times 20) + 2(20) + 0(1) = 3960 + 40 + 0 = 4000$

41.

43.
$$20 \overline{\smash{)}300}$$
with quotient 15; $\frac{20}{100}$, $\frac{100}{0}$

$300 = 15(20) + 0(1)$

45.
$$360 \overline{\smash{)}3181}$$
quotient 8; $\frac{2880}{301}$

$$20 \overline{\smash{)}301}$$
quotient 15; $\frac{300}{1}$

$3181 = 8(18 \times 20) + 15(20) + 1(1)$

47. Advantages: In general, a place-value system is more compact than an additive or multiplicative system, there are fewer symbols to memorize in a place-value system compared to a ciphered system, large and small numbers can be written more easily.

Disadvantage: If many of the place values are zero, then a place-value system may be less compact.

49. Hindu-Arabic: $10 + 10 + 10 + 1 + 1 + 1 = 33$
    Mayan: $33 = 1(20) + 13(1)$

51. $(\bigcirc \times \oplus^2) + (\square \times \oplus) + (\Delta \times 1)$

53. a) No largest number. The positional values are ..., $(60)^3$, $(60)^2$, 60, 1
    b) $999,999 = 4(60^3) + 37(60^2) + 46(60) + 39(1)$

55. $2(60) + 23(1) = 120 + 23 = 143$
    23
    $143 + 23 = 166$
    $166 = 2(60) + 46(1)$

57. $7(18 \times 20) + 6(20) + 15(1) = 2520 + 120 + 15 = 2655$
    $6(18 \times 20) + 7(20) + 13(1) = 2160 + 140 + 13 = 2313$
    $2655 + 2313 = 4968$
    $4968 = 13 (18 \times 20) + 14(20) + 8(1)$

Exercise Set 4.3

1. Answers will vary.

3. $7_8 = 7(1) = 7$

5. $23_5 = 2(5) + 3(1) = 13$

7. $1011_2 = 1(2^3) + 0(2^2) + 1(2) + 1(1) = 11$

9. $84_{12} = 8(12) + 4(1) = 100$

11. $465_7 = 4(7^2) + 6(7) + 5(1) = 4(49) + 42 + 5 = 243$

13. $20432_5 = 2(5^4) + 0(5^3) + 4(5^2) + 3(5) + 2(1) = 2(625) + 0 + 4(25) + 15 + 2 = 1367$

15. $4003_6 = 4(6^3) + 0(6^2) + 0(6) + 3(1) = 4(216) + 0 + 0 + 3 = 867$

17. $123_8 = 1(8^2) + 2(8) + 3(1) = 64 + 16 + 3 = 83$

19. $14705_8 = 1(8^4) + 4(8^3) + 7(8^2) + 0(8) + 5(1) = 4096 + 4(512) + 7(64) + 0 + 5 = 6597$

21. To convert 8 to base 2   ... 16 8 4 2 1

```
     1        0        0        0
 8 ⌐8    4 ⌐0    2 ⌐0    1 ⌐0
    8        0        0        0
    0        0        0        0      8 = 1000₂
```

23. To convert 22 to base 2   ... 32 16 8 4 2 1

```
     1         0        1        1        0
16 ⌐22    8 ⌐6    4 ⌐6    2 ⌐2    1 ⌐0
    16        0        4        2        0
     6        6        2        0        0     22 = 10110₂
```

25. To convert 435 to base 7   ... 2401 343 49 7 1

$$
\begin{array}{c}
\ \ 1 \\
343\,\overline{)\,435} \\
\underline{343} \\
92
\end{array}
\quad
\begin{array}{c}
\ \ 1 \\
49\,\overline{)\,92} \\
\underline{49} \\
43
\end{array}
\quad
\begin{array}{c}
\ \ 6 \\
7\,\overline{)\,43} \\
\underline{42} \\
1
\end{array}
\quad
\begin{array}{c}
\ \ 1 \\
1\,\overline{)\,1} \\
\underline{1} \\
0
\end{array}
\quad 435 = 1161_7
$$

27. To convert 2061 to base 12   ... 20,736 1728 144 12 1

$$
\begin{array}{c}
\ \ 1 \\
1728\,\overline{)\,2061} \\
\underline{1728} \\
333
\end{array}
\quad
\begin{array}{c}
\ \ 2 \\
144\,\overline{)\,333} \\
\underline{288} \\
45
\end{array}
\quad
\begin{array}{c}
\ \ 3 \\
12\,\overline{)\,45} \\
\underline{36} \\
9
\end{array}
\quad
\begin{array}{c}
\ \ 9 \\
1\,\overline{)\,9} \\
\underline{9} \\
0
\end{array}
\quad 2061 = 1239_{12}
$$

29. To convert 529 to base 8   ... 4096 512 64 8 1

$$
\begin{array}{c}
\ \ 1 \\
512\,\overline{)\,529} \\
\underline{512} \\
17
\end{array}
\quad
\begin{array}{c}
\ \ 0 \\
64\,\overline{)\,17} \\
\underline{0} \\
17
\end{array}
\quad
\begin{array}{c}
\ \ 2 \\
8\,\overline{)\,17} \\
\underline{16} \\
1
\end{array}
\quad
\begin{array}{c}
\ \ 1 \\
1\,\overline{)\,1} \\
\underline{1} \\
0
\end{array}
\quad 529 = 1021_8
$$

31. To convert 2867 to base 12   ... 20,736 1728 144 12 1

$$
\begin{array}{c}
\ \ 1 \\
1728\,\overline{)\,2867} \\
\underline{1728} \\
1139
\end{array}
\quad
\begin{array}{c}
\ \ 7 \\
144\,\overline{)\,1139} \\
\underline{1008} \\
131
\end{array}
\quad
\begin{array}{c}
\ \ 10 \\
12\,\overline{)\,131} \\
\underline{120} \\
11
\end{array}
\quad
\begin{array}{c}
\ \ 11 \\
1\,\overline{)\,11} \\
\underline{11} \\
0
\end{array}
\quad 2867 = 17TE_{12}
$$

33. To convert 1011 to base 2   ... 1024 512 256 128 64 32 16 8 4 2 1

$$
\begin{array}{c}
\ \ 1 \\
512\,\overline{)\,1011} \\
\underline{512} \\
499
\end{array}
\quad
\begin{array}{c}
\ \ 1 \\
256\,\overline{)\,499} \\
\underline{256} \\
243
\end{array}
\quad
\begin{array}{c}
\ \ 1 \\
128\,\overline{)\,243} \\
\underline{128} \\
115
\end{array}
\quad
\begin{array}{c}
\ \ 1 \\
64\,\overline{)\,115} \\
\underline{64} \\
51
\end{array}
\quad
\begin{array}{c}
\ \ 1 \\
32\,\overline{)\,51} \\
\underline{32} \\
19
\end{array}
$$

$$
\begin{array}{c}
\ \ 1 \\
16\,\overline{)\,19} \\
\underline{16} \\
3
\end{array}
\quad
\begin{array}{c}
\ \ 0 \\
8\,\overline{)\,3} \\
\underline{0} \\
3
\end{array}
\quad
\begin{array}{c}
\ \ 0 \\
4\,\overline{)\,3} \\
\underline{0} \\
3
\end{array}
\quad
\begin{array}{c}
\ \ 1 \\
2\,\overline{)\,3} \\
\underline{2} \\
1
\end{array}
\quad
\begin{array}{c}
\ \ 1 \\
1\,\overline{)\,1} \\
\underline{1} \\
0
\end{array}
\quad 1011 = 1111110011_2
$$

35. To convert 2307 to base 8   ... 4096 512 64 8 1

$$
\begin{array}{c}
\ \ 4 \\
512\,\overline{)\,2307} \\
\underline{2048} \\
259
\end{array}
\quad
\begin{array}{c}
\ \ 4 \\
64\,\overline{)\,259} \\
\underline{256} \\
3
\end{array}
\quad
\begin{array}{c}
\ \ 0 \\
8\,\overline{)\,3} \\
\underline{0} \\
3
\end{array}
\quad
\begin{array}{c}
\ \ 3 \\
1\,\overline{)\,3} \\
\underline{3} \\
0
\end{array}
\quad 2307 = 4403_8
$$

37. $826_{16} = 8(16^2) + 2(16) + 6(1) = 8(256) + 32 + 6 = 2086$

39. $6D3B7_{16} = 6(16^4) + 13(16^3) + 3(16^2) + 11(16) + 7(1) = 6(65{,}536) + 13(4096) + 3(256) + 176 + 7 = 447{,}415$

41. To convert 412 to base 16   ... 4096 256 16 1

$$
\begin{array}{c}
\ \ 1 \\
256\,\overline{)\,412} \\
\underline{256} \\
156
\end{array}
\quad
\begin{array}{c}
\ \ 9 \\
16\,\overline{)\,156} \\
\underline{144} \\
12
\end{array}
\quad
\begin{array}{c}
12 = C \\
\ \ 12 \\
1\,\overline{)\,12} \\
\underline{12} \\
0
\end{array}
\quad 412 = 19C_{16}
$$

43. To convert 5478 to base 16   ... 65,536 4096 256 16 1

$$
\begin{array}{c}
\ \ 1 \\
4096\,\overline{)\,5478} \\
\underline{4096} \\
1382
\end{array}
\quad
\begin{array}{c}
\ \ 5 \\
256\,\overline{)\,1382} \\
\underline{1280} \\
102
\end{array}
\quad
\begin{array}{c}
\ \ 6 \\
16\,\overline{)\,102} \\
\underline{96} \\
6
\end{array}
\quad
\begin{array}{c}
\ \ 6 \\
1\,\overline{)\,6} \\
\underline{6} \\
0
\end{array}
\quad 5478 = 1566_{16}
$$

45. To convert 2001 to base 2 ... 2048 1024 512 256 128 64 32 16 8 4 2 1

$$1024\overline{\smash{\big)}\,2001} \quad 512\overline{\smash{\big)}\,977} \quad 256\overline{\smash{\big)}\,465} \quad 128\overline{\smash{\big)}\,209} \quad 64\overline{\smash{\big)}\,81}$$

with quotients 1, 1, 1, 1, 1

$$\begin{array}{c} \underline{1024} \\ 977 \end{array} \quad \begin{array}{c} \underline{512} \\ 465 \end{array} \quad \begin{array}{c} \underline{256} \\ 209 \end{array} \quad \begin{array}{c} \underline{128} \\ 81 \end{array} \quad \begin{array}{c} \underline{64} \\ 17 \end{array}$$

$$32\overline{\smash{\big)}\,17} \quad 16\overline{\smash{\big)}\,17} \quad 8\overline{\smash{\big)}\,1} \quad 4\overline{\smash{\big)}\,1} \quad 2\overline{\smash{\big)}\,1} \quad 1\overline{\smash{\big)}\,1}$$

with quotients 0, 1, 0, 0, 0, 1

$$\begin{array}{c} \underline{0} \\ 17 \end{array} \quad \begin{array}{c} \underline{16} \\ 1 \end{array} \quad \begin{array}{c} \underline{0} \\ 1 \end{array} \quad \begin{array}{c} \underline{0} \\ 1 \end{array} \quad \begin{array}{c} \underline{0} \\ 1 \end{array} \quad \begin{array}{c} \underline{1} \\ 0 \end{array}$$

$$2001 = 11111010001_2$$

47. To convert 2001 to base 5 ... 3125 625 125 25 5 1

$$625\overline{\smash{\big)}\,2001} \quad 125\overline{\smash{\big)}\,126} \quad 25\overline{\smash{\big)}\,1} \quad 5\overline{\smash{\big)}\,1} \quad 1\overline{\smash{\big)}\,1}$$

with quotients 3, 1, 0, 0, 1

$$\begin{array}{c} \underline{1875} \\ 126 \end{array} \quad \begin{array}{c} \underline{125} \\ 1 \end{array} \quad \begin{array}{c} \underline{0} \\ 1 \end{array} \quad \begin{array}{c} \underline{0} \\ 1 \end{array} \quad \begin{array}{c} \underline{1} \\ 0 \end{array}$$

$$2001 = 31001_5$$

49. To convert 2001 to base 12 ... 20,736 1728 144 12 1

$$1728\overline{\smash{\big)}\,2001} \quad 144\overline{\smash{\big)}\,273} \quad 12\overline{\smash{\big)}\,129} \quad 1\overline{\smash{\big)}\,9}$$

with quotients 1, 1, 10 = T, 9

$$\begin{array}{c} \underline{1728} \\ 273 \end{array} \quad \begin{array}{c} \underline{144} \\ 129 \end{array} \quad \begin{array}{c} \underline{120} \\ 9 \end{array} \quad \begin{array}{c} \underline{9} \\ 0 \end{array}$$

$$2001 = 11T9_{12}$$

51. Incorrect, there is no 5 in base 5.

53. Correct

55. $2(5) + 3(1) = 13$

57. $2(5^2) + 4(5) + 3(1) = 2(25) + 20 + 3 = 73$

59. To convert ... 25 5 1

$$5\overline{\smash{\big)}\,17} \quad 1\overline{\smash{\big)}\,2}$$

with quotients 3 = ⊖, 2 = ①

$$\begin{array}{c} \underline{15} \\ 2 \end{array} \quad \begin{array}{c} \underline{2} \\ 0 \end{array}$$

$$17 = \ominus\,①_5$$

61. To convert ... 125 25 5 1

$$25\overline{\smash{\big)}\,74} \quad 5\overline{\smash{\big)}\,24} \quad 1\overline{\smash{\big)}\,4}$$

with quotients 2 = ①, 4 = ○, 4 = ○

$$\begin{array}{c} \underline{50} \\ 24 \end{array} \quad \begin{array}{c} \underline{20} \\ 4 \end{array} \quad \begin{array}{c} \underline{4} \\ 0 \end{array}$$

$$74 = ①\,○\,○_5$$

63. $1(4) + 3(1) = 7$

65. $2(4^2) + 1(4) + 0(1) = 2(16) + 4 + 0 = 36$

For #67-69, blue = 0 = b, red = 1 = r, gold = 2 = go, green = 3 = gr

67. To convert ... 16 4 1

$$4\overline{\smash{\big)}\,11} \quad 1\overline{\smash{\big)}\,3}$$

with quotients 2 = go, 3 = gr

$$\begin{array}{c} \underline{8} \\ 3 \end{array} \quad \begin{array}{c} \underline{3} \\ 0 \end{array}$$

$$11 = (go)\,(gr)_4$$

69. To convert ... 64 16 4 1

$$16\overline{\smash{\big)}\,60} \quad 4\overline{\smash{\big)}\,12} \quad 1\overline{\smash{\big)}\,0}$$

with quotients 3 = gr, 3 = gr, 0 = b

$$\begin{array}{c} \underline{48} \\ 12 \end{array} \quad \begin{array}{c} \underline{12} \\ 0 \end{array} \quad \begin{array}{c} \underline{0} \\ 0 \end{array}$$

$$60 = (gr)\,(gr)\,(b)_4$$

71. a) Each remainder is multiplied by the proper power of 5.

b)

5	683		
5	136	3	↑
5	27	1	↑
5	5	2	↑
5	1	0	↑
	0	1	↑

$683 = 10213_5$

c)

8	763		
8	95	3	↑
8	11	7	↑
8	1	3	↑
	0	1	↑

$763 = 1373_8$

73. Answers will vary.

75. $1(b^2) + 1(b) + 1 = 43$
$b^2 + b + 1 = 43$
$b^2 + b - 42 = 0$
$(b + 7)(b - 6) = 0$
$b + 7 = 0$ or $b - 6 = 0$
$b = -7$ or $b = 6$
Since the base cannot be negative, $b = 6$.

Exercise Set 4.4

1. a) b^0, b^1, b^2, b^3, b^4
   b) $6^0, 6^1, 6^2, 6^3, 6^4$

3. Answers will vary.

5.
$$\begin{array}{r} 32_5 \\ 41_5 \\ \hline 123_5 \end{array}$$

7.
$$\begin{array}{r} 3031_4 \\ 232_4 \\ \hline 3323_4 \end{array}$$

9.
$$\begin{array}{r} 799_{12} \\ 218_{12} \\ \hline 9E5_{12} \end{array}$$

11.
$$\begin{array}{r} 1112_3 \\ 1011_3 \\ \hline 2200_3 \end{array}$$

13.
$$\begin{array}{r} 14631_7 \\ 6040_7 \\ \hline 24001_7 \end{array}$$

15.
$$\begin{array}{r} 1011_2 \\ 110_2 \\ \hline 10001_2 \end{array}$$

17.
$$\begin{array}{r} 312_4 \\ -\ 103_4 \\ \hline 203_4 \end{array}$$

19.
$$\begin{array}{r} 2432_5 \\ -\ 1243_5 \\ \hline 1134_5 \end{array}$$

21.
$$\begin{array}{r} 782_{12} \\ -\ 13T_{12} \\ \hline 644_{12} \end{array}$$

23.
$$\begin{array}{r} 1001_2 \\ -\ 110_2 \\ \hline 11_2 \end{array}$$

25.
$$\begin{array}{r} 4223_7 \\ -\ 304_7 \\ \hline 3616_7 \end{array}$$

27.
$$\begin{array}{r} 2100_3 \\ -\ 1012_3 \\ \hline 1011_3 \end{array}$$

29.
$$\begin{array}{r} 34_5 \\ \times\ 2_5 \\ \hline 123_5 \end{array}$$

31.
$$\begin{array}{r} 342_7 \\ \times\ 5_7 \\ \hline 2403_7 \end{array}$$

33.
$$\begin{array}{r} 512_6 \\ \times\ 23_6 \\ \hline 2340 \\ 1424 \\ \hline 21020_6 \end{array}$$

35.
$$\begin{array}{r} 234_9 \\ \times\ 25_9 \\ \hline 1282 \\ 468 \\ \hline 6072_9 \end{array}$$

37.
$$\begin{array}{r} 111_2 \\ \times\ 101_2 \\ \hline 111 \\ 000 \\ 111 \\ \hline 100011_2 \end{array}$$

39.
$$\begin{array}{r} 316_7 \\ \times\ 16_7 \\ \hline 2541 \\ 316 \\ \hline 6031_7 \end{array}$$

41. $1_2 \times 1_2 = 1_2$

$$
1_2 \overline{\big)110_2} \quad \begin{array}{r} 110_2 \\ \hline 1 \\ \hline 01 \\ \underline{1} \\ 0 \\ \underline{0} \\ 0 \end{array}
$$

43. $4_5 \times 1_5 = 4_5$
$4_5 \times 2_5 = 13_5$
$4_5 \times 3_5 = 22_5$
$4_5 \times 4_5 = 31_5$

$$
4_5 \overline{\big)143_5} \quad \begin{array}{r} 22_5 \\ \hline 13 \\ \hline 13 \\ \underline{13} \\ 0 \end{array}
$$

45. $2_4 \times 1_4 = 2_4$
$2_4 \times 2_4 = 10_4$
$2_4 \times 3_4 = 12_4$

$$
2_4 \overline{\big)312_4} \quad \begin{array}{r} 123_4 \\ \hline 2 \\ \hline 11 \\ \underline{10} \\ 12 \\ \underline{12} \\ 0 \end{array}
$$

47. $3_4 \times 1_4 = 3_4$
$3_4 \times 2_4 = 12_4$
$3_4 \times 3_4 = 21_4$

$$
3_4 \overline{\big)232_4} \quad \begin{array}{r} 33_4 \quad R1 \\ \hline 21 \\ \hline 22 \\ \underline{21} \\ 1 \end{array}
$$

49. $3_5 \times 1_5 = 3_5$
$3_5 \times 2_5 = 11_5$
$3_5 \times 3_5 = 14_5$
$3_5 \times 4_5 = 22_5$

$$
3_5 \overline{\big)224_5} \quad \begin{array}{r} 41_5 \quad R1 \\ \hline 22 \\ \hline 04 \\ \underline{3} \\ 1 \end{array}
$$

51. $6_7 \times 1_7 = 6_7$
$6_7 \times 2_7 = 15_7$
$6_7 \times 3_7 = 24_7$
$6_7 \times 4_7 = 33_7$
$6_7 \times 5_7 = 42_7$
$6_7 \times 6_7 = 51_7$

$$
6_7 \overline{\big)404_7} \quad \begin{array}{r} 45_7 \quad R2 \\ \hline 33 \\ \hline 44 \\ \underline{42} \\ 2 \end{array}
$$

53.
$$
\begin{array}{r} 2_5 \\ + 3_5 \\ \hline 10_5 \end{array} = \bigcirc\bigcirc_5
$$

55.
$$
\begin{array}{r} 21_5 \\ + 43_5 \\ \hline 114_5 \end{array} = \bigcirc\bigcirc\bigcirc_5
$$

For #57-63, blue = 0 = b, red = 1 = r, gold = 2 = go, green = 3 = gr

57.
$$
\begin{array}{r} 3_4 \\ + 3_4 \\ \hline 12_4 \end{array} = \textcircled{r}\textcircled{go}_4
$$

59.
$$
\begin{array}{r} 32_4 \\ + 11_4 \\ \hline 103_4 \end{array} = \textcircled{r}\textcircled{b}\textcircled{gr}_4
$$

61.
$$
\begin{array}{r} 33_4 \\ - 12_4 \\ \hline 21_4 \end{array} = \textcircled{go}\textcircled{r}_4
$$

63.
$$
\begin{array}{r} 231_4 \\ - 103_4 \\ \hline 122_4 \end{array} = \textcircled{r}\textcircled{go}\textcircled{go}_4
$$

65. $2302_5 = 2(5^3) + 3(5^2) + 0(5) + 2(1) = 2(125) + 3(25) + 0 + 2 = 327$

67. $14_5 \times 1_5 = 14_5$
$14_5 \times 2_5 = 33_5$
$14_5 \times 3_5 = 102_5$
$14_5 \times 4_5 = 121_5$

$$
14_5 \overline{\big)242_5} \quad \begin{array}{r} 13_5 \\ \hline 14 \\ \hline 102 \\ \underline{102} \\ 0 \end{array}
$$

69. a) 462_8

$$\times \, 35_8$$

2772

1626

21252_8

b) $462_8 = 4(8^2) + 6(8) + 2(1) = 4(64) + 48 + 2 = 306$

$35_8 = 3(8) + 5(1) = 24 + 5 = 29$

c) $306 \times 29 = 8874$

d) $21252_8 = 2(8^4) + 1(8^3) + 2(8^2) + 5(8) + 2(1)$

$= 2(4096) + 512 + 2(64) + 40 + 2$

$= 8874$

e) Yes, in part a), the numbers were multiplied in base 8 and then converted to base 10 in part d). In part b), the numbers were converted to base 10 first, then multiplied in part c).

Exercise Set 4.5

1. Duplation and mediation, the galley method and Napier rods

3. a) Answers will vary.

b)

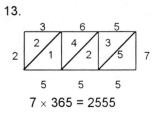

$423 \times 27 = 11,421$

5. $17 - 29$
    $8 = 58$
    $4 - 116$
    $2 - 232$
    $1 - 464$
    493

7. $9 - 162$
    $4 - 324$
    $2 - 648$
    $1 - 1296$
    1458

9. $35 - 236$
    $17 - 472$
    $8 - 944$
    $4 - 1888$
    $2 - 3776$
    $1 - 7552$
    8260

11. $85 - 85$
    $42 - 170$
    $21 - 340$
    $10 - 680$
    $5 - 1360$
    $2 - 2720$
    $1 - 5440$
    7225

13.

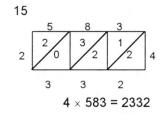

$7 \times 365 = 2555$

15.

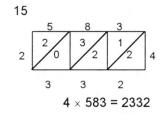

$4 \times 583 = 2332$

17.

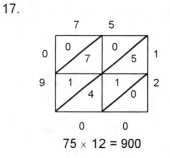

$75 \times 12 = 900$

19.

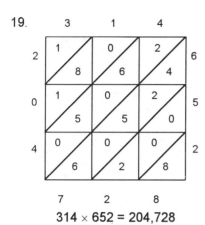

$$314 \times 652 = 204{,}728$$

21.

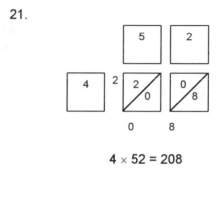

$$4 \times 52 = 208$$

23.

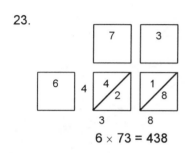

$$6 \times 73 = 438$$

25.

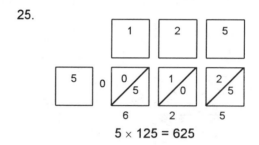

$$5 \times 125 = 625$$

27.

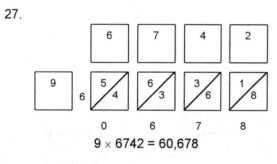

$$9 \times 6742 = 60{,}678$$

29. a) 253 × 46; Place the factors of 8 until the correct factors and placements are found so the rest of the rectangle can be completed.

b)

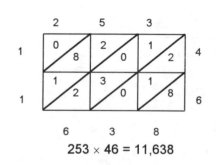

$$253 \times 46 = 11{,}638$$

31. a) 4 × 382; Place the factors of 12 until the correct factors and placements are found so the rest can be completed.

b)

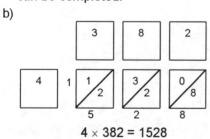

$$4 \times 382 = 1528$$

33. 13 – 22
~~6~~   ~~44~~
3 – 88
1 – 176
286 = 99 ∩∩∩∩∩∩∩∩ lllll

35. $12_3 \times 121_3 = 5 \times 16$

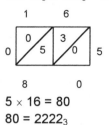

$5 \times 16 = 80$
$80 = 2222_3$

Review Exercises

1. $1000 + 1000 + 100 + 1 + 1 = 2102$
2. $1 + 10 + 100 + 1000 + 1 = 1112$
3. $10 + 100 + 100 + 100 + 1 + 1000 = 1311$
4. $100 + 10 + 1000 + 1 + 1000 + 1 + 1 + 1 = 2114$
5. $1000 + 1000 + 1000 + 100 + 100 + 10 + 1 + 1 + 1 + 1 = 3214$
6. $100 + 100 + 10 + 1 + 1000 + 1000 + 1 + 100 = 2312$
7. bbbbbaaaaaaa
8. cbbaaaaa
9. ccbbbbbbbbbaaa
10. dda
11. dddddccccccccbbbbba
12. ddcccbaaaa
13. $3(10) + 5 = 35$
14. $2(10) + 7 = 27$
15. $7(100) + 4(10) + 9 = 749$
16. $4(1000) + 6(10) + 8 = 4068$
17. $5(1000) + 6(100) + 4(10) + 8 = 5648$
18. $4(1000) + 8(100) + 9 = 4809$
19. gxd
20. byixe
21. hyfxb
22. bzbx
23. fzd
24. bza
25. $7(10) + 6(1) = 76$
26. $3(100) + 8(1) = 308$
27. $5(100) + 6(10) + 8(1) = 568$
28. $4(10,000) + 6(1000) + 8(100) + 8(10) + 3(1) = 46,883$
29. $4(10,000) + 8(10) + 2(1) = 40,082$
30. $6(10,000) + 5(100) + 2(10) + 9(1) = 60,529$
31. mb
32. xpe
33. vrc
34. BArg
35. ODvog
36. QFvrf

37. ₰ 9999 ∩∩∩∩∩ ll

38. MCDLXII

39. 一千四百六十二

40. α'υξβ

41.   24   ⟪lllll   ⟪⟨ll
       60) 1462
          1440
            22

$1462 = 24(60) + 22$

42.   4   1   ....
       360) 1462   20) 22   •
          1440   20   ••
            22   2

$1462 = 4(18 \times 20) + 1(20) + 2(1)$

43. $100{,}000 + 2(10{,}000) + 2(1000) + 2(10) + 5 = 122{,}025$

44. $8(1000) + 2(100) + 5(10) + 4 = 8254$

45. $500 + 80 + 5 = 585$

46. $1000 + (1000 - 100) + (100 - 10) + 1 = 1991$

47. $21(60) + (20 - 3) = 1277$

48. $5(18 \times 20) + 8(20) + 11(1) = 1971$

49. $54_9 = 5(9) + 4(1) = 49$

50. $101_2 = 1(2^2) + 0(2) + 1(1) = 4 + 0 + 1 = 5$

51. $130_4 = 1(4^2) + 3(4) + 0(1) = 16 + 12 + 0 = 28$

52. $2746_8 = 2(8^3) + 7(8^2) + 4(8) + 6(1) = 2(512) + 7(64) + 32 + 6 = 1510$

53. $T0E_{12} = 10(12^2) + 0(12) + 11(1) = 10(144) + 0 + 11 = 1451$

54. $20220_3 = 2(3^4) + 0(3^3) + 2(3^2) + 2(3) + 0(1) = 2(81) + 0 + 2(9) + 6 + 0 = 186$

55. To convert 463 to base 4   ... 1024   256   64   16   4   1

```
          1           3          0          3          3
   256 | 463   64 | 207   16 | 15    4 | 15    1 | 3
         256        192         0         12         3
         207         15         15         3          0    463 = 13033₄
```
$463 = 13033_4$

56. To convert 463 to base 3   ... 729   243   81   27   9   3   1

```
          1           2          2          0          1          1
   243 | 463   81 | 220   27 | 58    9 | 4     3 | 4     1 | 1
         243        162         54         0          3          1
         220         58          4         4          1          0   463 = 122011₃
```
$463 = 122011_3$

57. To convert 463 to base 2   ... 512   256   128   64   32   16   8   4   2   1

```
          1           1          1          0          0          1          1          1           1
   256 | 463  128 | 207  64 | 79   32 | 15   16 | 15    8 | 15    4 | 7     2 | 3      1 | 1
         256        128        64          0          0          8          4          2           1
         207         79         15         15         15          7          3          1           0
```
$463 = 111001111_2$

58. To convert 463 to base 5   ... 625   125   25   5   1

```
          3           3          2          3
   125 | 463   25 | 88    5 | 13    1 | 3
         375         75         10         3
          88         13          3         0
```
$463 = 3323_5$

59. To convert 463 to base 12   ... 1728   144   12   1

```
          3           2          7
   144 | 463   12 | 31    1 | 7
         432         24         7
          31          7         0
```
$463 = 327_{12}$

60. To convert 463 to base 8   ... 512   64   8   1

```
          7           1          7
    64 | 463    8 | 15    1 | 7
         448          8         7
          15          7         0
```
$463 = 717_8$

61.
$$\begin{array}{r} 42_6 \\ \underline{55_6} \\ 141_6 \end{array}$$

62.
$$\begin{array}{r} 10110_2 \\ \underline{11001_2} \\ 101111_2 \end{array}$$

63.
$$\begin{array}{r} TE_{12} \\ \underline{87_{12}} \\ 176_{12} \end{array}$$

64.
$$\begin{array}{r} 234_7 \\ \underline{456_7} \\ 1023_7 \end{array}$$

65.
$$3024_5$$
$$\underline{4023_5}$$
$$12102_5$$

66.
$$1407_8$$
$$\underline{7014_8}$$
$$10423_8$$

67.
$$4032_7$$
$$\underline{-\ 321_7}$$
$$3411_7$$

68.
$$1001_2$$
$$\underline{-\ 101_2}$$
$$100_2$$

69.
$$4TE_{12}$$
$$\underline{-\ E7_{12}}$$
$$3E4_{12}$$

70.
$$4321_5$$
$$\underline{-\ 442_5}$$
$$3324_5$$

71.
$$1713_8$$
$$\underline{-\ 1243_8}$$
$$450_8$$

72.
$$2021_3$$
$$\underline{-\ 212_3}$$
$$1102_3$$

73.
$$22_5$$
$$\underline{\times\ 4_5}$$
$$143_5$$

74.
$$23_4$$
$$\underline{\times\ 21_4}$$
$$23$$
$$\underline{112}$$
$$1203_4$$

75.
$$126_{12}$$
$$\underline{\times\ 47_{12}}$$
$$856$$
$$\underline{4T0}$$
$$5656_{12}$$

76.
$$221_3$$
$$\underline{\times\ 22_3}$$
$$1212$$
$$\underline{1212}$$
$$21102_3$$

77.
$$1011_2$$
$$\underline{\times\ 101_2}$$
$$1011$$
$$0000$$
$$\underline{1011}$$
$$110111_2$$

78.
$$476_8$$
$$\underline{\times\ 23_8}$$
$$1672$$
$$\underline{1174}$$
$$13632_8$$

79.
$$1_2 \times 1_2 = 1_2$$

```
        1011₂
   1₂ ) 1011₂
        1
        00
        00
        01
        1
        01
        1
        0
```

80.
$$2_4 \times 1_4 = 2_4$$
$$2_4 \times 2_4 = 10_4$$
$$2_4 \times 3_4 = 12_4$$

```
         130₄
   2₄ ) 320₄
         2
         12
         12
         0
         0
         0
```

81.
$$3_5 \times 1_5 = 3_5$$
$$3_5 \times 2_5 = 11_5$$
$$3_5 \times 3_5 = 14_5$$
$$3_5 \times 4_5 = 22_5$$

```
         30₅
   3₅ ) 140₅
         14
         00
         00
         0
```

82.
$$4_6 \times 1_6 = 4_6$$
$$4_6 \times 2_6 = 12_6$$
$$4_6 \times 3_6 = 20_6$$
$$4_6 \times 4_6 = 24_6$$
$$4_6 \times 5_6 = 32_6$$

```
         433₆
   4₆ ) 3020₆
         24
         22
         20
         20
         20
         0
```

83.
$$3_6 \times 1_6 = 3_6$$
$$3_6 \times 2_6 = 10_6$$
$$3_6 \times 3_6 = 13_6$$
$$3_6 \times 4_6 = 20_6$$
$$3_6 \times 5_6 = 23_6$$

```
         411₆    R1
   3₆ ) 2034₆
         20
         03
         3
         04
         3
         1
```

84.
$$6_8 \times 1_8 = 6_8$$
$$6_8 \times 2_8 = 14_8$$
$$6_8 \times 3_8 = 22_8$$
$$6_8 \times 4_8 = 30_8$$
$$6_8 \times 5_8 = 36_8$$
$$6_8 \times 6_8 = 44_8$$
$$6_8 \times 7_8 = 52_8$$

```
         664₈    R2
   6₈ ) 5072₈
         44
         47
         44
         32
         30
         2
```

85.
~~142   24~~
 71 - 48
 35 - 96
 17 - 192
 ~~8 - 384~~
 ~~4 - 768~~
 ~~2 - 1536~~
  1 - 3072
   3408

86.
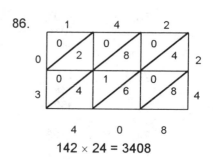
$142 \times 24 = 3408$

87.
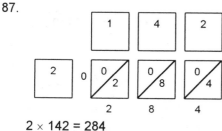
$2 \times 142 = 284$

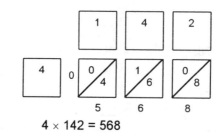
$4 \times 142 = 568$

$2 \times 142 = 284$, therefore $20 \times 142 = 2840$

Therefore, $142 \times 24 = 2840 + 568 = 3408$.

Chapter Test

1. A **number** is a quantity and answers the question "How many?". A **numeral** is the symbol used to represent the number.

2. $1000 + 1000 + 500 + 100 + (50 - 10) + 5 + 2$
= 2647

3. $21(60) + 15(1) = 1275$

4. $8(1000) + 9(10) = 8090$

5. $2(18 \times 20) + 11(20) + 4(1) = 944$

6. $10{,}000 + 10{,}000 + 1000 + 1000 + 100 + 10 + 10 + 10 + 10 + 1 + 1 = 22{,}142$

7. $9(1000) + 900 + 90 + 9 = 9999$

8. 999∩∩∩∩∩ ||

9. β'υο 2

10.
     4   3   ••••
 360 | 1512 20 | 72 •••
   1440   60 ••
    72   12 ═

$$1512 = 4(18 \times 20) + 3(20) + 12(1)$$

11.
     26 《《 ||||||| 《《《||||||
 60 | 1596
   1560
    36

$$1596 = 26(60) + 36(1)$$

12. MMCCCLXXVIII

13. In an additive system, the number represented by a particular set of numerals is the sum of the values of the numerals.

14. In a multiplicative system, there are numerals for each number less than the base and for powers of the base. Each numeral less than the base is multiplied by a numeral for the power of the base, and these products are added to obtain the number.

15. In a ciphered system, the number represented by a particular set of numerals is the sum of the values of the numerals. There are numerals for each number up to and including the base and multiples of the base.

16. In a place-value system, each number is multiplied by a power of the base. The position of the numeral indicates the power of the base by which it is multiplied.

17. $37_8 = 3(8) + 7(1) = 31$

18. $403_5 = 4(5^2) + 0(5) + 3(1) = 4(25) + 0 + 3 = 103$

19. $101101_2 = 1(2^5) + 0(2^4) + 1(2^3) + 1(2^2) + 0(2) + 1(1) = 32 + 0 + 8 + 4 + 0 + 1 = 45$

20. $368_9 = 3(9^2) + 6(9) + 8(1) = 3(81) + 54 + 8 = 305$

21. To convert 36 to base 2   ... 64   32   16   8   4   2   1

```
         1         0        0         1        0         0
   32 ⌐ 36   16 ⌐ 4    8 ⌐ 4    4 ⌐ 4    2 ⌐ 0    1 ⌐ 0
        32         0        0         4        0         0
         4         4        4         0        0         0
```
$$36 = 100100_2$$

22. To convert 84 to base 5   ... 125   25   5   1

```
        3        1        4
   25 ⌐ 84   5 ⌐ 9   1 ⌐ 4
        75        5        4
         9        4        0
```
$$84 = 314_5$$

23. To convert 2356 to base 12   ... 20,736   1728   144   12   1

```
           1              4           4    4
   1728 ⌐ 2356   144 ⌐ 628   12 ⌐ 52   1 ⌐ 4
          1728          576        48      4
           628           52         4      0
```
$$2356 = 1444_{12}$$

24. To convert 2938 to base 7   ... 16,807   2401   343   49   7   1

```
             1            1           3          6         5
   2401 ⌐ 2938   343 ⌐ 537   49 ⌐ 194   7 ⌐ 47   1 ⌐ 5
          2401          343        147        42         5
           537          194         47         5         0
```
$$2938 = 11365_7$$

25.
```
   133_5
   434_5
  1122_5
```

26.
```
   425_7
 − 154_7
   241_7
```

27.
```
    45_6
  × 23_6
    223
    134
  2003_6
```

28. $3_5 \times 1_5 = 3_5$
$3_5 \times 2_5 = 11_5$
$3_5 \times 3_5 = 14_5$
$3_5 \times 4_5 = 22_5$

```
         220_5
   3_5 ⌐ 1210_5
          11
          11
          11
          00
          00
           0
```

29.
```
  ~~14 - 28~~
    7 -  56
    3 - 112
    1 - 224
        392
```

30.
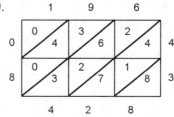

$43 \times 196 = 8428$

CHAPTER FIVE

NUMBER THEORY AND THE REAL NUMBER SYSTEM

Exercise Set 5.1

1. Number theory is the study of numbers and their properties.
3. a) *a* divides *b* means that *b* divided by *a* has a remainder of zero.
   b) *a* is divisible by *b* means that *a* divided by *b* has a remainder of zero.
5. A composite number is a natural number that is divisible by a number other than itself and 1. Any natural number that is not prime is composite.
7. a) The greatest common divisor (GCD) of a set of natural numbers is the largest natural number that divides (without remainder) every number in that set.

   b) Determine the prime factorization of each number. Then find the product of the prime factors with the smallest exponent that appears in each of the prime factorizations.

   c)

2	16
2	8
2	4
	2

   $16 = 2^4$

5	40
2	8
2	4
	2

   $40 = 2^3 \cdot 5$

   The prime factors with the smallest exponents that appear in each of the factorizations are 2^3.
   The GCD of 16 and 40 is $2^3 = 8$.
9. Mersenne Primes are prime numbers of the form $2^n - 1$ where n is a prime number.
11. Goldbach's conjecture states that every even number greater than or equal to 4 can be represented as the sum of two (not necessarily distinct) prime numbers.
13.

1	2	3	4	5	6	7	8	9	10
11	12	13	14	15	16	17	18	19	20
21	22	23	24	25	26	27	28	29	30
31	32	33	34	35	36	37	38	39	40
41	42	43	44	45	46	47	48	49	50
51	52	53	54	55	56	57	58	59	60
61	62	63	64	65	66	67	68	69	70
71	72	73	74	75					

The prime numbers between 1 and 75 are: 2, 3, 5, 7, 11, 13, 17, 19, 23, 29, 31, 37, 41, 43, 47, 53, 59, 61, 67, 71, 73.

15. True; since $42 \div 7 = 6$
17. True; since $6 \times 7 = 42$
19. False; 42 is divisible by 7.
21. True; If a number is divisible by 10, then it is also divisible by 5.

23. False; If a number is divisible by 3, then the sum of the number's digits is divisible by 3.

25. True; since $2 \times 3 = 6$.

27. Divisible by 2, 3, 4, and 6.

29. Divisible by 3 and 5.

31. Divisible by 2, 3, 4, 5, 6, 8, and 10.

33. $2 \cdot 3 \cdot 4 \cdot 5 \cdot 6 = 720$. (other answers are possible)

35.
```
2 | 44
2 | 22
    11
```
$44 = 2^2 \cdot 11$

37.
```
2 | 72
2 | 36
2 | 18
3 | 9
    3
```
$72 = 2^3 \cdot 3^2$

39.
```
3 | 303
    101
```
$303 = 3 \cdot 101$

41.
```
3 | 513
3 | 171
3 | 57
    19
```
$513 = 3^3 \cdot 19$

43.
```
2 | 1336
2 | 668
2 | 334
    167
```
$1336 = 2^3 \cdot 167$

45.
```
3  | 2001
23 | 667
     29
```
$2001 = 3 \cdot 23 \cdot 29$

47. The prime factors of 15 and 18 are:
$15 = 3 \cdot 5$, $18 = 2 \cdot 3^2$
a) The common factors are: 3; thus, the GCD = 3.
b) The factors with the greatest exponent that appear in either are: $2, 3^2, 5$; thus, the LCM $= 2 \cdot 3^2 \cdot 5 = 90$

49. The prime factors of 42 and 56 are:
$42 = 2 \cdot 3 \cdot 7$, $56 = 2^3 \cdot 7$
a) The common factors are: 2, 7; thus, the GCD $= 2 \cdot 7 = 14$.
b) The factors with the greatest exponent that appear in either are: $2^3, 3, 7$; thus, the LCM $= 2^3 \cdot 3 \cdot 7 = 168$

51. The prime factors of 40 and 900 are:
$40 = 2^3 \cdot 5$, $900 = 2^2 \cdot 3^2 \cdot 5^2$
a) The common factors are: $2^2, 5$; thus, the GCD $= 2^2 \cdot 5 = 20$.
b) The factors with the greatest exponent that appear in either are: $2^3, 3^2, 5^2$; thus, the LCM $= 2^2 \cdot 3^2 \cdot 5^2 = 1800$

53. The prime factors of 96 and 212 are:
$96 = 2^5 \cdot 3$, $212 = 2^2 \cdot 53$
a) The common factors are: 2^2; thus, the GCD $= 2^2 = 4$.
b) The factors with the greatest exponent that appear in either are: $2^5, 3, 53$; thus, the LCM $= 2^5 \cdot 3 \cdot 53 = 5088$

55. The prime factors of 24, 48, and 128 are:
$24 = 2^3 \cdot 3$, $48 = 2^4 \cdot 3$, $128 = 2^7$
a) The common factors are: 2^3; thus, the GCD $= 2^3 = 8$.
b) The factors with the greatest exponent that appear in either are: $2^7, 3$; thus, the LCM $= 2^7 \cdot 3 = 384$

57. Use the list of primes generated in exercise 13. The next two sets of twin primes are: 17, 19 and 29, 31.

59. $4 = 2 + 2, 6 = 3 + 3, 8 = 3 + 5, 10 = 3 + 7, 12 = 5 + 7, 14 = 7 + 7, 16 = 3 + 13, 18 = 5 + 13, 20 = 3 + 17$.

61. Fermat number $= 2^{2^n} + 1$, where n is a natural number. $2^{2^1} + 1 = 5$, $2^{2^2} + 1 = 2^4 + 1 = 17$, $2^{2^3} + 1 = 2^8 + 1 = 257$. These numbers are prime.

63. The lcm of 40 and 60 is 120. Thus, it will be 120 days before they are on sale at the same time again.

65. The least common multiple of 15 and 18 is 90. Thus, it will be 90 days before he visits both on the same day again.

67. The GCD of 288 and 192 is 96. Thus, each group should have 96 cars.

69. a)
$$5 = 6 - 1 \qquad 7 = 6 + 1$$
$$11 = 12 - 1 \qquad 13 = 12 + 1$$
$$17 = 18 - 1 \qquad 19 = 18 + 1$$
$$23 = 24 - 1 \qquad 29 = 30 - 1$$

b) Conjecture: Every prime number greater than 3 differs by 1 from a multiple of the number 6.

c) This conjecture appears to be correct.

71. $75 \div 35 = 2$ with remainder 5.
$35 \div 5 = 7$ with remainder 0.
Thus, the gcd of 35 and 75 is 5.

73. $112 \div 18 = 6$ with remainder 4.
$18 \div 4 = 4$ with remainder 2.
$4 \div 2 = 2$ with remainder 0.
Thus, the gcd of 18 and 112 is 2.

75. $180 \div 150 = 1$ with remainder 30.
$150 \div 30 = 5$ with remainder 0.
Thus, the gcd of 150 and 180 is 30.

77. The proper factors of 12 are:
1, 2, 3, 4, and 6.
$1 + 2 + 3 + 4 + 6 = 16 \neq 12$
Thus, 12 is not a perfect number.

79. The proper factors of 496 are:
1, 2, 4, 8, 16, 31, 62, 124, and 248.
$1 + 2 + 4 + 8 + 16 + 31 + 62 + 124 + 248 = 496$
Thus, 496 is a perfect number.

81. a) $60 = 2^2 \cdot 3^1 \cdot 5^1$ Adding 1 to each exponent and then multiplying these numbers, we get
$(2+1)(1+1)(1+1) = 3 \cdot 2 \cdot 2 = 12$ divisors of 60.
b) The divisors of 60 are: 1, 2, 3, 4, 5, 6, 10, 12, 15, 20, 30, and 60. Counting these we get 12, the same answer as in part (a).

83. The sum of the digits will be a number divisible by 3, thus the number is divisible by 6.

85. $36,018 = (36,000 + 18)$; $36,000 \div 18 = 2,000$ and $18 \div 18 = 1$
Thus, since $18 \mid 36000$ and $18 \mid 18$, $18 \mid 36018$.

87. $8 = 2+3+3$, $9 = 3+3+3$, $10 = 2+3+5$, $11 = 2+2+7$, $12 = 2+5+5$, $13 = 3+3+7$, $14 = 2+5+7$,
$15 = 3+5+7$, $16 = 2+7+7$, $17 = 5+5+7$, $18 = 2+5+11$, $19 = 3+5+11$, $20 = 2+7+11$.

Exercise Set 5.2

1. Begin at zero, draw an arrow to the value of the first number. From the tip of that arrow draw another arrow by moving a number of spaces equal to the value of the second number. Be sure to move left if the number is negative and move right if the number is positive. The sum of the two numbers is at the tip of the second arrow.

3. The product of two numbers with like signs is a positive number, and the product of two numbers with unlike signs is a negative number.

5. 0 times any real number is zero.

7. $-4 + 7 = 3$

9. $(-3) + 9 = 6$

11. $[6 + (-11)] + 0 = -5 + 0 = -5$

13. $[(-3) + (-4)] + 9 = -7 + 9 = 2$

15. $[(-23) + (-9)] + 11 = [-32] + 11 = -21$

17. $5 - 8 = 5 + (-8) = -3$

19. $-7 - 6 = (-7) + (-6) = -13$

21. $-5 - (-3) = -5 + 3 = -2$

23. $14 - 20 = 14 + (-20) = -6$

25. $[5 + (-3)] - 4 = 2 - 4 = 2 + (-4) = -2$

27. $-3 \cdot 6 = -18$

29. $(-7)(-7) = 49$

31. $[(-8)(-2)] \cdot 6 = 16 \cdot 6 = 96$

33. $(5 \cdot 6)(-2) = (30)(-2) = -60$

35. $[(-3)(-6)] \cdot [(-5)(8)] = (18)(-40) = -720$

37. $-27 \div (-9) = 3$

39. $13 \div (-13) = -1$

41. $\dfrac{56}{-8} = -7$

43. $\dfrac{-210}{14} = -15$

45. $144 \div (-3) = -48$

47. False; every integer is not a natural number.
49. False; the difference of two negative integers may be positive, negative, or zero.
51. True; the product of two integers with like signs is a positive integer.
53. True; the quotient of two integers with unlike signs is a negative number.
55. False; the sum of a positive integer and a negative integer could be positive, negative, or zero.

57. $(6 + 8) \div 2 = 14 \div 2 = 7$

59. $[6(-2)] - 5 = -12 + (-5) = -17$

61. $(4 - 8)(3) = (-4)(3) = -12$

63. $\{2 + (-17)\} \div 3 = [-15] \div 3 = -5$

65. $[(-22)(-3)] \div (2 - 13) = 66 \div (2 + (-13))$
    $= 66 \div (-11) = -6$

67. $-9, -5, -3, -1, 0, 7$

69. $-6, -5, -4, -3, -2, -1$

71. $15^0 - (-11^0) = 15^0 + 11^0 = 26^0 F$

73. $842 - (-927) = 842 + 927 = 1{,}769$
    1,769 feet

75. $7 - 2 - 3 - 2 + 1 = 5 - 3 - 2 + 1$
    $= 2 - 2 + 1 = 0 + 1 = 1.$
    Her net gain was 1 point.

77. a) $+1 - (-8) = +1 + 8 = 9.$ There is a 9 hour time difference.
    b) $-5 - (-7) = -5 + 7 = 2.$ There is a 2 hour time difference.

79. $\dfrac{1 + 23 + 45 + \ldots 99 + 100}{12 + 34 + 5 \ldots + 99100} = \dfrac{50}{50} = -1$

81. $0 + 1 - 2 + 3 + 4 - 5 + 6 - 7 - 8 + 9 = 1$ (other answers are possible)

Exercise Set 5.3

1. The set of rational numbers is the set of all numbers of the form p/q, where p and q are integers, and $q \neq 0$.
3. a) Divide both the numerator and the denominator by their greatest common divisor.
5. Divide the numerator by the denominator. The quotient is the the integer part of the mixed number. The fraction part of the mixed number is the remainder divided by the divisor.
7. a) The reciprocal of a number is 1 divided by the number.
   b) The reciprocal of -5 is $\dfrac{1}{-5} = -\dfrac{1}{5}$
9. a) To add or subtract two fractions with a common denominator, we add or subtract their numerators and keep the common denominator.
   b) $\dfrac{13}{27} + \dfrac{8}{27} = \dfrac{21}{27} = \dfrac{7}{9}$
11. We can multiply a fraction by the number one in the form of c/c (where c is a nonzero integer) and the number will maintain the same value.

13. The GCD of 14 and 21 is 7.
    $\dfrac{14}{21} = \dfrac{14 \div 7}{21 \div 7} = \dfrac{2}{3}$

15. The GCD of 63 and 98 is 7.
    $\dfrac{63}{98} = \dfrac{63 \div 7}{98 \div 7} = \dfrac{9}{14}$

17. The GCD of 525 and 800 is 25.
    $\dfrac{525}{800} = \dfrac{525 \div 25}{800 \div 25} = \dfrac{21}{32}$

19. The GCD of 112 and 176 is 16.
    $\dfrac{112}{176} = \dfrac{112 \div 16}{176 \div 16} = \dfrac{7}{11}$

21. The GCD of 45 and 495 is 45.
    $\dfrac{45}{495} = \dfrac{45 \div 45}{495 \div 45} = \dfrac{1}{11}$

23. $2\dfrac{5}{8} = \dfrac{2 \cdot 8 + 5}{8} = \dfrac{16 + 5}{8} = \dfrac{21}{8}$

25. $-2\dfrac{3}{4} = -\dfrac{2\cdot 4 + 3}{4} = -\dfrac{8+3}{4} = -\dfrac{11}{4}$

27. $-4\dfrac{15}{16} = -\dfrac{4\cdot 16 + 15}{16} = -\dfrac{64+15}{16} = -\dfrac{79}{16}$

29. $2\dfrac{1}{8} = \dfrac{2\cdot 8 + 1}{8} = \dfrac{16+1}{8} = \dfrac{17}{8}$

31. $1\dfrac{7}{8} = \dfrac{1\cdot 8 + 7}{8} = \dfrac{8+7}{8} = \dfrac{15}{8}$

33. $\dfrac{31}{16} = \dfrac{16+15}{16} = \dfrac{1\cdot 16 + 15}{16} = 1\dfrac{15}{16}$

35. $-\dfrac{213}{5} = -\dfrac{210+3}{5} = -\dfrac{42\cdot 5 + 3}{5} = -42\dfrac{3}{5}$

37. $-\dfrac{878}{15} = -\dfrac{870+8}{15} = -\dfrac{58\cdot 15 + 8}{15} = -58\dfrac{8}{15}$

39. $1 \div 4 = 0.25$

41. $4 \div 7 = 0.\overline{571428}$

43. $3 \div 8 = 0.375$

45. $13 \div 3 = 4.\overline{3}$

47. $85 \div 15 = 5.\overline{6}$

49. $0.6 = \dfrac{6}{10} = \dfrac{3}{5}$

51. $0.052 = \dfrac{52}{1000} = \dfrac{13}{250}$

53. $6.2 = \dfrac{62}{10} = \dfrac{31}{5}$

55. $1.452 = \dfrac{1452}{1000} = \dfrac{363}{250}$

57. $3.0001 = \dfrac{30001}{10000}$

59. Let n = $0.\overline{3}$, then
$$
\begin{aligned}
10n &= 3.\overline{3}\\
- \quad n &= 0.\overline{3}\\
\hline
9n &= 3\\
\dfrac{9n}{9} &= \dfrac{3}{9}\\
n &= \dfrac{3}{9} = \dfrac{1}{3}
\end{aligned}
$$

61. Let n = $2.\overline{9}$, then
$$
\begin{aligned}
10n &= 29.\overline{9}\\
- \quad n &= 2.\overline{9}\\
\hline
9n &= 27\\
\dfrac{9n}{9} &= \dfrac{27}{9}\\
n &= \dfrac{27}{9} = 3
\end{aligned}
$$

63. Let n = $1.\overline{36}$, then
$$
\begin{aligned}
100n &= 136.\overline{36}\\
- \quad n &= 1.\overline{36}\\
\hline
99n &= 135\\
\dfrac{99n}{99} &= \dfrac{135}{99}\\
n &= \dfrac{135}{99} = \dfrac{15}{11}
\end{aligned}
$$

65. Let n = $1.0\overline{2}$, then
$$
\begin{aligned}
100n &= 102.\overline{2}\\
- \quad 10n &= 10.\overline{2}\\
\hline
90n &= 92\\
\dfrac{90n}{90} &= \dfrac{92}{90}\\
n &= \dfrac{92}{90} = \dfrac{46}{45}
\end{aligned}
$$

67. Let n = $3.4\overline{78}$, then
$$
\begin{aligned}
1000n &= 3478.\overline{78}\\
- \quad 10n &= 34.\overline{78}\\
\hline
990n &= 3444\\
\dfrac{990n}{990} &= \dfrac{3444}{990}\\
n &= \dfrac{3444}{990} = \dfrac{574}{165}
\end{aligned}
$$

69. $\dfrac{2}{7} \div \dfrac{5}{3} = \dfrac{2}{7} \times \dfrac{3}{5} = \dfrac{6}{35}$

71. $\dfrac{-3}{8} \times \dfrac{-16}{15} = \dfrac{48}{120} = \dfrac{2}{5}$

73. $\dfrac{7}{8} \div \dfrac{8}{7} = \dfrac{7}{8} \times \dfrac{7}{8} = \dfrac{49}{64}$

75. $\left(\dfrac{3}{5} \times \dfrac{4}{7}\right) \div \dfrac{1}{3} = \dfrac{12}{35} \div \dfrac{1}{3} = \dfrac{12}{35} \times \dfrac{3}{1} = \dfrac{36}{35}$

77. $\left[\left(\dfrac{-3}{4}\right)\left(\dfrac{-2}{7}\right)\right] \div \dfrac{3}{5} = \left(\dfrac{6}{28}\right) \div \dfrac{3}{5} = \dfrac{3}{14} \times \dfrac{5}{3} = \dfrac{15}{42} = \dfrac{5}{14}$

79. The lcm of 5 and 6 is 30.
$$\dfrac{1}{5} + \dfrac{1}{6} = \left(\dfrac{1}{5} \cdot \dfrac{6}{6}\right) + \left(\dfrac{1}{6} \cdot \dfrac{5}{5}\right) = \dfrac{6}{30} + \dfrac{5}{30} = \dfrac{11}{30}$$

81. The lcm of 11 and 110 is 110.

$$\frac{2}{11}+\frac{3}{110}=\left(\frac{2}{11}\cdot\frac{10}{10}\right)+\frac{3}{110}=\frac{20}{110}+\frac{3}{110}=\frac{23}{110}$$

83. The lcm of 9 and 54 is 54.

$$\frac{5}{9}-\frac{7}{54}=\left(\frac{5}{9}\cdot\frac{6}{6}\right)-\frac{7}{54}=\frac{30}{54}-\frac{7}{54}=\frac{23}{54}$$

85. The lcm of 12, 48, and 72 is 144.

$$\frac{1}{12}+\frac{1}{48}+\frac{1}{72}=\left(\frac{1}{12}\cdot\frac{12}{12}\right)+\left(\frac{1}{48}\cdot\frac{3}{3}\right)+\left(\frac{1}{72}\cdot\frac{2}{2}\right)=\frac{12}{144}+\frac{3}{144}+\frac{2}{144}=\frac{17}{144}$$

87. The lcm of 30, 40, and 50 is 600.

$$\frac{1}{30}-\frac{3}{40}-\frac{7}{50}=\left(\frac{1}{30}\cdot\frac{20}{20}\right)\left(\frac{3}{40}\cdot\frac{15}{15}\right)\left(\frac{7}{50}\cdot\frac{12}{12}\right)=\frac{20}{600}-\frac{45}{600}-\frac{84}{600}=-\frac{109}{600}$$

89. $$\frac{2}{3}+\frac{3}{4}=\frac{2\cdot4+3\cdot3}{3\cdot4}=\frac{8+9}{12}=\frac{17}{12}$$

91. $$\frac{5}{7}+\frac{3}{4}=\frac{5\cdot4+7\cdot3}{7\cdot4}=\frac{20+21}{28}=\frac{41}{28}$$

93. $$\frac{3}{8}+\frac{5}{12}=\frac{3\cdot12+8\cdot5}{8\cdot12}=\frac{36+40}{96}=\frac{76}{96}=\frac{19}{24}$$

95. $$\left(\frac{1}{5}\cdot\frac{1}{4}\right)+\frac{1}{3}=\frac{1}{20}+\frac{1}{3}=\left(\frac{1}{20}\cdot\frac{3}{3}\right)+\left(\frac{1}{3}\cdot\frac{20}{20}\right)=\frac{3}{60}+\frac{20}{60}=\frac{23}{60}$$

97. $$\left(\frac{1}{2}+\frac{3}{10}\right)\div\left(\frac{1}{5}+2\right)=\left(\frac{1}{2}\cdot\frac{5}{5}+\frac{3}{10}\right)\div\left(\frac{1}{5}+\frac{2}{1}\cdot\frac{5}{5}\right)=\left(\frac{5}{10}+\frac{3}{10}\right)\div\left(\frac{1}{5}+\frac{10}{5}\right)=\frac{8}{10}\div\frac{11}{5}=\frac{4}{5}\cdot\frac{5}{11}=\frac{20}{55}=\frac{4}{11}$$

99. $$\left(3\frac{4}{9}\right)\div\left(4+\frac{2}{3}\right)=\left(\frac{3}{1}\cdot\frac{9}{9}-\frac{4}{9}\right)\div\left(\frac{4}{1}\cdot\frac{3}{3}+\frac{2}{3}\right)=\left(\frac{27}{9}-\frac{4}{9}\right)\div\left(\frac{12}{3}+\frac{2}{3}\right)=\frac{23}{9}\div\frac{14}{3}=\frac{23}{9}\cdot\frac{3}{14}=\frac{69}{126}=\frac{23}{42}$$

101. The LCM of 4, 5, 3 is 60. $$\frac{1}{4}+\frac{2}{5}+\frac{1}{3}=\left(\frac{1}{4}\cdot\frac{15}{15}\right)+\left(\frac{2}{5}\cdot\frac{12}{12}\right)+\left(\frac{1}{3}\cdot\frac{20}{20}\right)=\frac{15}{60}+\frac{24}{60}+\frac{20}{60}=\frac{59}{60}$$

103. $$1-\left(\frac{1}{2}+\frac{2}{5}\right)=1-\left(\frac{5}{10}+\frac{4}{10}\right)=1-\frac{9}{10}=\frac{10}{10}-\frac{9}{10}=\frac{1}{10}.$$ Student tutors is $\frac{1}{10}$ of the budget.

105. $$1-\left(\frac{1}{4}+\frac{1}{5}+\frac{1}{2}\right)=1-\left(\frac{5}{20}+\frac{4}{20}+\frac{10}{20}\right)=1-\frac{19}{20}=\frac{20}{20}-\frac{19}{20}=\frac{1}{20}$$

She must proofread 1/20 of the book or $(1/20)\cdot540 = 27$ pages.

107. $$27\frac{7}{8}-25\frac{1}{2}=\frac{223}{8}-\frac{204}{8}=\frac{19}{8}=2\frac{3}{8}.$$ The stock decreased by $2\frac{3}{8}$ points.

109. $$\left(1\frac{1}{4}\right)(15)=\frac{5}{4}\cdot\frac{15}{1}=\frac{75}{4}=18\frac{3}{4}$$ cups of flour

111. $$46\frac{3}{4}+3\frac{5}{16}=46+3+\frac{3}{4}+\frac{5}{16}=49+\frac{17}{16}=49+1\frac{1}{16}=50\frac{1}{16}$$ in.

113. $$\left(24\frac{7}{8}\right)\div2=\frac{199}{8}\times\frac{1}{2}=\frac{199}{16}=12\frac{7}{16}$$ in.

115. $$8\frac{3}{4}\text{ ft}=\left(\frac{35}{4}\cdot\frac{12}{1}\right)\text{in.}=105\text{ in.}$$

$$\left[105-(3)\left(\frac{1}{8}\right)\right]\div4=\left[\frac{840}{8}-\frac{3}{8}\right]\div4=\frac{837}{8}\cdot\frac{1}{4}=\frac{837}{32}=26\frac{5}{32}.$$ The length of each piece is $26\frac{5}{32}$ in.

117. width = 8 ft. 3 in. = 96 in. + 3 in. = 99 in.; length = 10 ft. 8 in. = 120 in. + 8 in. = 128 in.
 a) perimeter = 2L + 2W = 2(128) + 2(99) = 454 in.=454/12 ft. =37$\frac{10}{12}$ ft. or 37 ft. 10 in.

 b) width = 8ft. 3in. = $8\frac{3}{12}$ ft. = $8\frac{1}{4}$ ft. = $\frac{33}{4}$ ft .; length = 10ft. 8in. = $10\frac{8}{12}$ ft. = $10\frac{2}{3}$ ft. = $\frac{32}{3}$ ft

 Area = L × w = $\frac{32}{3} \times \frac{33}{4} = \frac{1056}{12} = 88$ sq.ft

 c) Volume = L · W· H = $\frac{32}{3} \times \frac{33}{4} \times \frac{55}{6} = \frac{58080}{72} = 806.7$ cu. ft.

In Exercises 119 -125 other answers are possible.

119. $\frac{0.25+0.26}{2} = \frac{0.51}{2} = 0.255$

121. $\frac{-2.176+(-2.175)}{2} = \frac{-4.351}{2} = -2.1755$

123. $\frac{3.12345+3.123451}{2} = \frac{6.246901}{2} = 3.1234505$

125. $\frac{4.872+4.873}{2} = \frac{9.745}{2} = 4.8725$

127. $\left(\frac{3}{5}+\frac{4}{5}\right)\div 2 = \frac{7}{5} \times \frac{1}{2} = \frac{7}{10}$

129. $\left(\frac{1}{20}+\frac{1}{10}\right)\div 2 = \left(\frac{1}{20}+\frac{2}{20}\right)\cdot\frac{1}{2} = \frac{3}{20}\cdot\frac{1}{2} = \frac{3}{40}$

131. $\left(\frac{1}{4}+\frac{1}{5}\right)\div 2 = \left(\frac{5}{20}+\frac{4}{20}\right)\cdot\frac{1}{2} = \frac{9}{20}\cdot\frac{1}{2} = \frac{9}{40}$

133. $\left(\frac{1}{10}+\frac{1}{100}\right)\div 2 = \left(\frac{10}{100}+\frac{1}{100}\right)\cdot\frac{1}{2} = \frac{11}{100}\cdot\frac{1}{2} = \frac{11}{200}$

135. a) Water (or milk): $\left(1+1\frac{3}{4}\right)\div 2 = \left(\frac{4}{4}+\frac{7}{4}\right)\cdot\frac{1}{2} = \frac{11}{4}\cdot\frac{1}{2} = \frac{11}{8} = 1\frac{3}{8}$ cup; Oats: $\left(\frac{1}{2}+1\right)\div 2 = \frac{3}{2}\cdot\frac{1}{2} = \frac{3}{4}$ cup

 b) Water (or milk): $1+\frac{1}{2} = 1\frac{1}{2}$ cup; Oats: $\frac{1}{2}+\frac{1}{4} = \frac{2}{4}+\frac{1}{4} = \frac{3}{4}$ cup

Exercise Set 5.4
1. A rational number can be written as a ratio of two integers, p/q, with q not equal to zero. Numbers that cannot be written as the ratio of two integers are called irrational numbers.
3. A perfect square number is any number that is the square of a natural number.
5. a) To add or subtract two or more square roots with the same radicand, add or subtract their coefficients and then multiply by the common radical.
 b) $7\sqrt{3} - 2\sqrt{3} + 3\sqrt{3} = 5\sqrt{3} + 3\sqrt{3} = 8\sqrt{3}$
7. A rationalized denominator contains no radical expressions.

9. Rational; $\sqrt{49}$ = 7 is an integer.

11. Rational; quotient of two integers is rational.

13. Irrational; nonterminating, nonrepeating decimal.

15. Rational; quotient of two integers.

17. Irrational; nonterminating, nonrepeating decimal.

19. $\sqrt{81} = 9$

21. $\sqrt{49} = 7$

23. $-\sqrt{169} = -13$

25. $-\sqrt{225} = -15$

27. $-\sqrt{100} = -10$

29. rational, integer, natural

31. rational, integer, natural

33. rational

35. rational

37. rational

39. $\sqrt{12} = \sqrt{4}\sqrt{3} = 2\sqrt{3}$

41. $\sqrt{52} = \sqrt{4}\sqrt{13} = 2\sqrt{13}$

43. $\sqrt{63} = \sqrt{9}\sqrt{7} = 3\sqrt{7}$

45. $\sqrt{80} = \sqrt{16}\sqrt{5} = 4\sqrt{5}$

47. $\sqrt{162} = \sqrt{81}\sqrt{2} = 9\sqrt{2}$

49. $3\sqrt{5} + 4\sqrt{5} = (3+4)\sqrt{5} = 7\sqrt{5}$

51. $3\sqrt{7} - 5\sqrt{7} = (3-5)\sqrt{7} = -2\sqrt{7}$

53. $4\sqrt{12} - 7\sqrt{27} = 4 \cdot 2\sqrt{3} - 7 \cdot 3\sqrt{3} = 8\sqrt{3} - 21\sqrt{3} = (8-21)\sqrt{3} = -13\sqrt{3}$

55. $5\sqrt{3} + 7\sqrt{12} - 3\sqrt{75} = 5\sqrt{3} + 7 \cdot 2\sqrt{3} - 3 \cdot 5\sqrt{3} = 5\sqrt{3} + 14\sqrt{3} - 15\sqrt{3} = (5+14-15)\sqrt{3} = 4\sqrt{3}$

57. $\sqrt{8} - 3\sqrt{50} + 9\sqrt{32} = 2\sqrt{2} - 3 \cdot 5\sqrt{2} + 9 \cdot 4\sqrt{2} = 2\sqrt{2} - 15\sqrt{2} + 36\sqrt{2} = (2-15+36)\sqrt{2} = 23\sqrt{2}$

59. $\sqrt{3} \cdot \sqrt{2} = \sqrt{6}$

61. $\sqrt{9} \cdot \sqrt{15} = \sqrt{135} = \sqrt{9} \cdot \sqrt{15} = 3\sqrt{15}$

63. $\sqrt{10} \cdot \sqrt{20} = \sqrt{200} = \sqrt{100} \cdot \sqrt{2} = 10\sqrt{2}$

65. $\dfrac{\sqrt{8}}{\sqrt{4}} = \sqrt{2}$

67. $\dfrac{\sqrt{72}}{\sqrt{8}} = \sqrt{9} = 3$

69. $\dfrac{7}{\sqrt{2}} = \dfrac{7}{\sqrt{2}} \dfrac{\sqrt{2}}{\sqrt{2}} = \dfrac{7\sqrt{2}}{\sqrt{4}} = \dfrac{7\sqrt{2}}{2}$

71. $\dfrac{\sqrt{5}}{\sqrt{13}} = \dfrac{\sqrt{5}}{\sqrt{13}} \cdot \dfrac{\sqrt{13}}{\sqrt{13}} = \dfrac{\sqrt{65}}{13}$

73. $\dfrac{\sqrt{20}}{\sqrt{3}} = \dfrac{\sqrt{20}}{\sqrt{3}} \dfrac{\sqrt{3}}{\sqrt{3}} = \dfrac{\sqrt{60}}{\sqrt{9}} = \dfrac{\sqrt{4}\sqrt{15}}{3} = \dfrac{2\sqrt{15}}{3}$

75. $\dfrac{\sqrt{9}}{\sqrt{2}} \cdot \dfrac{\sqrt{2}}{\sqrt{2}} = \dfrac{3\sqrt{2}}{2}$

77. $\dfrac{\sqrt{10}}{\sqrt{6}} \cdot \dfrac{\sqrt{6}}{\sqrt{6}} = \dfrac{\sqrt{60}}{6} = \dfrac{2\sqrt{15}}{6} = \dfrac{\sqrt{15}}{3}$

79. $\sqrt{15}$ is between 3 and 4 since $\sqrt{15}$ is between $\sqrt{9} = 3$ and $\sqrt{16} = 4$. $\sqrt{15}$ is between 3.5 and 4 since 15 is closer to 16 than to 9. Using a calculator $\sqrt{15} \approx 3.9$.

81. $\sqrt{107}$ is between 10 and 11 since $\sqrt{107}$ is between $\sqrt{100} = 10$ and $\sqrt{121} = 11$. $\sqrt{107}$ is between 10 and 10.5 since 107 is closer to 100 than to 121. Using a calculator $\sqrt{107} \approx 10.3$.

83. $\sqrt{170}$ is between 13 and 14 since $\sqrt{170}$ is between $\sqrt{169} = 13$ and $\sqrt{196} = 14$. $\sqrt{170}$ is between 13 and 13.5 since 170 is closer to 169 than to 196. Using a calculator $\sqrt{170} \approx 13.04$.

85. True. Prime numbers are not perfect square numbers.

87. False. The result may be a rational number or an irrational number.

89. False. The result may be a rational number or an irrational number.

91. $\sqrt{3} + 5\sqrt{3} = 6\sqrt{3}$

93. $\sqrt{2} \cdot \sqrt{3} = \sqrt{6}$

95. No. $\sqrt{3} \neq 1.732$ since $\sqrt{3}$ is an irrational number and 1.732 is a rational number.

97.
$$\sqrt{9+16} \neq \sqrt{9} + \sqrt{16}$$
$$\sqrt{25} \neq 3 + 4$$
$$5 \neq 7$$

99. $T = 2\pi\sqrt{\dfrac{35}{980}} = 2\pi\sqrt{\dfrac{7}{196}} = 2\pi \cdot \dfrac{\sqrt{7}}{14} = \dfrac{\pi\sqrt{7}}{7} \approx 1.2$ sec.

101. a) $t = \dfrac{\sqrt{100}}{4} = \dfrac{10}{4} = 2.5$ sec

    b) $t = \dfrac{\sqrt{400}}{4} = \dfrac{20}{4} = 5$ sec

    c) $t = \dfrac{\sqrt{900}}{4} = \dfrac{30}{4} = 7.5$ sec

    d) $t = \dfrac{\sqrt{1600}}{4} = \dfrac{40}{4} = 10$ sec

103. No. The sum of two irrational numbers may not be irrational. (i.e. $-\sqrt{3}+\sqrt{3} = 0$)

Exercise Set 5.5
 1. The set of real numbers is the union of the rational numbers and the irrational numbers.
 3. If the given operation is preformed on any two elements of the set and the result is an element of the set, then the set is <u>closed</u> under the given operation.
 5. The order in which two numbers are multiplied does not make a difference in the result.
    Ex. $2 \times 3 = 3 \times 2$
 7. The associative property of multiplication states that when multiplying three real numbers, parentheses may be placed around any two adjacent numbers.
    One example is $(2 \times 3) \times 4 = 2 \times (3 \times 4)$.
 9. Not closed. (i.e. $3 - 5 = -2$ is not a natural number).
11. Closed. The product of two natural numbers is a natural number.
13. Closed. The sum of two integers is an integer.
15. Closed. The product of two integers is an integer.
17. Closed
19. Not closed
21. Not closed
23. Not closed
25. Closed
27. Closed

29. Commutative property. The order is changed from 7 + 8 to 8 + 7.

31. $(-4) \cdot (-5) = 20 = (-5) \cdot (-4)$
33. No. $6 \div 3 = 2$, but $3 \div 6 = 1/2$
35. $[-3 \cdot (-5)] \cdot (-7) = (15) \cdot (-7) = -105$
    $(-3) \cdot [-5 \cdot (-7)] = (-3) \cdot (35) = -105$
37. No. $(8 \div 4) \div 2 = 2 \div 2 = 1$,
    but $8 \div (4 \div 2) = 8 \div 2 = 4$
39. No. $(8 \div 4) \div 2 = 2 \div 2 = 1$,
    but $8 \div (4 \div 2) = 8 \div 2 = 4$
41. Associative property of addition
43. Commutative property of multiplication
45. Associative property of addition
47. Associative property of addition
49. Commutative property of addition
51. Commutative property of addition
53. Distributive property
55. Commutative property of addition
57. $3(y + 4) = 3y + 12$
59. $\sqrt{2}\left(3 + \sqrt{6}\right) = 3\sqrt{2} + \sqrt{12} = 3\sqrt{2} + 2\sqrt{3}$
61. $\sqrt{5}(x + \sqrt{5}) = x\sqrt{5} + \sqrt{25} = x\sqrt{5} + 5$
63. $\sqrt{3}\left(\sqrt{3} - \sqrt{6}\right) = \sqrt{9} - \sqrt{18} = 3 - 3\sqrt{2}$
65. Distributive property
67. Distributive property
69. Commutative property of addition
71. Distributive property
73. Associative property of addition
75. No. The computer would not work if it were not turned on first.
77. Yes. The order of placing sugar and cream in coffee is not important.
79. No. The book cannot be read before the lamp is turned on.
81. Yes. The order of these events does not matter.
83. No. The egg cannot be poured before it is cracked.
85. No. The machine must drop the cup before dispensing the coffee.
87. No. The car will not start if it is put into drive first.

89. Yes. Since it is possible to remove the sweater without removing the coat; the result will be the same whether the coat is removed first and then the sweater or the sweater removed first and then the coat.

91. No. $0 \div a = 0$ and $a \div 0$ is undefined.

Exercise Set 5.6

1. 4 is the base and 6 is the exponent or power.

3. a) If m and n are natural numbers and a is any real number, then $a^m a^n = a^{m+n}$
   b) $3^3 \times 3^5 = 3^{3+5} = 3^8$

5. a) If n is a natural number and a is any real number except 0, then $a^{-n} = \dfrac{1}{a^n}$.

   b) $3^{-5} = \dfrac{1}{3^5}$

7. a) If m and n are natural numbers and a is any real number, then $\left(a^m\right)^n = a^{m \cdot n}$

   b) $\left(4^4\right)^3 = 4^{4 \cdot 3} = 4^{12}$

9. a) Move the decimal point in the original number to the right or left until you obtain a number greater or equal to 1 and less than 10. Count the number of places the decimal was moved. If it was moved to the left the count is a positive number and if it was moved to the right the count is a negative number. Multiply the number obtained in the first step by 10 raised to the count number.

   b) $0.000426 = 4.26 \times 10^{-4}$. note: the count number is -4

11. a) The number is greater than or equal to 10.

   b) The number is greater than or equal 1 but less than 10.

   c) The number is less than 1.

13. $3^2 = 3 \times 3 = 9$

15. $(-5)^2 = (-5)(-5) = 25$

17. $-2^5 = -(2 \times 2 \times 2 \times 2 \times 2) = -32$

19. $\left(\dfrac{4}{5}\right)^2 = \dfrac{4}{5} \times \dfrac{4}{5} = \dfrac{16}{25}$

21. $(-2)^4 = (-2)(-2)(-2)(-2) = 16$

23. $2^3 \cdot 3^2 = 2 \times 2 \times 2 \times 3 \times 3 = 8 \times 9 = 72$

25. $\dfrac{5^7}{5^5} = 5^{7-5} = 5^2 = 5 \cdot 5 = 25$

27. $\dfrac{7}{7^3} = 7^{1-3} = 7^{-2} = \dfrac{1}{7^2} = \dfrac{1}{7 \times 7} = \dfrac{1}{49}$

29. $(-13)^0 = 1$

31. $3^4 = 3 \times 3 \times 3 \times 3 = 81$

33. $3^{-2} = \dfrac{1}{3^2} = \dfrac{1}{9}$

35. $(2^3)^4 = 2^{(3)(4)} = 2^{12} = 4096$

37. $\dfrac{11^{25}}{11^{23}} = 11^{25-23} = 11^2 = 121$

39. $(-4)^2 = (-4)(-4) = 16$

41. $-4^2 = -4 \cdot 4 = -16$

43. $\left(2^2\right)^{-3} = 2^{2(-3)} = 2^{-6} = \dfrac{1}{2^6} = \dfrac{1}{64}$

45. 1.2×10^5
47. 4.5×10^1
49. 5.3×10^{-2}
51. 1.9×10^4
53. 1.86×10^{-4}
55. 4.23×10^{-6}
57. 7.11×10^2
59. 1.53×10^{-1}
61. 84,000
63. 0.012
65. 0.0000213
67. 0.312
69. 9,000,000
71. 231
73. 35,000
75. 10,000

77. $(4.0 \times 10^2)(3.0 \times 10^5) = 12 \times 10^7 = 120{,}000{,}000$

79. $(5.1 \times 10^1)(3.0 \times 10^{-4}) = 15.3 \times 10^{-3} = 0.0153$

81. $\dfrac{6.4 \times 10^5}{2 \times 10^3} = 3.2 \times 10^2 = 320$

83. $\dfrac{8.4 \times 10^{-6}}{4 \times 10^{-3}} = 2.1 \times 10^{-3} = 0.0021$

85. $\dfrac{4 \times 10^5}{2 \times 10^4} = 2.0 \times 10^1 = 20$

87. $(7 \times 10^5)(6 \times 10^6) = 42 \times 10^{11} = 4.2 \times 10^{12}$

89. $(3 \times 10^{-3})(1.5 \times 10^{-4}) = 4.5 \times 10^{-7}$

91. $\dfrac{1.4 \times 10^6}{7 \times 10^2} = 0.2 \times 10^4 = 2.0 \times 10^3$

93. $\dfrac{4 \times 10^{-5}}{2 \times 10^2} = 2.0 \times 10^{-7}$

95. $\dfrac{1.5 \times 10^5}{5 \times 10^{-4}} = 0.3 \times 10^9 = 3 \times 10^8$

97. 8.3×10^{-4}, 3.2×10^{-1}, 4.6, 5.8×10^5

99. 8.3×10^{-5}; 0.00079; 4.1×10^3; $40{,}000$; Note: $0.00079 = 7.9 \times 10^{-4}$, $40{,}000 = 4 \times 10^4$

101. $(6.008 \times 10^9) - (1.256 \times 10^9) = (6.008 - 1.256) \times 10^9 = 4.752 \times 10^9$
    a) $4{,}752{,}000{,}000$ people   b) 4.752×10^9 people

103. time $= \dfrac{dist.}{rate} = \dfrac{239000 \ mi}{20000 \ mph} = 11.95$ a) 11.95 hrs   b) 1.195×10^1 hrs

105. $50 \times 5{,}800{,}000 = (5 \times 10^1)(5.8 \times 10^6) = 29 \times 10^7 = 2.9 \times 10^8$
    a) $290{,}000{,}000$ cells   b) 2.9×10^8 cells

107. a) $(100{,}000 \text{ cu.ft./sec}) \times (60 \text{ sec/min}) \times (60 \text{ min/hr}) \times (24 \text{ hr}) = 8{,}640{,}000{,}000 \text{ ft}^3$
    b) $8.64 \times 10^9 \text{ ft}^3$

109. a) 18 billion $= 18{,}000{,}000{,}000 = 1.8 \times 10^{10}$ diapers
    b) $14 \times 2.38 \times 10^5 = 33.32 \times 10^5 = 3.332 \times 10^6$ or $3{,}332{,}000$ miles

111. a) $(0.40) \times (3{,}400{,}000{,}000) = \$1{,}360{,}000{,}000$
    b) $(0.40) \times (3{,}400{,}000{,}000) = \$1{,}360{,}000{,}000$
    c) $(0.10) \times (3{,}400{,}000{,}000) = \$340{,}000{,}000$
    d) $(0.10) \times (3{,}400{,}000{,}000) = \$340{,}000{,}000$

113. Since 1 gram $= 10^3$ milligrams and 1 gram $= 10^{-3}$ kilograms,
    10^{-3} kilograms $= 10^3$ milligrams
    $\dfrac{10^{-3} \text{ Kilograms}}{10^{-3}} = \dfrac{10^3 \text{ milligrams}}{10^{-3}}$,   Thus,   1 kilogram $= 10^6$ milligrams

115. a) 2×6 billion $= 12$ billion $= 12{,}000{,}000{,}000$ people
    b) $\dfrac{6{,}000{,}000{,}000}{(35)(365)} = \dfrac{6{,}000{,}000{,}000}{12775} = 469{,}667$ people per day

117. a) $1{,}000{,}000 = 1.0 \times 10^6$; $1{,}000{,}000{,}000 = 1.0 \times 10^9$; $1{,}000{,}000{,}000{,}000 = 1.0 \times 10^{12}$
    b) $\dfrac{1.0 \times 10^6}{1.0 \times 10^3} = 1.0 \times 10^3$ days or $1{,}000$ days $= 2.74$ years
    c) $\dfrac{1.0 \times 10^9}{1.0 \times 10^3} = 1.0 \times 10^6$ days or $1{,}000{,}000$ days $= 2{,}739.73$ years
    d) $\dfrac{1.0 \times 10^{12}}{1.0 \times 10^3} = 1.0 \times 10^9$ days or $1{,}000{,}000{,}000$ days $= 2{,}739{,}726.03$ years
    e) $\dfrac{1 \text{ billion}}{1 \text{ million}} = \dfrac{1.0 \times 10^9}{1.0 \times 10^6} = 1.0 \times 10^3 = 1{,}000$ times greater

119. a) $E(0) = 2^{10} \cdot 2^0 = 2^{10} \cdot 1 = 1024$ bacteria   b) $E(1/2) = 2^{10} \cdot 2^{1/2} = 2^{10.5} = 1448.2$ bacteria

Exercise Set 5.7

1. A sequence is a list of numbers that are related to each other by a given rule. One example is 2, 4, 6, 8, ...
3. An arithmetic sequence is a sequence in which each term differs from the preceding term by a constant amount. One example is 1, 4, 7, 10, ...
5. A geometric sequence is one in which the ratio of any term to the term that directly precedes it is a constant. One example is 1, 3, 9, 27, ...

7. 2, 6, 10, 14, 18

9. $-3, 0, 3, 6, 9$

11. 5, 3, 1, $-1, -3$

13. 1/2, 1, 3/2, 2, 5/2

15. $a_5 = a_1 + (5-1)d = 4+(4)(3) = 4+12 = 16$

17. $a_9 = -5 + (9-1)(2) = -5+(8)(2)$
$= -5 + 16 = 11$

19. $a_{20} = 4/5 + (19)(-1) = 4/5 - 19 = -91/5$

21. $a_{11} = 4 + (10)(1/2) = 4 + 5 = 9$

23. $a_n = 2 + (n-1)2 = 2 + 2n - 2 = 2n$

25. $a_n = 6 + (n-1)10 = 10n - 4$

27. $a_n = -5/3 + (n-1)(1/3) = (1/3)n - 2$

29. $a_n = -3 + (n-1)(3/2) = (3/2)n - (9/2)$

31. $s_{14} = \dfrac{14(14+1)}{2} = \dfrac{14 \cdot 15}{2} = 105$

33. $s_9 = \dfrac{9(45+5)}{2} = \dfrac{9 \cdot 50}{2} = 225$

35. $s_8 = \dfrac{8(11+(-24))}{2} = \dfrac{8 \cdot (-13)}{2} = -52$

37. $s_8 = \dfrac{8\left(\frac{1}{2}+\frac{29}{2}\right)}{2} = \dfrac{8 \cdot \left(\frac{30}{2}\right)}{2} = \dfrac{8 \cdot 15}{2} = 60$

39. 2, 8, 32, 128, 512

41. 4, $-12, 36, -108, 324$

43. $-3, 3, -3, 3, -3$

45. $-16, 8, -4, 2, -1$

47. $a_6 = 3(4)^5 = 3 \cdot 1024 = 3072$

49. $a_8 = 5(3)^7 = 5 \cdot 2187 = 10{,}935$

51. $a_7 = 10(-3)^6 = 10(729) = 7290$

53. $a_7 = -3(-3)^6 = -3(729) = -2187$

55. $a_n = a_1 r^{n-1} = 3(3)^{n-1} = 3^n$

57. $a_n = a_1 r^{n-1} = -5(-1)^{n-1}$

59. $a_n = a_1 r^{n-1} = (1/4)(2)^{n-1}$

61. $a_n = a_1 r^{n-1} = 9(1/3)^{n-1}$

63. $s_4 = \dfrac{a_1\left(1-r^4\right)}{1-r} = \dfrac{3\left(1-2^4\right)}{1-2} = \dfrac{3(-15)}{-1} = 45$

65. $s_7 = \dfrac{a_1\left(1-r^7\right)}{1-r} = \dfrac{5\left(1-4^7\right)}{1-4} = \dfrac{5(-16383)}{-3} = 27{,}305$

67. $s_{11} = \dfrac{a_1\left(1-r^{11}\right)}{1-r} = \dfrac{-7\left(1-3^{11}\right)}{1-3} = \dfrac{-7(-177146)}{-2}$
$= -620{,}011$

69. $s_{13} = \dfrac{a_1\left(1-r^{13}\right)}{1-r} = \dfrac{-8\left(1-(-3)^{13}\right)}{1-(-3)} = \dfrac{-8(1594324)}{4}$
$= -3{,}188{,}648$

71. $\dfrac{50(1+50)}{2} = \dfrac{50 \cdot 51}{2} = 1{,}275$

73. $\dfrac{50(1+99)}{2} = \dfrac{50 \cdot 100}{2} = 2{,}500$

75. a) Using the formula $a_n = a_1 + (n-1)d$, we get
$a_8 = 20{,}200 + (8-1) \times 1200 = \$28{,}600$

b) $\dfrac{8(20200+28600)}{2} = \dfrac{8(48800)}{2} = \$195{,}200$

77. $a_6 = 200(0.8)^6 = 200(0.262144) = 52.4288$ g

79. $s_{12} = \dfrac{12(1+12)}{2} = \dfrac{12 \cdot 13}{2} = 78$ times

81. $a_{15} = a_1 r^{15} = 1(2)^{15} = 32{,}768$ layers

83. The visitors sequence is arithmetic.
Runs scored in the 8th is a_8.
$a_8 = a_1 + (8-1)d = 1 + 7(1) = 8$ runs
Visitors total score after 8 is s_8.

$s_8 = \dfrac{8(a_1+a_8)}{2} = \dfrac{8(1+8)}{2} = 36$ runs

The home team scored runs in a geometric sequence.
Runs scored in the 8th is $a_8 = a_1 r^{8-1} = 1(2)^7 = 128$

Home team total score after 8 is s_8.

$s_8 = \dfrac{a_1(1-2^8)}{1-2} = \dfrac{1(-255)}{-1} = 255$ runs

85. The sequence of bets during a losing streak is geometric.

a) $a_6 = a_1 r^{n-1} = 1(2)^{6-1} = 1(32) = \$32$ $S_5 = \dfrac{a_1\left(1-r^n\right)}{1-r} = \dfrac{1\left(1-2^5\right)}{1-2} = \dfrac{-31}{-1} = \$31$

b) $a_6 = a_1 r^{n-1} = 10(2)^{6-1} = 10(32) = \$320$ $S_5 = \dfrac{a_1\left(1-r^n\right)}{1-r} = \dfrac{10\left(1-2^5\right)}{1-2} = \dfrac{10(-31)}{-1} = \$310$

c) $a_{11} = a_1 r^{n-1} = 1(2)^{11-1} = 1(1024) = \$1{,}024$ $S_{10} = \dfrac{a_1\left(1-r^n\right)}{1-r} = \dfrac{1\left(1-2^{10}\right)}{1-2} = \dfrac{1(-1023)}{-1} = \$1{,}023$

d) $a_{11} = a_1 r^{n-1} = 10(2)^{11-1} = 10(1024) = \$10{,}240$ $S_{10} = \dfrac{a_1\left(1-r^n\right)}{1-r} = \dfrac{10\left(1-2^{10}\right)}{1-2} = \dfrac{10(-1023)}{-1} = \$10{,}230$

e) If you lose too many times in a row, then you will run out of money.

87. The arithmetic sequence $180^0, 360^0, 540^0, 720^0, \ldots$ has a common difference of 180. Thus, $a_n = 180(n - 2) = 180n - 360,\ n \geq 3$

89. Since $a_5 = a_1 r^4$ and $a_2 = a_1 r$, $a_5/a_2 = r^3$. Thus $r^3 = 648/24 = 27$ or $r = 3$.
Then $24 = a_2 = a_1 r = a_1(3)$ thus $a_1 = 24/3 = 8$.

Exercise Set 5.8

1. Begin with the numbers 1, 1, then add 1 and 1 to get 2 and continue to add the previous two numbers in the sequence to get the next number in the sequence.

3. $\dfrac{a_n}{a_{n+1}} \approx \dfrac{1}{1.618} \approx 0.618$ as n increases.

5. Student research question.

7. a) $\dfrac{\sqrt{5}+1}{2} \approx 1.618$ b) $\dfrac{\sqrt{51}}{2} \approx 0.618$ c) $1.618 - 0.618 = 1.000$

9. 1/1 = 1, 2/1 = 2, 3/2 = 1.5, 5/3 = 1.6, 8/5 = 1.6, 13/8 = 1.625, 21/13 = 1.6154, 34/21 = 1.619, 55/34 = 1.6176, 89/55 = 1.61818. The consecutive ratios alternate increasing then decreasing about the golden ratio.

11.

Fib. No.	prime factors	Fib. No.	prime factors
1	-------	34	$2 \cdot 17$
1	-------	55	$5 \cdot 11$
2	prime	89	prime
3	prime	144	$2^4 \cdot 3^2$
5	prime	233	prime
8	2^3	377	$13 \cdot 29$
13	prime	610	$2 \cdot 5 \cdot 61$

13. If 5 is selected the result is $2(5) - 8 = 10 - 8 = 2$ which is the second number preceding 5.

15. Answers will vary.

17. Answers will vary.   19. Answers will vary.   21. Answers will vary.

23. Fibonacci type; $19 + 31 = 50$; $31 + 50 = 81$

25. Not Fibonacci. Each term is not the sum of the two preceding terms.

27. Fibonacci type; 40 + 65 = 105; 65 + 105 = 170.

29. Fibonacci type; $-1 + 0 = -1$; $0 + (-1) = -1$

31. a) If 6 and 10 are selected the sequence is 6, 10, 16, 26, 42, 68, 110, ...

   b) 10/6 = 1.666, 16/10 = 1.600, 26/16 = 1.625, 42/26 = 1.615, 68/42 = 1.619, 110/68 = 1.618, ...

33. a) If 5, 8, and 13 are selected the result is $8^2 - (5)(13) = 64 - 65 = -1$.

   b) If 21, 34, and 55 are selected the result is $34^2 - (21)(55) = 1156 - 1155 = 1$.

   c) The square of the middle term of three consecutive terms in a Fibonacci sequence differs from the product of the 1st and 2nd term by 1.

35. a) Lucas sequence: 1, 3, 4, 7, 11, 18, 29, 47, ...

   b) 8 + 21 = 29; 13 + 34 = 47

   c) The first column is a Fibonacci-type sequence.

37.
$$1 + 1/x = x$$
$$x(1 + 1/x) = x(x) \text{ multiply by } x$$
$$x + 1 = x^2$$
$$x^2 - x - 1 = 0 \text{ solve for } x$$
Using the quadratic formula,
$$x = \frac{1 \pm \sqrt{1 - 4(1)(-1)}}{2(1)} = \frac{1 \pm \sqrt{5}}{2}$$

39. Answers will vary.

Review Exercises

1. Use the divisibility rules in section 5.1.
    670,920 is divisible by 2, 3, 4, 5, 6, 8 and 10

2. Use the divisibility rules in section 5.1.
    400,644 is divisible by 2, 3, 4, 6, and 9

3.
2	328
2	164
2	82
	41

$328 = 2^3 \cdot 41$

4.
2	350
5	175
5	35
	7

$350 = 2 \cdot 5^2 \cdot 7$

5.
2	840
2	420
2	210
5	105
3	21
	7

$840 = 2^3 \cdot 3 \cdot 5 \cdot 7$

6.
2	882
3	441
3	147
7	49
	7

$882 = 2 \cdot 3^2 \cdot 7^2$

7.
2	1452
2	726
3	363
11	121
	11

$1452 = 2^2 \cdot 3 \cdot 11^2$

8. $12 = 2^2 \cdot 3$, $36 = 2^2 \cdot 3^2$; gcd $= 2^2 \cdot 3 = 12$; lcm $= 2^2 \cdot 3^2 = 36$

9. $72 = 2^3 \cdot 3^2$, $52 = 2^2 \cdot 13$; gcd $= 2^2 = 4$; lcm $= 2^3 \cdot 3^2 \cdot 13 = 936$

10. $45 = 3^2 \cdot 5$, $250 = 2 \cdot 5^3$; gcd $= 5$; lcm $= 2 \cdot 3^2 \cdot 5^3 = 2250$

11. $840 = 2^3 \cdot 3 \cdot 5 \cdot 7$, $320 = 2^6 \cdot 5$; gcd $= 2^3 \cdot 5 = 40$; lcm $= 2^6 \cdot 3 \cdot 5 \cdot 7 = 6720$

12. $60 = 2^2 \cdot 3 \cdot 5$, $40 = 2^3 \cdot 5$, $96 = 2^5 \cdot 3$; gcd $= 2^2 = 4$; lcm $= 2^5 \cdot 3 \cdot 5 = 480$

13. $36 = 2^2 \cdot 3^2$, $108 = 2^2 \cdot 3^3$, $144 = 2^4 \cdot 3^2$; gcd $= 2^2 \cdot 3^2 = 36$; lcm $= 2^4 \cdot 3^3 = 432$

14. $15 = 3 \cdot 5$, $9 = 3^2$; lcm $= 3^2 \cdot 5 = 45$. In 45 days the train will stop in both cities.

15. $-5 + 3 = -2$

16. $7 + (-5) = 2$

17. $4 - 8 = 4 + (-8) = -4$

18. $(-2) + (-4) = -6$

19. $-5 - 4 = -5 + (-4) = -9$

20. $-3 - (-6) = -3 + 6 = 3$

21. $(-3 + 7) - 4 = 4 + (-4) = 0$

22. $-1 + (9 - 4) = -1 + 5 = 4$

23. $(-4)(-6) = 24$

24. $(-3)(7) = -21$

25. $5(-3) = -15$

26. $\dfrac{-35}{-7} = 5$

27. $\dfrac{12}{-6} = -2$

28. $[8 \div (-4)](-3) = (-2)(-3) = 6$

29. $[(-4)(-3)] \div 2 = 12 \div 2 = 6$

30. $[-30 \div (10)] \div (-1) = -3 \div (-1) = 3$

31. $4/5 = 0.8$

32. $7/10 = 0.7$

33. $12/16 = 3/4 = 0.75$

34. $13/4 = 3.25$

35. $3/7 = 0.\overline{428571}$

36. $7/12 = 0.58\overline{3}$

37. $3/8 = 0.375$

38. $7/8 = 0.875$

39. $5/7 = 0.\overline{714285}$

40. $0.175 = \dfrac{175}{1000} = \dfrac{7}{40}$

41. Let $n = 0.\overline{3}$, then

$$10n = 3.\overline{3}$$
$$-\ n = -0.\overline{3}$$
$$\overline{9n = 3}$$
$$\dfrac{9n}{9} = \dfrac{3}{9}$$
$$n = \dfrac{3}{9} = \dfrac{1}{3}$$

42. $5.31 = \dfrac{531}{100}$

43. Let $n = 2.\overline{37}$, then

$$100n = 237.\overline{37}$$
$$-\ n = -2.\overline{37}$$
$$\overline{99n = 235}$$
$$\dfrac{99n}{99} = \dfrac{235}{99}$$
$$n = \dfrac{235}{99}$$

44. $12.083 = \dfrac{12083}{1000}$

45. $0.0042 = \dfrac{42}{10000} = \dfrac{21}{5000}$

46. Let $n = 2.3\overline{4}$, then

$$100n = 234.\overline{4}$$
$$-\ 10n = -23.\overline{4}$$
$$\overline{90n = 211}$$
$$\dfrac{90n}{90} = \dfrac{211}{90}$$
$$n = \dfrac{211}{90}$$

47. $5\frac{1}{2} = \dfrac{(5 \cdot 2) + 1}{2} = \dfrac{11}{2}$

48. $12\frac{3}{4} = \dfrac{(12 \cdot 4) + 3}{4} = \dfrac{51}{4}$

49. $-3\frac{1}{4} = \dfrac{(-3 \cdot 4) - 1}{4} = \dfrac{-13}{4}$

50. $-35\frac{3}{8} = \frac{(-35 \cdot 8) - 3}{8} = \frac{-283}{8}$

51. $\frac{27}{4} = \frac{6 \cdot 4 + 3}{4} = 6\frac{3}{4}$

52. $\frac{39}{12} = \frac{3 \cdot 12 + 3}{12} = 3\frac{3}{12} = 3\frac{1}{4}$

53. $\frac{-12}{7} = \frac{(-1) \cdot 7 - 5}{7} = -1\frac{5}{7}$

54. $\frac{-136}{5} = \frac{(-27) \cdot 5 - 1}{5} = -27\frac{1}{5}$

55. $\frac{1}{3} + \frac{1}{7} = \frac{7}{7} \cdot \frac{1}{3} + \frac{3}{3} \cdot \frac{1}{7} = \frac{7}{21} + \frac{3}{21} = \frac{10}{21}$

56. $\frac{3}{4} - \frac{1}{3} = \frac{3}{3} \cdot \frac{3}{4} - \frac{4}{4} \cdot \frac{1}{3} = \frac{9}{12} - \frac{4}{12} = \frac{5}{12}$

57. $\frac{7}{12} + \frac{5}{14} = \frac{7}{7} \cdot \frac{7}{12} + \frac{6}{6} \cdot \frac{5}{14} = \frac{49}{84} + \frac{30}{84} = \frac{79}{84}$

58. $\frac{2}{3} \cdot \frac{3}{11} = \frac{2 \cdot 3}{3 \cdot 11} = \frac{6}{33} = \frac{2}{11}$

59. $\frac{5}{9} \div \frac{6}{7} = \frac{5}{9} \cdot \frac{7}{6} = \frac{35}{54}$

60. $\left(\frac{4}{5} + \frac{5}{7}\right) \div \frac{4}{5} = \frac{28 + 25}{35} \cdot \frac{5}{4} = \frac{53}{35} \cdot \frac{5}{4} = \frac{53}{28}$

61. $\left(\frac{2}{3} \cdot \frac{1}{7}\right) \div \frac{4}{7} = \frac{2}{21} \cdot \frac{7}{4} = \frac{1}{6}$

62. $\left(\frac{1}{5} + \frac{2}{3}\right) \cdot \frac{3}{8} = \frac{3 + 10}{15} \cdot \frac{3}{8} = \frac{13}{15} \cdot \frac{3}{8} = \frac{13}{40}$

63. $\left(\frac{1}{5} \cdot \frac{2}{3}\right) + \left(\frac{1}{5} \div \frac{1}{2}\right) = \frac{2}{15} + \left(\frac{1}{5} \cdot \frac{2}{1}\right) = \frac{2}{15} + \frac{2}{5} = \frac{2}{15} + \frac{6}{15} = \frac{8}{15}$

64. $\frac{1}{8} \cdot 17\frac{3}{4} = \frac{1}{8} \cdot \frac{71}{4} = \frac{71}{32} = 2\frac{7}{32}$ teaspoons

65. $\sqrt{20} = \sqrt{4 \cdot 5} = \sqrt{4} \cdot \sqrt{5} = 2\sqrt{5}$

66. $\sqrt{32} = \sqrt{16 \cdot 2} = \sqrt{16} \cdot \sqrt{2} = 4\sqrt{2}$

67. $\sqrt{5} + 7\sqrt{5} = 8\sqrt{5}$

68. $\sqrt{3} - 4\sqrt{3} = -3\sqrt{3}$

69. $\sqrt{8} + 6\sqrt{2} = 2\sqrt{2} + 6\sqrt{2} = 8\sqrt{2}$

70. $\sqrt{3} - 7\sqrt{27} = \sqrt{3} - 21\sqrt{3} = -20\sqrt{3}$

71. $\sqrt{75} + \sqrt{27} = 5\sqrt{3} + 3\sqrt{3} = 8\sqrt{3}$

72. $\sqrt{3} \cdot \sqrt{6} = \sqrt{18} = \sqrt{9 \cdot 2} = \sqrt{9} \cdot \sqrt{2} = 3\sqrt{2}$

73. $\sqrt{8} \cdot \sqrt{6} = \sqrt{48} = \sqrt{16 \cdot 3} = \sqrt{16} \cdot \sqrt{3} = 4\sqrt{3}$

74. $\frac{\sqrt{18}}{\sqrt{2}} = \sqrt{\frac{18}{2}} = \sqrt{9} = 3$

75. $\frac{\sqrt{56}}{\sqrt{2}} = \sqrt{\frac{56}{2}} = \sqrt{28} = 2\sqrt{7}$

76. $\frac{3}{\sqrt{2}} \cdot \frac{\sqrt{2}}{\sqrt{2}} = \frac{3\sqrt{2}}{2}$

77. $\frac{\sqrt{3}}{\sqrt{5}} \cdot \frac{\sqrt{5}}{\sqrt{5}} = \frac{\sqrt{15}}{5}$

78. $5(3 + \sqrt{5}) = 15 + 5\sqrt{5}$

79. $\sqrt{3}(4 + \sqrt{6}) = 4\sqrt{3} + \sqrt{18} = 4\sqrt{3} + 3\sqrt{2}$

80. $\sqrt{3}(\sqrt{6} + \sqrt{15}) = \sqrt{18} + \sqrt{45} = 3\sqrt{2} + 3\sqrt{5}$

81. Commutative property of addition

82. Commutative property of multiplication

83. Associative property of addition

84. Distributive property

85. Commutative property of addition

86. Commutative property of addition

87. Associative property of multiplication

88. Commutative property of multiplication

89. Distributive property

90. Commutative property of multiplication

91. Closed

92. Closed

93. Not closed; $1 \div 2$ is not an integer

94. Closed

95. Not closed; $\sqrt{2} \cdot \sqrt{2} = 2$ is not irrational

96. Not closed; $1 \div 0$ is undefined

97. $2^4 = 2 \cdot 2 \cdot 2 \cdot 2 = 16$

98. $2^{-3} = \frac{1}{2^3} = \frac{1}{2 \cdot 2 \cdot 2} = \frac{1}{8}$

99. $\frac{7^5}{7^4} = 7^{5-4} = 7^1 = 7$

100. $5^2 \cdot 5^1 = 5^3 = 125$

101. $7^0 = 1$

102. $4^{-3} = \dfrac{1}{4^3} = \dfrac{1}{64}$

103. $(2^3)^2 = 2^{3 \cdot 2} = 2^6 = 64$

104. $(3^2)^2 = 3^{2 \cdot 2} = 3^4 = 81$

105. $230{,}000 = 2.3 \times 10^5$

106. $0.0000158 = 1.58 \times 10^{-5}$

107. $0.00275 = 2.75 \times 10^{-3}$

108. $4{,}950{,}000 = 4.95 \times 10^6$

109. $2.5 \times 10^4 = 25{,}000$

110. $1.39 \times 10^{-4} = 0.000139$

111. $1.75 \times 10^{-4} = 0.000175$

112. $1 \times 10^5 = 100{,}000$

113. a) $(5 \times 10^6)(1.7 \times 10^{-4})$
$(5)(1.7) \times 10^6 \cdot 10^{-4}$
8.5×10^2

114. a) $(4 \times 10^2)(2.5 \times 10^2)$
$(4)(2.5) \times 10^2 \cdot 10^2$
10×10^4
1.0×10^5

115. a) $\dfrac{8.4 \times 10^3}{4 \times 10^2} = \dfrac{8.4}{4} \times \dfrac{10^3}{10^2} = 2.1 \times 10^1$

116. a) $\dfrac{1.5 \times 10^{-3}}{5 \times 10^{-4}} = \dfrac{1.5}{5} \times \dfrac{10^{-3}}{10^{-4}} = 0.3 \times 10^1 = 3.0 \times 10^0$

117. a) $(25{,}000)(600{,}000) = (2.5 \times 10^4)(6.0 \times 10^5)$
$= (2.5)(6) \times 10^4 \cdot 10^5 = 15 \times 10^9$
$= 1.5 \times 10^{10} = 15{,}000{,}000{,}000$

118. a) $(35{,}000)(0.00002) = (3.5 \times 10^4)(2.0 \times 10^{-5})$
$= (3.5)(2) \times 10^4 \cdot 10^{-5} = 7 \times 10^{-1} = 0.7$

119. $\dfrac{9600000}{3000} = \dfrac{9.6 \times 10^6}{3 \times 10^3} = 3.2 \times 10^3 = 3{,}200$

120. $\dfrac{0.000002}{0.0000004} = \dfrac{2 \times 10^{-6}}{4 \times 10^{-7}} = 0.5 \times 10^1 = 5.0$

121. $\dfrac{300000}{12000} = \dfrac{3 \times 10^5}{1.2 \times 10^4} = 2.5 \times 10^1 = 25$ times

122. $\dfrac{20{,}000{,}000}{3{,}600} = \dfrac{2.0 \times 10^7}{3.6 \times 10^3} \approx 0.555556 \times 10^4 = \$5{,}555.56$

123. Arithmetic: $d = 5$; 21 and 26

124. Geometric: $r = -3$; -243 and 729

125. Arithmetic: $d = -3$; -15 and -18

126. Geometric: $r = 1/2$; 1/32 and 1/64

127. Arithmetic: $d = 3$; 16 and 19

128. Geometric: $r = -1$; -2 and 2

129. $a_6 = -6 + (6-1)3 = -6 + (5)(3) = 9$

130. $a_8 = -6 + (8-1)(-4) = -6 + (7)(-4) = -34$

131. $a_{10} = -20 + (10-1)5 = -20 + (9)(5) = 25$

132. $a_4 = 8(3)^{4-1} = 8(3)^3 = 8(27) = 216$

133. $a_5 = 4(1/2)^{5-1} = 4(1/2)^4 = 4(1/16) = 1/4$

134. $a_4 = -6(2)^{4-1} = -6(2)^3 = -6(8) = -48$

135. $s_{10} = \dfrac{10(2+38)}{2} = \dfrac{(10)(40)}{2} = 200$

136. $s_8 = \dfrac{8\left(-4 + (-2\,\frac{1}{4})\right)}{2} = \dfrac{(8)(-6\,\frac{1}{4})}{2} = -25$

137. $s_8 = \dfrac{8(100+58)}{2} = \dfrac{(8)(158)}{2} = 632$

138. $s_{20} = \dfrac{20(0.5+5.25)}{2} = \dfrac{(20)(5.75)}{2} = 57.5$

139. $s_3 = \dfrac{4(1-2^3)}{1-2} = \dfrac{(4)(1-8)}{-1} = \dfrac{(4)(-7)}{-1} = 28$

140. $s_4 = \dfrac{2(1-3^4)}{1-3} = \dfrac{(2)(1-81)}{-2} = \dfrac{(2)(-80)}{-2} = 80$

141. $s_5 = \dfrac{3(1-(-2)^5)}{1-(-2)} = \dfrac{(3)(1+32)}{3} = \dfrac{(3)(33)}{3} = 33$

142. $s_6 = \dfrac{1(1-(-2)^6)}{1-(-2)} = \dfrac{(1)(1-64)}{3} = \dfrac{(1)(-63)}{3} = -21$

143. Arithmetic: $a_n = -3n + 10$

144. Arithmetic: $a_n = 5n - 5$

145. Arithmetic: $a_n = -(3/2)n + (11/2)$

146. Geometric: $a_n = 3(2)^{n-1}$

147. Geometric: $a_n = 4(-1)^{n-1}$

148. Geometric: $a_n = 5(1/3)^{n-1}$

149. Yes; 13, 21

150. Yes; 17, 28

151. No

152. No

Chapter Test

1. 481,248 is divisible by:
   2, 3, 4, 6, 8, and 9.

2.

$$
\begin{array}{r|r}
2 & 420 \\
2 & 210 \\
3 & 105 \\
5 & 35 \\
\hline
 & 7
\end{array}
$$

$$420 = 2^2 \cdot 3 \cdot 5 \cdot 7$$

3. $[(-6) + (-9)] + 8 = -15 + 8 = -7$

4. $-5 - 15 = -5 + (-15) = -20$

5. $[(-70)(-5)] \div (8 - 10)$
   $= 350 \div [8 + (-10)] = 350 \div (-2) = -175$

6. $4\frac{5}{8} = \frac{(8\cdot4)+5}{8} = \frac{32+5}{8} = \frac{37}{8}$

7. $\frac{176}{9} = \frac{(19\cdot9)+5}{9} = 19\frac{5}{9}$

8. $\frac{5}{8} = 0.625$

9. $6.45 = \frac{645}{100} = \frac{129}{20}$

10. $\frac{5}{16} \div \frac{4}{5} \cdot \frac{1}{2} = \frac{5}{16} \cdot \frac{1}{3} + \frac{2}{5} = \frac{5}{48} + \frac{2}{5} = \frac{25}{240} + \frac{96}{240} = \frac{121}{240}$

11. $\frac{15}{24} - \frac{3}{20} = \frac{5}{5} \cdot \frac{15}{24} - \frac{6}{6} \cdot \frac{3}{20} = \frac{75}{120} - \frac{18}{120} = \frac{57}{120} = \frac{19}{40}$

12. $\sqrt{75} + \sqrt{48} = \sqrt{25}\sqrt{3} + \sqrt{16}\sqrt{3} = 5\sqrt{3} + 4\sqrt{3} = 9\sqrt{3}$

13. $\frac{\sqrt{5}}{\sqrt{6}} = \frac{\sqrt{5}}{\sqrt{6}} \cdot \frac{\sqrt{6}}{\sqrt{6}} = \frac{\sqrt{30}}{\sqrt{36}} = \frac{\sqrt{30}}{6}$

14. The integers are closed under multiplication since the product of two integers is always an integer.

15. Associative property of addition

16. Distributive property

17. $\frac{6^7}{6^5} = 6^{7-5} = 6^2 = 36$

18. $4^3 \cdot 4^2 = 4^5 = 4 \cdot 4 \cdot 4 \cdot 4 \cdot 4 = 1024$

19. $9^{-2} = \frac{1}{9^2} = \frac{1}{81}$

20. $\frac{64000}{0.008} = \frac{5.4 \times 10^4}{8 \times 10^{-3}} = 0.8 \times 10^7 = 8 \times 10^6$

21. $a_n = -4n + 2$

22. $\frac{11[-2+(-32)]}{2} = \frac{11(-34)}{2} = -187$

23. $a_5 = 3(3)^4 = 3^5 = 243$

24. $\frac{3(1-4^5)}{1-4} = \frac{3(1-1024)}{-3} = 1023$

25. $a_n = 3 \cdot (2)^{n-1}$

26. 1, 1, 2, 3, 5, 8, 13, 21, 34, 55

CHAPTER SIX

ALGEBRA, GRAPHS, AND FUNCTIONS

Exercise Set 6.1

1. **Variables** are letters of the alphabet used to represent numbers.

3. An **algebraic expression** is a collection of variables, numbers, parentheses, and operation symbols. An example is $5x^2y - 11$.

5. a) Base: 4, exponent: 5
   b) Multiply 4 by itself 5 times.

7. $6 + 12 \div 2 = 6 + 6 = 12$

9. $x = -4, x^2 = (-4)^2 = 16$

11. $x = -7, -x^2 = -(-7)^2 = -49$

13. $x = -7, -2x^3 = -2(-7)^3 = -2(-343) = 686$

15. $x = 4, x - 7 = 4 - 7 = -3$

17. $x = -4, -5x + 8 = -5(-4) + 8 = 20 + 8 = 28$

19. $x = -2, -x^2 - 7x + 5 = -(-2)^2 - 7(-2) + 5$
    $$= -4 + 14 + 5 = 15$$

21. $x = \dfrac{2}{3}, \dfrac{1}{2}x^2 - 5x + 2 = \dfrac{1}{2}\left(\dfrac{2}{3}\right)^2 - 5\left(\dfrac{2}{3}\right) + 2$
    $$= \dfrac{1}{2}\left(\dfrac{4}{9}\right) - \dfrac{10}{3} + 2$$
    $$= \dfrac{4}{18} - \dfrac{10}{3} + 2$$
    $$= \dfrac{4}{18} - \dfrac{60}{18} + \dfrac{36}{18} = -\dfrac{20}{18} = -\dfrac{10}{9}$$

23. $x = \dfrac{1}{2}, 8x^3 - 4x^2 + 7 = 8\left(\dfrac{1}{2}\right)^3 - 4\left(\dfrac{1}{2}\right)^2 + 7$
    $$= 8\left(\dfrac{1}{8}\right) - 4\left(\dfrac{1}{4}\right) + 7$$
    $$= 1 - 1 + 7 = 7$$

25. $x = 1, y = -2, 3x^2 - xy + 2y^2 = 3(1)^2 - 1(-2) + 2(-2)^2$
    $$= 3 + 2 + 8 = 13$$

27. $x = 3, y = 2, 4x^2 - 12xy + 9y^2 = 4(3)^2 - 12(3)(2) + 9(2)^2$
    $$= 36 - 72 + 36 = 0$$

29. $6x - 9 = 12, x = 3$
    $6(3) - 9 = 18 - 9 = 9$
    $9 \neq 12, x = 3$ is not a solution.

31. $x + 2y = 0, x = -6, y = 3$

    $-6 + 2(3) = -6 + 6 = 0$

    $0 = 0, x = -6, y = 3$ is a solution.

33. $x^2 + 3x - 4 = 5, x = 2$

    $(2)^2 + 3(2) - 4 = 4 + 6 - 4 = 6$

    $6 \neq 5, x = 2$ is not a solution.

35. $2x^2 + x = 28, x = -4$

    $2(-4)^2 + (-4) = 2(16) - 4 = 32 - 4 = 28$

    $28 = 28, x = -4$ is a solution.

37. $y = -x^2 + 4x - 1, x = 3, y = 2$

    $-3^2 + 4(3) - 1 = -9 + 12 - 1 = 2$

    $2 = 2, x = 3, y = 2$ is a solution.

39. a) $t = 8, 6.55t = 6.55(8) = \$52.40$

    b) $t = 20, 6.55t = 6.55(20) = \$131$

41. $x = \$12,500, x + 0.05x = \$12,500 + 0.05(\$12,500)$

    $\qquad\qquad\qquad = \$12,500 + \$625 = \$13,125$

43. $x = 60, 25x - 0.2x^2 = 25(60) - 0.2(60)^2$

    $\qquad\qquad\qquad\quad = 1500 - 0.2(3600)$

    $\qquad\qquad\qquad\quad = 1500 - 720$

    $\qquad\qquad\qquad\quad = 780$ baskets of oranges

45. $R = 2, T = 70, 0.2R^2 + 0.003RT + 0.0001T^2 = 0.2(2)^2 + 0.003(2)(70) + 0.0001(70)^2 = 0.8 + 0.42 + 0.49 = 1.71$ in.

47.

x	y	$(x+y)^2$	$x^2 + y^2$
2	3	$5^2 = 25$	$4 + 9 = 13$
-2	-3	$(-5)^2 = 25$	$4 + 9 = 13$
-2	3	$1^2 = 1$	$4 + 9 = 13$
2	-3	$(-1)^2 = 1$	$4 + 9 = 13$

     The two expressions are not equal.

Exercise Set 6.2

1. The parts that are added or subtracted in an algebraic expression are called **terms**.
   In $3x - 2y$, the $3x$ and $-2y$ are terms.

3. The numerical part of a term is called its **numerical coefficient.**
   For the term $3x$, 3 is the numerical coefficient.

5. A **linear equation** is one in which the exponent on the variable is 1. Example: $4x + 6 = 10$

7. If $a = b$, then $a - c = b - c$ for all real numbers a, b, and c. Example: If $2x + 3 = 5$, then $2x + 3 - 3 = 5 - 3$.

9. If $a = b$, then $\dfrac{a}{c} = \dfrac{b}{c}$ for all real numbers a, b, and c, where $c \neq 0$. Example: If $4x = 8$ then $\dfrac{4x}{4} = \dfrac{8}{4}$.

11. A **ratio** is a quotient of two quantities. Example: $\dfrac{7}{9}$

13. Yes. They have the same variable and the same exponent on the variable.

15. $3x + 8x = 11x$

17. $8x + 2x - 11 = 10x - 11$

19. $7x + 3y - 4x + 8y = 3x + 11y$

21. $-3x + 2 - 5x = -8x + 2$

23. $2 - 3x - 2x + 1 = -5x + 3$

25. $3.7x - 5.8 + 2.6x = 6.3x - 5.8$

27. $\dfrac{1}{3}x - \dfrac{1}{4}x - 2 = \dfrac{4}{12}x - \dfrac{3}{12}x - 2 = \dfrac{1}{12}x - 2$

29. $5x - 4y - 3y + 8x + 3 = 13x - 7y + 3$

31. $2(s+3) + 6(s-4) + 1 = 2s + 6 + 6s - 24 + 1 = 8s - 17$

33. $0.2(x-3) - 1.6(x+2)$
$= 0.2x - 0.6 - 1.6x - 3.2$
$= -1.4x - 3.8$

35. $\dfrac{3}{4}x + \dfrac{3}{5} - \dfrac{2}{5}x + \dfrac{1}{2} = \dfrac{15}{20}x - \dfrac{8}{20}x + \dfrac{6}{10} + \dfrac{5}{10}$

$= \dfrac{7}{20}x + \dfrac{11}{10}$

37. $0.5(2.6x - 4) + 2.3(1.4x - 5) = 1.3x - 2 + 3.22 - 11.5$
$= 4.52x - 13.5$

39. $\quad y + 3 = 8$

$y + 3 - 3 = 8 - 3$ Subtract 3 from both sides of the equation

$y = 5$

41. $\quad 16 = 2x + 6$

$16 - 6 = 2x + 6 - 6$ Subtract 6 from both sides of the equation

$10 = 2x$

$\dfrac{10}{2} = \dfrac{2x}{2}$ Divide both sides of the equation by 2

$5 = x$

43. $\quad \dfrac{3}{x} = \dfrac{7}{8}$

$3(8) = 7x$ Cross multiplication

$24 = 7x$

$\dfrac{24}{7} = \dfrac{7x}{7}$ Divide both sides of the equation by 7

$\dfrac{24}{7} = x$

45. $\quad \dfrac{1}{2}x + \dfrac{1}{3} = \dfrac{2}{3}$

$6\left(\dfrac{1}{2}x + \dfrac{1}{3}\right) = 6\left(\dfrac{2}{3}\right)$ Multiply both sides of the equation by the LCD

$3x + 2 = 4$ Distributive Property

$3x + 2 - 2 = 4 - 2$ Subtract 2 from both sides of the equation

$3x = 2$

$\dfrac{3x}{3} = \dfrac{2}{3}$ Divide both sides of the equation by 3

$x = \dfrac{2}{3}$

47. $0.7x - 0.3 = 1.8$

$0.7x - 0.3 + 0.3 = 1.8 + 0.3$ Add 0.3 to both sides of the equation

$0.7x = 2.1$

$\dfrac{0.7x}{0.7} = \dfrac{2.1}{0.7}$ Divide both sides of the equation by 0.7

$x = 3$

49. $3t - 4 = 2t - 1$

$3t - 2t - 4 = 2t - 2t - 1$ Subtract $2t$ from both sides of the equation

$t - 4 = -1$

$t - 4 + 4 = -1 + 4$ Add 4 to both sides of the equation

$t = 3$

51. $\dfrac{x-5}{4} = \dfrac{x-9}{3}$

$3(x-5) = 4(x-9)$ Cross multiplication

$3x - 15 = 4x - 36$ Distributive Property

$3x - 3x - 15 = 4x - 3x - 36$ Subtract $3x$ from both sides of the equation

$-15 = x - 36$

$-15 + 36 = x - 36 + 36$ Add 36 to both sides of the equation

$21 = x$

53. $\dfrac{x}{15} = 2 + \dfrac{x}{5}$

$15\left(\dfrac{x}{15}\right) = 15\left(2 + \dfrac{x}{5}\right)$ Multiply both sides of the equation by the LCD

$x = 30 + 3x$ Distributive Property

$x - 3x = 30 + 3x - 3x$ Subtract $3x$ from both sides of the equation

$-2x = 30$

$\dfrac{-2x}{-2} = \dfrac{30}{-2}$ Divide both sides of the equation by -2

$x = -15$

55. $2(x+3) - 4 = 2(x-4)$

$2x + 6 - 4 = 2x - 8$ Distributive Property

$2x + 2 = 2x - 8$

$2x - 2x + 2 = 2x - 2x - 8$ Subtract $2x$ from both sides of the equation

$2 = -8$ False

No solution

57. $6(x+1) = 4x + 2(x+3)$

    $6x + 6 = 4x + 2x + 6$ Distributive Property

    $6x + 6 = 6x + 6$

This equation is an identity. Therefore, the solution is all real numbers.

59. $\dfrac{1}{4}(x+4) = \dfrac{2}{5}(x+2)$

    $20\left(\dfrac{1}{4}\right)(x+4) = 20\left(\dfrac{2}{5}\right)(x+2)$ Multiply both sides of the equation by the LCD

    $5(x+4) = 8(x+2)$

    $5x + 20 = 8x + 16$ Distributive Property

    $5x - 8x + 20 = 8x - 8x + 16$ Subtract $8x$ from both sides of the equation

    $-3x + 20 = 16$

    $-3x + 20 - 20 = 16 - 20$ Subtract 20 from both sides of the equation

    $-3x = -4$

    $\dfrac{-3x}{-3} = \dfrac{-4}{-3},\ x = \dfrac{4}{3}$ Divide both sides of the equation by -3

61. $3x + 2 - 6x = -x - 15 + 8 - 5x$

    $-3x + 2 = -6x - 7$

    $-3x + 6x + 2 = -6x + 6x - 7$ Add $6x$ to both sides of the equation

    $3x + 2 = -7$

    $3x + 2 - 2 = -7 - 2$ Subtract 2 from both sides of the equation

    $3x = -9$

    $\dfrac{3x}{3} = \dfrac{-9}{3}$ Divide both sides of the equation by 3

    $x = -3$

63. $2(x-3) + 2 = 2(2x-6)$

    $2x - 6 + 2 = 4x - 12$ Distributive Property

    $2x - 4 = 4x - 12$

    $2x - 4x - 4 = 4x - 4x - 12$ Subtract $4x$ from both sides of the equation

    $-2x - 4 = -12$

    $-2x - 4 + 4 = -12 + 4$ Add 4 to both sides of the equation

    $-2x = -8$

    $\dfrac{-2x}{-2} = \dfrac{-8}{-2}$ Divide both sides of the equation by -2

    $x = 4$

65. $\dfrac{1.95}{1000} = \dfrac{x}{35,300}$

$$1.95(35,300) = 1000x$$

$$68,835 = 1000x$$

$$\dfrac{68,835}{1000} = \dfrac{1000x}{1000}$$

$$x \approx \$68.84$$

67. $\dfrac{8.025}{1000} = \dfrac{x}{132,600}$

$$8.025(132,600) = 1000x$$

$$1,064,115 = 1000x$$

$$\dfrac{1,064,115}{1000} = \dfrac{1000x}{1000}$$

$$x \approx \$1064.12$$

69. a) $\dfrac{700}{3} = \dfrac{x}{60}$

$$700(60) = 3x$$

$$42,000 = 3x$$

$$\dfrac{42,000}{3} = \dfrac{3x}{3}$$

$$x = 14,000 \ \textbf{toys}$$

b) $\dfrac{700}{3} = \dfrac{2800}{x}$

$$700x = 3(2800)$$

$$700x = 8400$$

$$\dfrac{700x}{700} = \dfrac{8400}{700}$$

$$x = 12 \ \textbf{hours}$$

71. a) $\dfrac{50}{80} = \dfrac{1}{x}$

$$50x = 80$$

$$\dfrac{50x}{50} = \dfrac{80}{50}$$

$$x = 1.6 \ \textbf{kph}$$

b) $\dfrac{50}{80} = \dfrac{x}{90}$

$$80x = 50(90)$$

$$80x = 4500$$

$$\dfrac{80x}{80} = \dfrac{4500}{80}$$

$$x = 56.25 \ \textbf{mph}$$

73. $\dfrac{40}{1} = \dfrac{12}{x}$

$$40x = 12$$

$$\dfrac{40x}{40} = \dfrac{12}{40}$$

$$x = 0.3 \ \textbf{cc}$$

75. a) Answers will vary.

   b) $2(x+3)=4x+3-5x$

   $2x+6=-x+3$ Distributive Property

   $2x+x+6=-x+x+3$ Add x to both sides of the equation

   $3x+6=3$

   $3x+6-6=3-6$ Subtract 6 from both sides of the equation

   $3x=-3$

   $\dfrac{3x}{3}=\dfrac{-3}{3}$ Divide both sides of the equation by 3

   $x=-1$

77. a) An **inconsistent equation** is an equation with no solution.
   b) When solving an equation, if you obtain a false statement, then the equation is inconsistent.

79. a) $2:5$
   b) $m:m+n$

Exercise Set 6.3

1. A **formula** is an equation that typically has a real-life application.
3. **Subscripts** are numbers (or letters) placed below and to the right of variables. They are used to help clarify a formula.
5. An **exponential equation** is of the form $y=a^x, a>0, a\neq 1$.

7. $A=bh=15(4)=60$

9. $P=2l+2w$
   $P=2(12)+2(16)=24+32=56$

11. $E=mc^2$
   $400=m(4)^2$
   $400=16m$
   $\dfrac{400}{16}=\dfrac{16m}{16}$
   $25=m$

13. $m=\dfrac{a+b}{2}$
   $\dfrac{55}{1}=\dfrac{27+b}{2}$
   $55(2)=27+b$
   $110=27+b$
   $110-27=27-27+b$
   $83=b$

15.
$$z = \frac{x - \mu}{\sigma}$$
$$\frac{2.5}{1} = \frac{42.1 - \mu}{2}$$
$$2.5(2) = 42.1 - \mu$$
$$5 = 42.1 - \mu$$
$$5 - 42.1 = 42.1 - 42.1 - \mu$$
$$-37.1 = -\mu$$
$$\frac{-37.1}{-1} = \frac{-\mu}{-1}$$
$$37.1 = \mu$$

17.
$$T = \frac{PV}{k}$$
$$\frac{80}{1} = \frac{P(20)}{0.5}$$
$$80(0.5) = 20P$$
$$40 = 20P$$
$$\frac{40}{20} = \frac{20P}{20}$$
$$2 = P$$

19.
$$A = P(1 + rt)$$
$$3600 = P(1 + 0.04(5))$$
$$3600 = P(1 + 0.2)$$
$$3600 = 1.2P$$
$$\frac{3600}{1.2} = \frac{1.2P}{1.2}$$
$$3000 = P$$

21.
$$V = \frac{1}{2}at^2$$
$$576 = \frac{1}{2}a(12)^2$$
$$\frac{576}{1} = \frac{144a}{2}$$
$$576(2) = 144a$$
$$1152 = 144a$$
$$\frac{1152}{144} = \frac{144a}{144}$$
$$8 = a$$

23.
$$C = \frac{5}{9}(F - 32)$$
$$C = \frac{5}{9}(77 - 32)$$
$$C = \frac{5}{9}(45) = 25$$

25.
$$z = \frac{\bar{x} - \mu}{\frac{\sigma}{\sqrt{n}}}$$
$$z = \frac{66 - 60}{\frac{15}{\sqrt{25}}}$$
$$z = \frac{6}{\frac{15}{5}} = \frac{6}{3} = 2$$

27.
$$S = R - rR$$
$$186 = 1R - 0.07R$$
$$186 = 0.93R$$
$$\frac{186}{0.93} = \frac{0.93R}{0.93}$$
$$200 = R$$

29.
$$E = a_1 p_1 + a_2 p_2 + a_3 p_3$$
$$E = 5(0.2) + 7(0.6) + 10(0.2)$$
$$E = 1 + 4.2 + 2 = 7.2$$

31. $x = \dfrac{-b - \sqrt{b^2 - 4ac}}{2a}$

$x = \dfrac{-(-5) - \sqrt{(-5)^2 - 4(2)(-12)}}{2(2)}$

$x = \dfrac{5 - \sqrt{25 + 96}}{4}$

$x = \dfrac{5 - \sqrt{121}}{4} = \dfrac{5 - 11}{4} = \dfrac{-6}{4} = -\dfrac{3}{2}$

33. $P = \dfrac{f}{1 + i}$

$3000 = \dfrac{f}{1 + 0.08}$

$\dfrac{3000}{1} = \dfrac{f}{1.08}$

$3000(1.08) = f$

$3240 = f$

35. $F = \dfrac{G m_1 m_2}{r^2}$

$625 = \dfrac{G(100)(200)}{(4)^2}$

$625 = 1250G$

$\dfrac{625}{1250} = \dfrac{1250G}{1250}$

$0.5 = G$

37. $S_n = \dfrac{a_1 \left(1 - r^n\right)}{1 - r}$

$S_n = \dfrac{8\left(1 - \left(\dfrac{1}{2}\right)^3\right)}{1 - \dfrac{1}{2}}$

$S_n = \dfrac{8\left(1 - \dfrac{1}{8}\right)}{1 - \dfrac{1}{2}}$

$S_n = \dfrac{8\left(\dfrac{7}{8}\right)}{\dfrac{1}{2}} = \dfrac{7}{\dfrac{1}{2}} = 7(2) = 14$

39. $7x - 6y = 15$

$-7x + 7x - 6y = -7x + 15$ Subtract $7x$ from both sides of the equation

$-6y = -7x + 15$

$\dfrac{-6y}{-6} = \dfrac{-7x + 15}{-6}$ Divide both sides of the equation by -6

$y = \dfrac{7x - 15}{6} = \dfrac{7}{6}x - \dfrac{5}{2}$

41. $4x + 7y = 14$

$-4x + 4x + 7y = -4x + 14$ Subtract $4x$ from both sides of the equation

$7y = -4x + 14$

$\dfrac{7y}{7} = \dfrac{-4x + 14}{7}$ Divide both sides of the equation by 7

$y = \dfrac{-4x + 14}{7} = -\dfrac{4}{7}x + 2$

43.
$$2x - 3y + 6 = 0$$
$$2x - 3y + 6 - 6 = 0 - 6 \qquad \text{Subtract } 6 \text{ from both sides of the equation}$$
$$2x - 3y = -6$$
$$-2x + 2x - 3y = -2x - 6 \qquad \text{Subtract } 2x \text{ from both sides of the equation}$$
$$-3y = -2x - 6$$
$$\frac{-3y}{-3} = \frac{-2x - 6}{-3} \qquad \text{Divide both sides of the equation by } -3$$
$$y = \frac{-2x - 6}{-3} = \frac{2x + 6}{3} = \frac{2}{3}x + 2$$

45.
$$-3x - 2y = 20$$
$$-3x + 3x - 2y = 3x + 20 \qquad \text{Add } 3x \text{ to both sides of the equation}$$
$$-2y = 3x + 20$$
$$\frac{-2y}{-2} = \frac{3x + 20}{-2} \qquad \text{Divide both sides of the equation by } -2$$
$$y = \frac{3x + 20}{-2} = -\frac{3}{2}x - 10$$

47.
$$9x + 4z = 7 + 8y$$
$$9x + 4z - 7 = 7 - 7 + 8y \qquad \text{Subtract } 7 \text{ from both sides of the equation}$$
$$9x + 4z - 7 = 8y$$
$$\frac{9x + 4z - 7}{8} = \frac{8y}{8} \qquad \text{Divide both sides of the equation by } 8$$
$$y = \frac{9x + 4z - 7}{8} = \frac{9}{8}x + \frac{1}{2}z - \frac{7}{8}$$

49.
$$A = bh$$
$$\frac{A}{h} = \frac{bh}{h} \qquad \text{Divide both sides of the equation by } h$$
$$b = \frac{A}{h}$$

51.
$$p = a + b + c$$
$$p - b = a + b - b + c \qquad \text{Subtract } b \text{ from both sides of the equation}$$
$$p - b = a + c$$
$$p - b - c = a + c - c \qquad \text{Subtract } c \text{ from both sides of the equation}$$
$$a = p - b - c$$

53. $V = lwh$

$\dfrac{V}{l} = \dfrac{lwh}{l}$ Divide both sides of the equation by l

$\dfrac{V}{l} = wh$

$\dfrac{V}{lh} = \dfrac{wh}{h}$ Divide both sides of the equation by h

$w = \dfrac{V}{lh}$

55. $C = 2\pi r$

$\dfrac{C}{2} = \dfrac{2\pi r}{2}$ Divide both sides of the equation by 2

$\dfrac{C}{2} = \pi r$

$\dfrac{C}{2\pi} = \dfrac{\pi r}{\pi}$ Divide both sides of the equation by π

$r = \dfrac{C}{2\pi}$

57. $y = mx + b$

$y - mx = mx - mx + b$ Subtract mx from both sides of the equation

$b = y - mx$

59. $P = 2l + 2w$

$P - 2l = 2l - 2l + 2w$ Subtract $2l$ from both sides of the equation

$P - 2l = 2w$

$\dfrac{P - 2l}{2} = \dfrac{2w}{2}$ Divide both sides of the equation by 2

$w = \dfrac{P - 2l}{2}$

61. $A = \dfrac{a + b + c}{3}$

$3A = 3\left(\dfrac{a + b + c}{3}\right)$ Multiply both sides of the equation by 3

$3A = a + b + c$

$3A - a = a - a + b + c$ Subtract a from both sides of the equation

$3A - a = b + c$

$3A - a - b = b - b + c$ Subtract b from both sides of the equation

$c = 3A - a - b$

63. $P = \dfrac{KT}{V}$

$PV = \left(\dfrac{KT}{V}\right)V$ Multiply both sides of the equation by V

$PV = KT$

$\dfrac{PV}{K} = \dfrac{KT}{K}$ Divide both sides of the equation by K

$T = \dfrac{PV}{K}$

65. $F = \dfrac{9}{5}C + 32$

$F - 32 = \dfrac{9}{5}C + 32 - 32$ Subtract 32 from both sides of the equation

$F - 32 = \dfrac{9}{5}C$

$\dfrac{5}{9}(F - 32) = \dfrac{5}{9}\left(\dfrac{9}{5}C\right)$ Multiply both sides of the equation by $\dfrac{5}{9}$

$C = \dfrac{5}{9}(F - 32)$

67. $S = \pi r^2 + \pi rs$

$S - \pi r^2 = \pi r^2 - \pi r^2 + \pi rs$ Subtract πr^2 from both sides of the equation

$S - \pi r^2 = \pi rs$

$\dfrac{S - \pi r^2}{\pi} = \dfrac{\pi rs}{\pi}$ Divide both sides of the equation by π

$\dfrac{S - \pi r^2}{\pi} = rs$

$\dfrac{S - \pi r^2}{\pi r} = \dfrac{rs}{r}$ Divide both sides of the equation by r

$s = \dfrac{S - \pi r^2}{\pi r}$

69. a) $i = prt$

$i = 3500(0.03)(1) = \$105$

b) $\$3500 + \$105 = \$3605$

71.   Radius $= \dfrac{2.5}{2} = 1.25\ in.$

$V = \pi r^2 h$

$V = \pi(1.25)^2 (3.75)$

$V = \pi(1.5625)(3.75)$

$V = 18.40776945\ in.^3 \approx 18.41\ in.^3$

73. $P = P_0 2^{-t/5600}$

$P = (20)2^{-500/5600}$

$P = (20)2^{-0.0892857143}$

$P = (20)(0.9399880269)$

$P = 18.79976054 \ mg. \approx 18.8 \ mg.$

75. $V = 24e^{0.08t}$

$V = 24e^{0.08(374)}$

$V = 24e^{29.92}$

$V = \$236,756,624,900,000$

77. $V = lwh - \pi r^2 h$

$V = 12(8)(12) - \pi(2)^2(8)$

$V = 1152 - 100.5309649$

$V = 1051.469035 \ in.^3 \approx 1051.47 \ in.^3$

Exercise Set 6.4

1. A **mathematical expression** is a collection of variables, numbers, parentheses and operation symbols. An **equation** is two algebraic expressions joined by an equals sign.

3. $9 - 6x$

5. $6r + 5$

7. $15 - 2r$

9. $x + 6$

11. $\dfrac{3+n}{8}$

13. $(5y - 6) + 3$

15. Let $x =$ the number
$x + 7 =$ the sum of the number and 7
$x + 7 = 19$
$x + 7 - 7 = 19 - 7$
$x = 12$

17. Let $x =$ the number
$x - 10 =$ the number decreased by 10
$x - 10 = 25$
$x - 10 + 10 = 25 + 10$
$x = 35$

19. Let $x =$ the number
$12 + 5x = 12$ increased by 5 times the number
$12 + 5x = 47$
$12 - 12 + 5x = 47 - 12$
$5x = 35$
$\dfrac{5x}{5} = \dfrac{35}{5}$
$x = 7$

21. Let $x =$ the number
$8x + 16 = 16$ more than 8 times the number
$8x + 16 = 88$
$8x + 16 - 16 = 88 - 16$
$8x = 72$
$\dfrac{8x}{8} = \dfrac{72}{8}$
$x = 9$

23. Let $x=$ the number
$x+11=$ the number increased by 11
$3x+1=1$ more than 3 times the number
$$x+11=3x+1$$
$$x-x+11=3x-x+1$$
$$11=2x+1$$
$$11-1=2x+1-1$$
$$10=2x$$
$$\frac{10}{2}=\frac{2x}{2}$$
$$5=x$$

25. Let $x=$ the number
$x+3=3$ more than the number
$5(x+7)=5$ times the sum of the number and 7
$$x+3=5(x+7)$$
$$x+3=5x+35$$
$$x-x+3=5x-x+35$$
$$3=4x+35$$
$$3-35=4x+35-35$$
$$-32=4x$$
$$\frac{-32}{4}=\frac{4x}{4}$$
$$-8=x$$

27. Let $x=$ amount invested in mutual funds
$2x=$ amount invested in bonds
$$x+2x=9000$$
$$3x=9000$$
$$\frac{3x}{3}=\frac{9000}{3}$$
$$x=\$3000 \text{ in mutual funds}$$
$$2x=2(3000)=\$6000 \text{ in bonds}$$

29. Let $x=$ number of years until the population reaches $12,200$
$500x=$ the amount the population increases by each year
$$6200+500x=12,200$$
$$6200-6200+500x=12,200-6200$$
$$500x=6000$$
$$\frac{500x}{500}=\frac{6000}{500}$$
$$x=12 \text{ years}$$

31. Let $x=$ the original price before tax
$0.10x=$ amount saved on spending x dollars
$$x-0.10x=15.72$$
$$0.9x=15.72$$
$$\frac{0.9x}{0.9}=\frac{15.72}{0.9}$$
$$x\approx\$17.47$$

33. Let $x=$ number of discs for Samantha
$3x=$ number of discs for Josie
$$x+3x=12$$
$$4x=12$$
$$\frac{4x}{4}=\frac{12}{4}$$
$$x=3 \text{ discs for Samantha}$$
$$3x=3(3)=9 \text{ discs for Josie}$$

35. Let $x=$ the number of miles traveled
$0.20x=$ the amount spent for x miles at $\$.20$ per mile
$$60+0.20x=100$$
$$60-60+0.20x=100-60$$
$$0.20x=40$$
$$\frac{0.20x}{0.20}=\frac{40}{0.20}$$
$$x=200 \text{ miles}$$

37. a) Let $x=$ area of smaller ones
$3x=$ area of largest one
$$x+x+3x=45,000$$
$$5x=45,000$$
$$\frac{5x}{5}=\frac{45,000}{5}$$
$$x=9000 \; ft.^2 \text{ for the two smaller barns}$$
$$3x=3(9000)=27,000 \; ft.^2 \text{ for the largest barn}$$
   b) Yes

39. Let $x =$ the weight on Earth

$\dfrac{1}{6}x =$ the weight on the moon

$$x + \dfrac{1}{6}x = 203$$

$$\dfrac{7}{6}x = 203$$

$$\dfrac{6}{7}\left(\dfrac{7}{6}x\right) = \dfrac{6}{7}(203)$$

$$x = 174 \text{ lbs. on Earth}$$

41. Let $w =$ width

$2w =$ length of entire enclosed region

$3w + 2(2w) =$ total amount of fencing

$$3w + 2(2w) = 140$$

$$3w + 4w = 140$$

$$7w = 140$$

$$\dfrac{7w}{7} = \dfrac{140}{7}$$

width $= 20$ ft., length $= 2w = 2(20) = 40$ ft.

43. Let $x =$ the number of months

$70x =$ cost of laundry for x months

$$70x = 760$$

$$\dfrac{70x}{70} = \dfrac{760}{70}$$

$$x = 10.85714286 \text{ months} \approx 11 \text{ months}$$

45. Let $x =$ regular fare

$0.50x =$ half off regular fare

$0.07x =$ tax on regular fare

$$0.50x + 0.07x = 227$$

$$0.57x = 227$$

$$\dfrac{0.57x}{0.57} = \dfrac{227}{0.57}$$

$x = \$398.245614 \approx \$398.25$ regular fare

regular fare including tax:

$\$398.25 + 0.07(\$398.25)$

$= \$398.25 + \$27.88 = \$426.13$

47. Let $x =$ amount of tax reduction to be deducted from Mr. McAdam's income

$3640 - x =$ amount of tax reduction to be deducted from Mrs. McAdam's income

$$24{,}200 - x = 26{,}400 - (3640 - x)$$

$$24{,}200 - x = 26{,}400 - 3640 + x$$

$$24{,}200 - x = 22{,}760 + x$$

$$24{,}200 - x + x = 22{,}760 + x + x$$

$$24{,}200 = 22{,}760 + 2x$$

$$24{,}200 - 22{,}760 = 22{,}760 - 22{,}760 + 2x$$

$$1440 = 2x$$

$$\dfrac{1440}{2} = \dfrac{2x}{2}$$

$x = \$720$ deducted from Mr. McAdam's income

$3640 - x = 3640 - 720 = \$2920$ deducted from Mrs. McAdam's income

49. Let $x =$ the first integer

$x + 1 =$ the second integer

$x + 2 =$ the third integer (the largest)

$$x + (x+1) + (x+2) = 3(x+2) - 3$$

$$3x + 3 = 3x + 6 - 3$$

$$3x + 3 = 3x + 3$$

Exercise Set 6.5

1. **Direct variation** - As one variable increases, so does the other, and as one variable decreases, so does the other.

3. **Joint variation** - One quantity varies directly as the product of two or more other quantities.

5. Inverse

7. Direct

9. Direct

11. Inverse

13. Inverse

15. Inverse

17. Direct

19. Direct

21. Answers will vary.

25. $y = \dfrac{k}{x^2}$

    $y = \dfrac{320}{(8)^2} = \dfrac{320}{64} = 5$

29. $F = kDE$
    $F = 7(3)(10) = 210$

33. $Z = kWY$

    $12 = k(9)(4)$

    $12 = 36k$

    $\dfrac{12}{36} = \dfrac{36k}{36}$

    $k = \dfrac{1}{3}$

    $Z = \dfrac{1}{3}WY$

    $Z = \dfrac{1}{3}(50)(6) = \dfrac{300}{3} = 100$

37. $A = kB^2$

    $245 = k(7)^2$

    $245 = 49k$

    $\dfrac{245}{49} = \dfrac{49k}{49}$

    $k = 5$

    $A = 5B^2$

    $A = 5(9)^2 = 5(81) = 405$

41. $F = km$

    $256 = k(8)$

    $k = \dfrac{256}{8} = 32$

    $F = 32m$

    $F = 32(50) = 1600$ newtons

23. $r = ks$
    $r = 3(11) = 33$

27. $R = \dfrac{k}{W}$

    $R = \dfrac{8}{160} = 0.05$

31. $T = \dfrac{kD^2}{F}$

    $T = \dfrac{12(8)^2}{15} = \dfrac{12(64)}{15} = \dfrac{768}{15} = 51.2$

35. $H = kL$

    $15 = k(50)$

    $\dfrac{15}{50} = \dfrac{50k}{50}$

    $k = 0.3$

    $H = 0.3L$

    $H = 0.3(10) = 3$

39. $F = \dfrac{kq_1 q_2}{d^2}$

    $8 = \dfrac{k(2)(8)}{(4)^2}$

    $8 = \dfrac{16k}{16}$

    $k = 8$

    $F = \dfrac{8q_1 q_2}{d^2}$

    $F = \dfrac{8(28)(12)}{(2)^2} = \dfrac{2688}{4} = 672$

43. $l = \dfrac{k}{d^2}$

    $20 = \dfrac{k}{(6)^2}$

    $k = 20(36) = 720$

    $l = \dfrac{720}{d^2}$

    $l = \dfrac{720}{(3)^2} = \dfrac{720}{9} = 80$ dB.

45.
$$R = \frac{kA}{P}$$
$$4800 = \frac{k(600)}{3}$$
$$600k = 14,400$$
$$k = \frac{14,400}{600} = 24$$
$$R = \frac{24A}{P}$$
$$R = \frac{24(700)}{3.50} = \frac{16,800}{3.50} = 4800 \text{ tapes}$$

47. $W = kI^2R$
$$1 = k(0.1)^2(100)$$
$$1 = 1k$$
$$k = \frac{1}{1} = 1$$
$$W = 1I^2R$$
$$W = 1(0.4)^2(250) = 0.16(250) = 40 \text{ watts}$$

49.
$$N = \frac{kp_1p_2}{d}$$
$$100,000 = \frac{k(60,000)(200,000)}{300}$$
$$12,000,000,000k = 30,000,000$$
$$k = \frac{30,000,000}{12,000,000,000} = 0.0025$$
$$N = \frac{0.0025p_1p_2}{d}$$
$$N = \frac{0.0025(125,000)(175,000)}{450}$$
$$N = \frac{54,687,500}{450} = 121,527.7778 \approx 121,528 \text{ calls}$$

51. a)
$$y = \frac{k}{x}$$
$$y = \frac{0.3}{x}$$
$$xy = 0.3$$
$$\frac{xy}{y} = \frac{0.3}{y}$$
$$x = \frac{0.3}{y}$$
Inversely

b) $k = 0.3$

53.
$$W = \frac{kTA\sqrt{F}}{R}$$
$$68 = \frac{k(78)(1000)\sqrt{4}}{5.6}$$
$$156,000k = 380.8$$
$$k = \frac{380.8}{156,000} = 0.0024410256$$
$$W = \frac{0.0024410256TA\sqrt{F}}{R}$$
$$W = \frac{0.0024410256(78)(1500)\sqrt{6}}{5.6}$$
$$W = \frac{699.5742588}{5.6} = 124.9239748 \approx \$124.92$$

Exercise Set 6.6

1. $a < b$ means that a is less than b, $a \leq b$ means that a is less than or equal to b, $a > b$ means that a is greater than b, $a \geq b$ means that a is greater than or equal to b
3. When both sides of an inequality are multiplied or divided by a negative number, the direction of the inequality symbol must be reversed.
5. Yes, the inequality symbol points to the x in both cases.

7. $x \le 10$

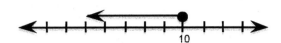

9. $x + 5 < 11$
    $x + 5 - 5 < 11 - 5$
    $x < 6$

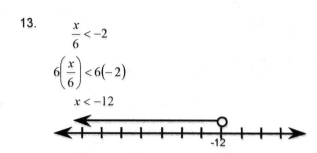

11. $-3x \le 18$
    $\dfrac{-3x}{-3} \ge \dfrac{18}{-3}$
    $x \ge -6$

13. $\dfrac{x}{6} < -2$
    $6\left(\dfrac{x}{6}\right) < 6(-2)$
    $x < -12$

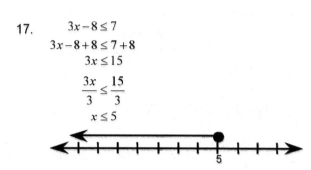

15. $\dfrac{-x}{3} \ge 3$
    $-3\left(\dfrac{-x}{3}\right) \le -3(3)$
    $x \le -9$

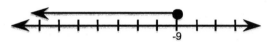

17. $3x - 8 \le 7$
    $3x - 8 + 8 \le 7 + 8$
    $3x \le 15$
    $\dfrac{3x}{3} \le \dfrac{15}{3}$
    $x \le 5$

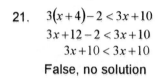

19. $2(x + 6) \le 15$
    $2x + 12 \le 15$
    $2x + 12 - 12 \le 15 - 12$
    $2x \le 3$
    $\dfrac{2x}{2} \le \dfrac{3}{2}$
    $x \le \dfrac{3}{2}$

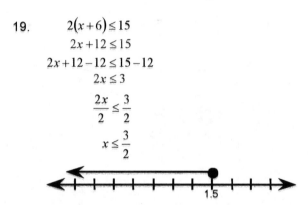

21. $3(x + 4) - 2 < 3x + 10$
    $3x + 12 - 2 < 3x + 10$
    $3x + 10 < 3x + 10$
    False, no solution

23. $3 < x - 7 \le 6$
    $3 + 7 < x - 7 + 7 \le 6 + 7$
    $10 < x \le 13$

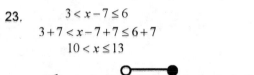

25. $x \ge 3$

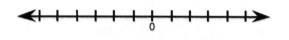

27. $-3x \leq 27$

$$\dfrac{-3x}{-3} \geq \dfrac{27}{-3}$$

$$x \geq -9$$

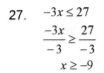

29. $x + 3 < 6$

$$x + 3 - 3 < 6 - 3$$

$$x < 3$$

31. $\dfrac{x}{6} < -2$

$$6\left(\dfrac{x}{6}\right) < 6(-2)$$

$$x < -12$$

33. $\dfrac{-x}{6} \geq 3$

$$-6\left(\dfrac{-x}{6}\right) \leq -6(3)$$

$$x \leq -18$$

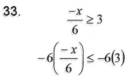

35. $-11 < -5x + 4$

$$-11 - 4 < -5x + 4 - 4$$

$$-15 < -5x$$

$$\dfrac{-15}{-5} > \dfrac{-5x}{-5}$$

$$3 > x$$

$$x < 3$$

37. $3(x + 4) \geq 4x + 13$

$$3x + 12 \geq 4x + 13$$

$$3x - 4x + 12 \geq 4x - 4x + 13$$

$$-x + 12 \geq 13$$

$$-x + 12 - 12 \geq 13 - 12$$

$$-x \geq 1$$

$$\dfrac{-x}{-1} \leq \dfrac{1}{-1}$$

$$x \leq -1$$

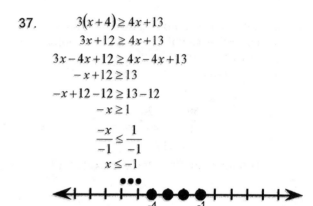

39. $5(x + 4) - 6 \leq 2x + 8$

$$5x + 20 - 6 \leq 2x + 8$$

$$5x + 14 \leq 2x + 8$$

$$5x - 2x + 14 \leq 2x - 2x + 8$$

$$3x + 14 \leq 8$$

$$3x + 14 - 14 \leq 8 - 14$$

$$3x \leq -6$$

$$\dfrac{3x}{3} \leq \dfrac{-6}{3}$$

$$x \leq -2$$

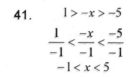

41. $1 > -x > -5$

$$\dfrac{1}{-1} < \dfrac{-x}{-1} < \dfrac{-5}{-1}$$

$$-1 < x < 5$$

43.

$$0.2 < \frac{x-3}{10} \le 0.4$$

$$10(0.2) < 10\left(\frac{x-3}{10}\right) \le 10(0.4)$$

$$2 < x - 3 \le 4$$

$$2 + 3 < x - 3 + 3 \le 4 + 3$$

$$5 < x \le 7$$

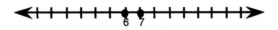

45. Let $x =$ the number of miles

$110 + 0.25x =$ cost of renting from Fred's

$$110 + 0.25x < 200$$

$$110 - 110 + 0.25x < 200 - 110$$

$$0.25x < 90$$

$$\frac{0.25x}{0.25} < \frac{90}{0.25}$$

$$x < 360 \text{ miles}$$

47. a) Let $x =$ the number of boxes of books

$60x =$ the weight of x boxes of books

$$60x + 180 \le 1200$$

b) $60x + 180 - 180 \le 1200 - 180$

$$60x \le 1020$$

$$\frac{60x}{60} \le \frac{1020}{60}$$

$$x \le 17$$

The maximum number of boxes is 17.

49.

$$12x > 2x + 200$$

$$12x - 2x > 2x - 2x + 200$$

$$10x > 200$$

$$\frac{10x}{10} > \frac{200}{10}$$

$$x > 20$$

More than 20 books must be sold weekly to make a profit.

51. Let $x =$ Devon's grade on the fifth test

$$80 \le \frac{78 + 64 + 88 + 76 + x}{5} < 90$$

$$80 \le \frac{306 + x}{5} < 90$$

$$5(80) \le 5\left(\frac{306 + x}{5}\right) < 5(90)$$

$$400 \le 306 + x < 450$$

$$400 - 306 \le 306 - 306 + x < 450 - 306$$

$$94 \le x < 144$$

Devon must have a score of $94 \le x \le 100$, assuming 100 is the highest grade possible.

53. Let $x =$ the number of people enrolled

$$18,000 \le 8000 + 175x \le 24,000$$

$$18,000 - 8,000 \le 8000 - 8000 + 175x \le 24,000 - 8000$$

$$10,000 \le 175x \le 16,000$$

$$\frac{10,000}{175} \le \frac{175x}{175} \le \frac{16,000}{175}$$

$$57.14285714 \le x \le 91.42857143$$

Minimum: 58   Maximum: 91

55. Let $x=$ the final exam grade

The semester average $=\dfrac{86+74+68+96+72}{5}=\dfrac{396}{5}=79.2$

The final grade is found by taking $\dfrac{2}{3}$ of the semester average and adding this to $\dfrac{1}{3}$ of the final exam. The

final grade is $\dfrac{2}{3}(79.2)+\dfrac{1}{3}x=52.8+\dfrac{1}{3}x$. In order for Teresa to receive a final grade of B in the course, she

must have an average greater than or equal to 80 and less than 90.

$$80 \le 52.8+\frac{1}{3}x<90$$

$$80-52.8 \le 52.8-52.8+\frac{1}{3}x<90-52.8$$

$$27.2 \le \frac{1}{3}x<37.2$$

$$3(27.2)\le 3\left(\frac{1}{3}x\right)<3(37.2)$$

$$81.6 \le x<111.6$$

Thus, Teresa must receive $81.6 \le x \le 100$, assuming 100 is the highest grade possible.

Exercise Set 6.7

1. A **graph** is an illustration of all the points whose coordinates satisfy an equation.

3. To find the **x-intercept**, set $y=0$ and solve the equation for x.

5. a) Divide the difference between the $y-$ coordinates by the difference between the $x-$ coordinates.

   b) $m=\dfrac{5-2}{-3-6}=\dfrac{3}{-9}=-\dfrac{1}{3}$

7. - 13.   15. - 21.

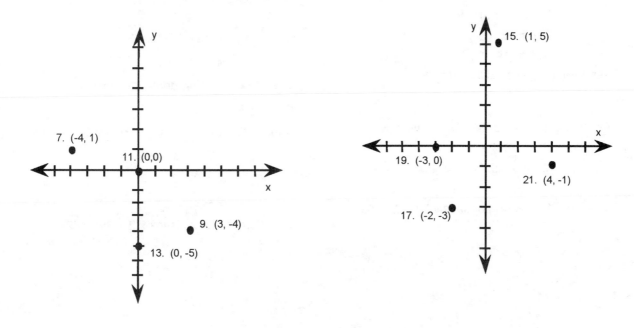

23. (2, 2)   25. (0, 2)   27. (-2, 0)   29. (-5, -3)   31. (2, -3)

33. Substituting (2, -1) into $x - 3y = 8$, we have
$$2 - 3(-1) = 8$$
$$2 + 3 = 8$$
$$5 \neq 8$$
Therefore, (2, -1) does not satisfy $x - 3y = 8$.

Substituting (2, -2) into $x - 3y = 8$, we have
$$2 - 3(-2) = 8$$
$$2 + 6 = 8$$
$$8 = 8$$
Therefore, (2, -2) satisfies $x - 3y = 8$.

Substituting (2, -3) into $x - 3y = 8$, we have
$$2 - 3(-3) = 8$$
$$2 + 9 = 8$$
$$11 \neq 8$$
Therefore, (2, -3) does not satisfy $x - 3y = 8$.

35. Substituting (0, 4) into $3x + 2y = 8$, we have
$$3(0) + 2(4) = 8$$
$$0 + 8 = 8$$
$$8 = 8$$
Therefore, (0, 4) satisfies $3x + 2y = 8$.

Substituting (1, 5/2) into $3x + 2y = 8$, we have
$$3(1) + 2(5/2) = 8$$
$$3 + 5 = 8$$
$$8 = 8$$
Therefore, (1, 5/2) satisfies $3x + 2y = 8$.

Substituting (-1, 3) into $3x + 2y = 8$, we have
$$3(-1) + 2(3) = 8$$
$$-3 + 6 = 8$$
$$3 \neq 8$$
Therefore, (-1, 3) does not satisfy $3x + 2y = 8$.

37. Substituting (1, -1) into $7y = 3x - 5$, we have
$$7(-1) = 3(1) - 5$$
$$-7 = 3 - 5$$
$$-7 \neq -2$$
Therefore, (1, -1) does not satisfy $7y = 3x - 5$.

Substituting (-3, -2) into $7y = 3x - 5$, we have
$$7(-2) = 3(-3) - 5$$
$$-14 = -9 - 5$$
$$-14 = -14$$
Therefore, (-3, -2) satisfies $7y = 3x - 5$.

Substituting (2, 5) into $7y = 3x - 5$, we have
$$7(5) = 3(2) - 5$$
$$35 = 6 - 5$$
$$35 \neq 1$$
Therefore, (2, 5) does not satisfy $7y = 3x - 5$.

39. Substituting (0, 8/3) into $x/2 + 3y/4 = 2$, we have
$$0/2 + 8/4 = 2$$
$$0 + 2 = 2$$
$$2 = 2$$
Therefore, (0, 8/3) satisfies $x/2 + 3y/4 = 2$.

Substituting (1,11/4) into $x/2 + 3y/4 = 2$, we have
$$1/2 + 33/16 = 2$$
$$8/16 + 33/16 = 2$$
$$41/16 \neq 2$$
Therefore, (1, 11/4) does not satisfy
$x/2 + 3y/4 = 2$.

Substituting (4, 0) into $x/2 + 3y/4 = 2$, we have
$$4/2 + 0/4 = 2$$
$$2 + 0 = 2$$
$$2 = 2$$
Therefore, (4, 0) satisfies $x/2 + 3y/4 = 2$.

41. Since the line is vertical, its slope is undefined.

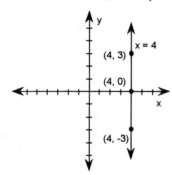

43. Since the line is horizontal, its slope is 0.

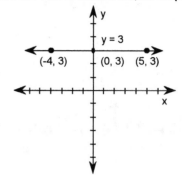

45. y = x - 2

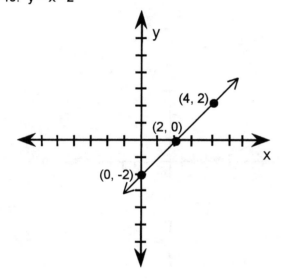

47. y = -x + 3

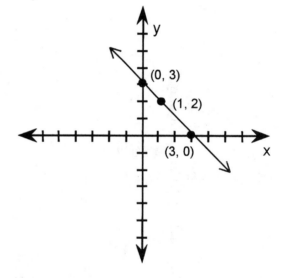

49. y + 3x = 6 or y = -3x + 6

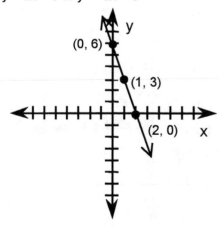

51. $y = \frac{1}{2}x + 4$

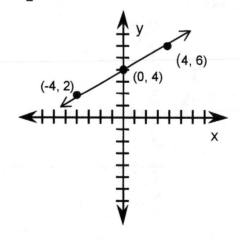

53. $2y = -x + 6$ or $y = -\frac{1}{2}x + 3$

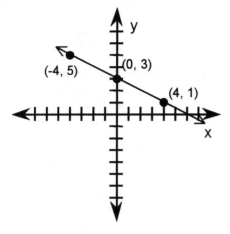

55. $x - y = 5$

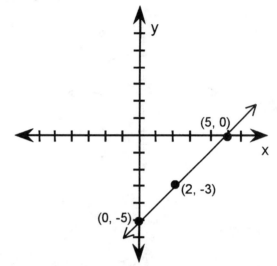

57. $3x + y = 6$

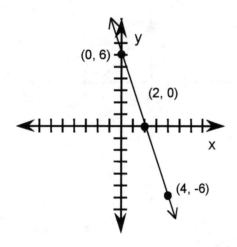

59. $2x = -4y - 8$

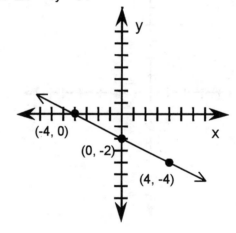

61. $y = -2x - 5$

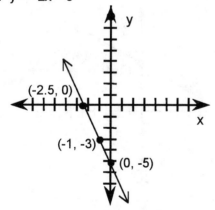

63. $-3x + y = 4$

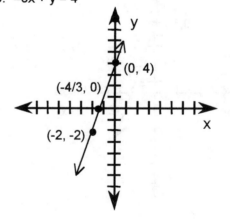

65. $(2, 8), (4, 16)$ $m = \dfrac{16 - 8}{4 - 2} = \dfrac{8}{2} = 4$

67. $(-1, -6), (3, 5)$ $m = \dfrac{5 - (-6)}{3 - (-1)} = \dfrac{11}{4}$

69. $(5, 2), (-3, 2)$ $m = \dfrac{2 - 2}{-3 - 5} = \dfrac{0}{-8} = 0$

71. $(8, -3), (8, 3)$ $m = \dfrac{3 - (-3)}{8 - 8} = \dfrac{6}{0}$ Undefined

73. (-2, 3), (1, -1) $m = \dfrac{-1-3}{1-(-2)} = \dfrac{-4}{3} = -\dfrac{4}{3}$

75. $y = x - 2$

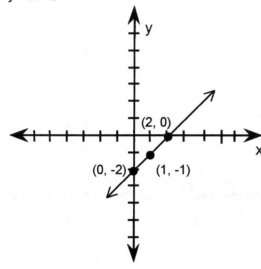

77. $y = -2x + 1$

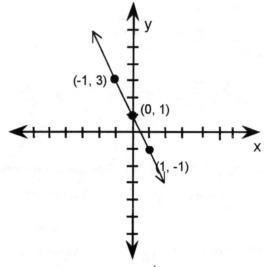

79. $y = -\dfrac{3}{5}x + 3$

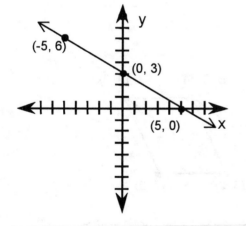

81. $7y = 4x - 7$ or $y = \dfrac{4}{7}x - 1$

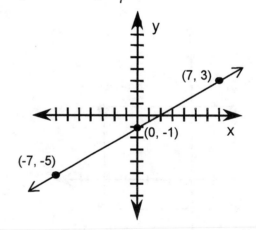

83. $3x - 2y + 6 = 0$ or $y = \frac{3}{2}x + 3$

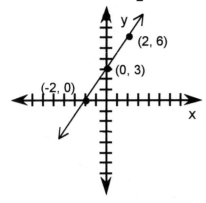

85. The y-intercept is 3; thus b = 3. The slope is negative since the graph falls from left to right. The change in y is 3, while the change in x is 4. Thus m, the slope, is $-\frac{3}{4}$. The equation is $y = -\frac{3}{4}x + 3$.

87. The y-intercept is -1; thus b = -1. The slope is positive since the graph rises from left to right. The change in y is 1, while the change in x is 2. Thus m, the slope, is $\frac{1}{2}$. The equation is $y = \frac{1}{2}x - 1$.

89. a)

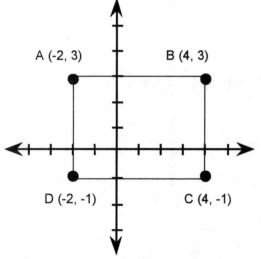

91.

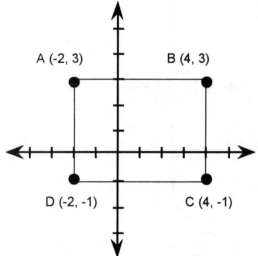

b) $A = l \times w = 6 \times 4 = 24$ square units

93. For the line joining points P and Q to be parallel to the x-axis, both ordered pairs must have the same y-value. Thus, b = 8.

95. For the line joining points P and Q to be parallel to the y-axis, both ordered pairs must have the same x-value.
$3b - 1 = 8$
$3b - 1 + 1 = 8 + 1$
$3b = 9$
$b = 3$

97. a)

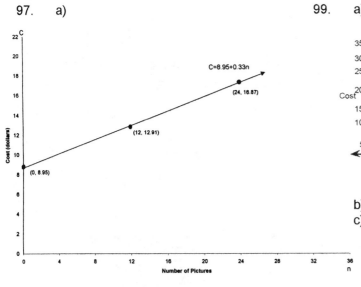

C=8.95+0.33n

(24, 16.87)

(12, 12.91)

(0, 8.95)

Cost (dollars)

Number of Pictures

99. a)

(1000, 330)

C

Cost

C= 80 + 0.25n

200 400 600 800 1000

Number of Miles

b) C = 80 + 0.25(600) = $230
c) 180 = 80 + 0.25n
    100 = 0.25n
    n = 400 miles

b) 8.95 + 0.33(20) = $15.55
c) 8.95 + 0.33n = 20.83
    0.33n = 11.88
    n = 36 pictures

101. a) $m = \dfrac{96-53}{4-0} = \dfrac{43}{4} = 10.75$

b) $y = 10.75x + 53$

c) $y = 10.75(3) + 53 = 85.25$

d) $80 = 10.75x + 53$
    $27 = 10.75x$
    $x = 2.511627907 \approx 2.5$ hours

103. a) $m = \dfrac{790-370}{17-0} = \dfrac{420}{17} = 24.70588235 \approx 24.71$

b) $y = 24.71x + 370$

c) $y = 24.71(6) + 370 = \$518.26$

d) $600 = 24.71x + 370$
    $230 = 24.71x$
    $x = 9.307972481 \approx 9.3$ years after 1980,
    or in 1989

105. a) Solve the equations for y to put them in slope-intercept form. Then compare the slopes and
     y-intercepts. If the slopes are equal but the y-intercepts are different, then the lines are parallel.

b) $2x - 3y = 6$ $4x = 6y + 6$

     $2x - 2x - 3y = -2x + 6$ $4x - 6 = 6y + 6 - 6$

          $-3y = -2x + 6$ $4x - 6 = 6y$

     $\dfrac{-3y}{-3} = \dfrac{-2x}{-3} + \dfrac{6}{-3}$ $\dfrac{4x}{6} - \dfrac{6}{6} = \dfrac{6y}{6}$

          $y = \dfrac{2}{3}x - 2$ $\dfrac{2}{3}x - 1 = y$

Since the two equations have the same slope, m = $\dfrac{2}{3}$, the graphs of the equations are parallel lines.

Exercise Set 6.8

1. (1) Mentally substitute the equal sign for the inequality sign and plot points as if you were graphing the
    equation. (2) If the inequality is < or >, draw a dashed line through the points. If the inequality is ≤ or ≥,
    draw a solid line through the points. (3) Select a test point not on the line and substitute the
    x- and y- coordinates into the inequality. If the substitution results in a true statement, shade in the area
    on the same side of the line as the test point. If the substitution results in a false statement, shade in the
    area on the opposite side of the line as the test point.

3. Graph x = 2. Since the original statement is less than or equal to, a solid line is drawn. Since the point (0, 0) satisfies the inequality x ≤ 2, all points on the line and in the half-plane to the left of the line x = 2 are in the solution set.

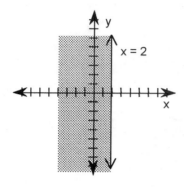

5. Graph y = x − 2. Since the original statement is strictly less than, a dashed line is drawn. Since the point (0, 0) does not satisfy the inequality y < x − 2, all points in the half-plane below the line y = x − 2 are in the solution set.

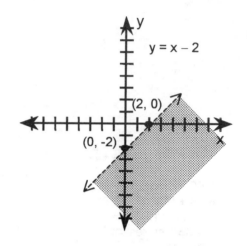

7. Graph y = 2x − 6. Since the original statement is greater than or equal to, a solid line is drawn. Since the point (0, 0) satisfies the inequality y ≥ 2x - 6, all points on the line and in the half-plane above the line y = 2x − 6 are in the solution set.

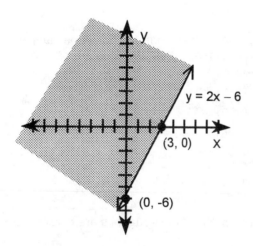

9. Graph 3x − 4y = 12. Since the original statement is strictly greater than, a dashed line is drawn. Since the point (0, 0) does not satisfy the inequality 3x − 4y > 12, all points in the half-plane below the line 3x − 4y = 12 are in the solution set.

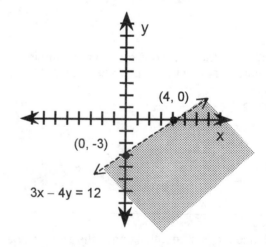

11. Graph $3x - 4y = 9$. Since the original statement is less than or equal to, a solid line is drawn. Since the point (0, 0) satisfies the inequality $3x - 4y \leq 9$, all points on the line and in the half-plane above the line $3x - 4y = 9$ are in the solution set.

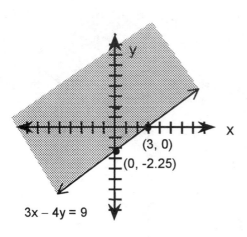

13. Graph $3x + 2y = 6$. Since the original statement is strictly less than, a dashed line is drawn. Since the point (0, 0) satisfies the inequality $3x + 2y < 6$, all points in the half-plane to the left of the line $3x + 2y = 6$ are in the solution set.

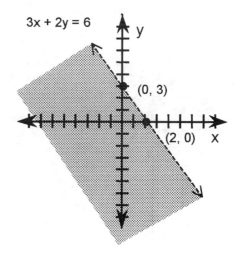

15. Graph $x + y = 0$. Since the original statement is strictly greater than, a dashed line is drawn. Since the point (1,1) satisfies the inequality $x + y > 0$, all points in the half-plane above the line $x + y = 0$ are in the solution set.

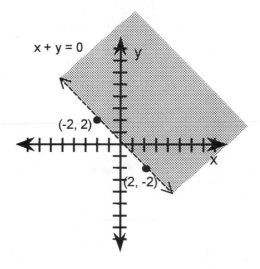

17. Graph $3y - 2x = 0$. Since the original statement is less than or equal to, a solid line is drawn. Since the point (0, 1) does not satisfy the inequality $3y - 2x \leq 0$, all points on the line and in the half-plane below the line $3y - 2x = 0$ are in the solution set.

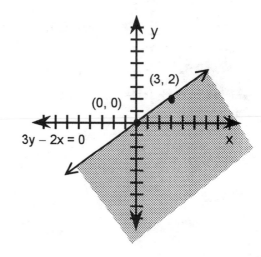

19. Graph $3x + 2y = 12$. Since the original statement is strictly greater than, a dashed line is drawn. Since the point $(0, 0)$ does not satisfy the inequality $3x + 2y > 12$, all points in the half-plane above the line $3x + 2y = 12$ are in the solution set.

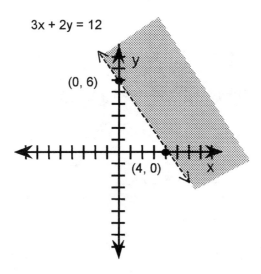

21. Graph $(2/5)x - (1/2)y = 1$. Since the original statement is less than or equal to, a solid line is drawn. Since the point $(0, 0)$ satisfies the inequality $(2/5)x - (1/2)y \leq 1$, all points on the line and in the half-plane above the line $(2/5)x - (1/2)y = 1$ are in the solution set.

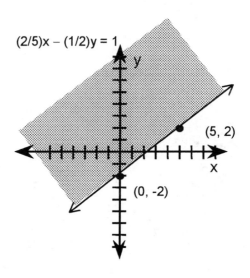

23. Graph $0.2x + 0.5y = 0.3$. Since the original statement is less than or equal to, a solid line is drawn. Since the point $(0, 0)$ satisfies the inequality $0.2x + 0.5y \leq 0.3$, all points on the line and in the half-plane below the line $0.2x + 0.5y = 0.3$ are in the solution set.

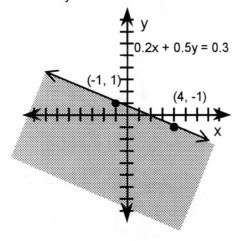

25. a) $2l + 2w \le 40$ or $l + w \le 20$, where $0 \le l \le 20$
and $0 \le w \le 20$

b) Let the x-coordinate represent w and the
y-coordinate represent l.

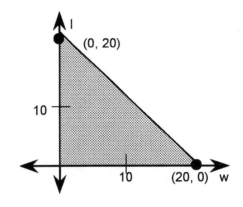

27. a) No, you can not have a negative number of shirts.
b)

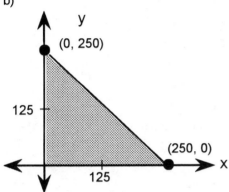

c) Answers will vary.

Exercise Set 6.9

1. A **binomial** is an expression that contains two terms in which each exponent that appears on the variable
is a whole number. Examples: $2x + 3$, $x - 7$

3. The **foil method** is a method that obtains the products of the First, Outer, Inner, and Last terms of the
binomials.

5. If the product of two factors is 0, then one or both of the factors must have a value of 0.

7. $x^2 + 10x + 21 = (x + 3)(x + 7)$

9. $x^2 - 4x - 5 = (x - 5)(x + 1)$

11. $x^2 + 2x - 24 = (x + 6)(x - 4)$

13. $x^2 - 2x - 3 = (x - 3)(x + 1)$

15. $x^2 - 10x + 21 = (x - 3)(x - 7)$

17. $x^2 - 16 = (x + 4)(x - 4)$

19. $x^2 + 3x - 28 = (x + 7)(x - 4)$

21. $x^2 + 2x - 63 = (x + 9)(x - 7)$

23. $2x^2 + 5x + 3 = (2x + 3)(x + 1)$

25. $3x^2 - 14x - 5 = (3x + 1)(x - 5)$

27. $5x^2 + 12x + 4 = (5x + 2)(x + 2)$

29. $5x^2 - 13x - 6 = (5x + 2)(x - 3)$

31. $5x^2 - 13x + 6 = (5x - 3)(x - 2)$

33. $3x^2 - 14x - 24 = (3x + 4)(x - 6)$

35. $(x+2)(x-5)=0$

$x+2=0$ or $x-5=0$

$x=-2$ $x=5$

37. $(2x-3)(3x+7)=0$

$2x-3=0$ or $3x+7=0$

$2x=3$ $3x=-7$

$x=\dfrac{3}{2}$ $x=-\dfrac{7}{3}$

39. $x^2+5x+6=0$

$(x+3)(x+2)=0$

$x+3=0$ or $x+2=0$

$x=-3$ $x=-2$

41. $x^2-6x+8=0$

$(x-4)(x-2)=0$

$x-4=0$ or $x-2=0$

$x=4$ $x=2$

43. $x^2-15=2x$

$x^2-2x-15=0$

$(x-5)(x+3)=0$

$x-5=0$ or $x+3=0$

$x=5$ $x=-3$

45. $x^2=4x-3$

$x^2-4x+3=0$

$(x-1)(x-3)=0$

$x-1=0$ or $x-3=0$

$x=1$ $x=3$

47. $x^2-81=0$

$(x+9)(x-9)=0$

$x+9=0$ or $x-9=0$

$x=-9$ $x=9$

49. $x^2+5x-36=0$

$(x+9)(x-4)=0$

$x+9=0$ or $x-4=0$

$x=-9$ $x=4$

51. $3x^2+7x=-2$

$3x^2+7x+2=0$

$(3x+1)(x+2)=0$

$3x+1=0$ or $x+2=0$

$3x=-1$ $x=-2$

$x=-\dfrac{1}{3}$

53. $5x^2+11x=-2$

$5x^2+11x+2=0$

$(5x+1)(x+2)=0$

$5x+1=0$ or $x+2=0$

$5x=-1$ $x=-2$

$x=-\dfrac{1}{5}$

55. $3x^2-4x=-1$

$3x^2-4x+1=0$

$(3x-1)(x-1)=0$

$3x-1=0$ or $x-1=0$

$3x=1$ $x=1$

$x=\dfrac{1}{3}$

57. $4x^2-9x+2=0$

$(4x-1)(x-2)=0$

$4x-1=0$ or $x-2=0$

$4x=1$ $x=2$

$x=\dfrac{1}{4}$

59. $x^2-x-30=0$

$a=1,\ b=-1,\ c=-30$

$x=\dfrac{-(-1)\pm\sqrt{(-1)^2-4(1)(-30)}}{2(1)}$

$x=\dfrac{1\pm\sqrt{1+120}}{2}=\dfrac{1\pm\sqrt{121}}{2}=\dfrac{1\pm11}{2}$

$x=\dfrac{12}{2}=6$ or $x=\dfrac{-10}{2}=-5$

61. $x^2-3x-10=0$

$a=1,\ b=-3,\ c=-10$

$x=\dfrac{-(-3)\pm\sqrt{(-3)^2-4(1)(-10)}}{2(1)}$

$x=\dfrac{3\pm\sqrt{9+40}}{2}=\dfrac{3\pm\sqrt{49}}{2}=\dfrac{3\pm7}{2}$

$x=\dfrac{10}{2}=5$ or $x=\dfrac{-4}{2}=-2$

63. $x^2 - 8x = 9$

$x^2 - 8x - 9 = 0$

$a = 1, \; b = -8, \; c = -9$

$x = \dfrac{-(-8) \pm \sqrt{(-8)^2 - 4(1)(-9)}}{2(1)}$

$x = \dfrac{8 \pm \sqrt{64 + 36}}{2} = \dfrac{8 \pm \sqrt{100}}{2} = \dfrac{8 \pm 10}{2}$

$x = \dfrac{18}{2} = 9 \;$ or $\; x = \dfrac{-2}{2} = -1$

65. $x^2 - 2x + 3 = 0$

$a = 1, \; b = -2, \; c = 3$

$x = \dfrac{-(-2) \pm \sqrt{(-2)^2 - 4(1)(3)}}{2(1)}$

$x = \dfrac{2 \pm \sqrt{4 - 12}}{2} = \dfrac{2 \pm \sqrt{-8}}{2}$

No real solution

67. $x^2 - 4x + 2 = 0$

$a = 1, \; b = -4, \; c = 2$

$x = \dfrac{-(-4) \pm \sqrt{(-4)^2 - 4(1)(2)}}{2(1)}$

$x = \dfrac{4 \pm \sqrt{16 - 8}}{2} = \dfrac{4 \pm \sqrt{8}}{2} = \dfrac{4 \pm 2\sqrt{2}}{2}$

$x = 2 \pm \sqrt{2}$

69. $2x^2 - x = 4$

$2x^2 - x - 4 = 0$

$a = 2, \; b = -1, \; c = -4$

$x = \dfrac{-(-1) \pm \sqrt{(-1)^2 - 4(2)(-4)}}{2(2)}$

$x = \dfrac{1 \pm \sqrt{1 + 32}}{4} = \dfrac{1 \pm \sqrt{33}}{4}$

71. $4x^2 - x - 1 = 0$

$a = 4, \; b = -1, \; c = -1$

$x = \dfrac{-(-1) \pm \sqrt{(-1)^2 - 4(4)(-1)}}{2(4)}$

$x = \dfrac{1 \pm \sqrt{1 + 16}}{8} = \dfrac{1 \pm \sqrt{17}}{8}$

73. $2x^2 + 7x + 5 = 0$

$a = 2, \; b = 7, \; c = 5$

$x = \dfrac{-7 \pm \sqrt{(7)^2 - 4(2)(5)}}{2(2)}$

$x = \dfrac{-7 \pm \sqrt{49 - 40}}{4} = \dfrac{-7 \pm \sqrt{9}}{4} = \dfrac{-7 \pm 3}{4}$

$x = \dfrac{-4}{4} = -1 \;$ or $\; x = \dfrac{-10}{4} = -\dfrac{5}{2}$

75. $3x^2 - 10x + 7 = 0$

$a = 3, \; b = -10, \; c = 7$

$x = \dfrac{-(-10) \pm \sqrt{(-10)^2 - 4(3)(7)}}{2(3)}$

$x = \dfrac{10 \pm \sqrt{100 - 84}}{6} = \dfrac{10 \pm \sqrt{16}}{6} = \dfrac{10 \pm 4}{6}$

$x = \dfrac{14}{6} = \dfrac{7}{3} \;$ or $\; x = \dfrac{6}{6} = 1$

77. $4x^2 - 11x + 13 = 0$

$a = 4, \; b = -11, \; c = 13$

$x = \dfrac{-(-11) \pm \sqrt{(-11)^2 - 4(4)(13)}}{2(4)}$

$x = \dfrac{11 \pm \sqrt{121 - 208}}{8} = \dfrac{11 \pm \sqrt{-87}}{8}$

No real solution

79. $45,000 = x^2 + 15x - 100$

$x^2 + 15x - 45,100 = 0$

$(x + 220)(x - 205) = 0$

$x + 220 = 0 \;$ or $\; x - 205 = 0$

$x = -220 \qquad x = 205$

Cannot produce a negative number of air conditioners. Thus, $x = 205$.

81. $x = \dfrac{-b \pm \sqrt{b^2 - 4ac}}{2a}$

The $b^2 - 4ac$ is the radicand in the quadratic formula, the part under the square root sign.

a) If $b^2 - 4ac > 0$, then you are taking the square root of a positive number and there are two solutions.

These solutions are $x = \dfrac{-b + \sqrt{b^2 - 4ac}}{2a}$ and $x = \dfrac{-b - \sqrt{b^2 - 4ac}}{2a}$.

b) If $b^2 - 4ac = 0$, then you are taking the square root of zero and there is one solution. This solution

is $x = \dfrac{-b \pm \sqrt{0}}{2a} = \dfrac{-b}{2a}$.

c) If $b^2 - 4ac < 0$, then you are taking the square root of a negative number and there is no real solution.

Exercise Set 6.10

1. A **function** is a special type of relation where each value of the independent variable corresponds to a unique value of the dependent variable.

3. The **domain** of a function is the set of values that can be used for the independent variable.

5. The vertical line test can be used to determine if a graph represents a function. If a vertical line can be drawn so that it intersects the graph at more than one point, then each value of x does not have a unique value of y and the graph does not represent a function. If a vertical line cannot be made to intersect the graph in at least two different places, then the graph represents a function.

7. Function since each value of x is paired with a unique value of y.
D: -2, -1, 1, 2, 3   R: -1, 1, 2, 3

9. Function since each vertical line intersects the graph at only one point.
D: all real numbers   R: all real numbers

11. Function since each vertical line intersects the graph at only one point.
D: all real numbers   R: y = 2

13. Function since each vertical line intersects the graph at only one point.
D: all real numbers   R: y ≥ -4

15. Not a function since it is possible to draw a vertical line that intersects the graph at more than one point.

17. Function since each vertical line intersects the graph at only one point.
D: 0 ≤ x < 12   R: y = 1, 2, 3

19. Not a function since it is possible to draw a vertical line that intersects the graph at more than one point.

21. Function since each vertical line intersects the graph at only one point.
D: all real numbers   R: y > 0

23. Function since each value of x is paired with a unique value of y.

25. Not a function since x = 2 is paired with two different values of y.

27. Function since each value of x is paired with a unique value of y.

29. $f(x) = x + 6, \; x = 9$
$f(9) = 9 + 6 = 15$

31. $f(x) = -2x - 7, \; x = -4$
$f(-4) = -2(-4) - 7 = 8 - 7 = 1$

33. $f(x) = 10x - 6, \; x = 0$
$f(0) = 10(0) - 6 = 0 - 6 = -6$

35. $f(x) = x^2 + 2x + 4, \; x = 6$
$f(6) = (6)^2 + 2(6) + 4 = 36 + 12 + 4 = 52$

37. $f(x) = 2x^2 - 2x - 8, \; x = -2$
$f(-2) = 2(-2)^2 - 2(-2) - 8 = 8 + 4 - 8 = 4$

39. $f(x) = -3x^2 + 5x + 4, \; x = -3$
$f(-3) = -3(-3)^2 + 5(-3) + 4 = -27 - 15 + 4 = -38$

41. $f(x) = -6x^2 - 6x - 12, \; x = -3$
$f(-3) = -6(-3)^2 - 6(-3) - 12 = -54 + 18 - 12 = -48$

43.

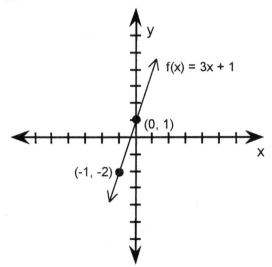

45.

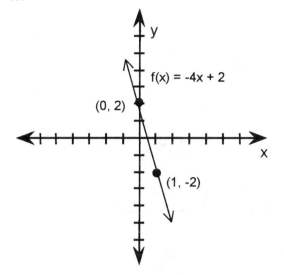

47.

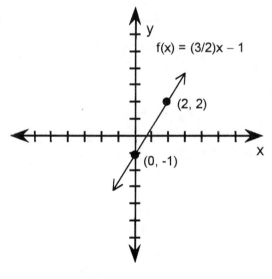

49. $y = x^2 - 1$

a) $a = 1 > 0$, opens upward

b) $x = 0$ c) $(0, -1)$ d) $(0, -1)$

e) $(-1, 0), (1, 0)$

f)

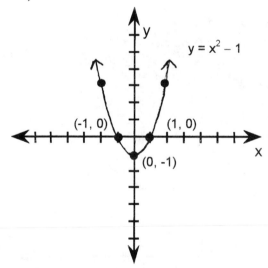

g)   D: all real numbers   R: $y \geq -1$

51. $y = -x^2 + 4$
    a) $a = -1 < 0$, opens downward
    b) $x = 0$ c) $(0, 4)$ d) $(0, 4)$
    e) $(-2, 0), (2, 0)$
    f)

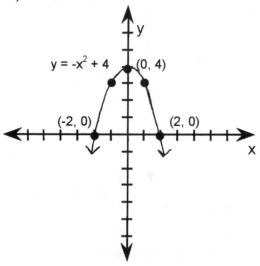

    g) D: all real numbers   R: $y \leq 4$

53. $f(x) = -x^2 - 4$
    a) $a = -1 < 0$, opens downward
    b) $x = 0$ c) $(0,-4)$ d) $(0,-4)$
    e) no x-intercepts
    f)

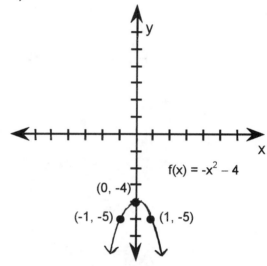

    g) D : all real numbers   R: $y \leq -4$

55. $y = 2x^2 - 3$
    a) $a = 2 > 0$, opens upward
    b) $x = 0$ c) $(0,-3)$ d) $(0,-3)$
    e) $(-1.22, 0)$, $(1.22, 0)$
    f)

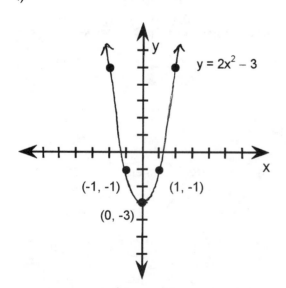

    g) D: all real numbers   R: $y \geq -3$

57. $f(x) = x^2 + 4x + 10$
    a) $a = 1 > 0$, opens upward
    b) $x = -2$ c) $(-2, 6)$ d) $(0, 10)$
    e) no x-intercepts
    f)

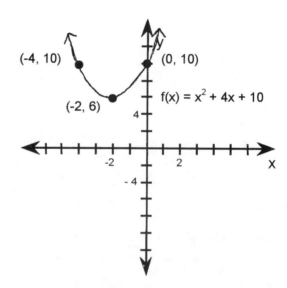

    g) D: all real numbers   R: $y \geq 6$

59. $y = x^2 + 5x + 6$

    a) $a = 1 > 0$, opens upward

    b) $x = -\dfrac{5}{2}$ c) $(-2.5, -0.25)$ d) $(0, 6)$

    e) $(-3, 0), (-2, 0)$

    f)

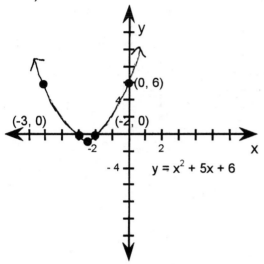

    g) D: all real numbers   R: $y \geq -0.25$

61. $y = -x^2 + 4x - 6$

    a) $a = -1 < 0$, opens downward

    b) $x = 2$ c) $(2, -2)$ d) $(0, -6)$

    e) no x-intercepts

    f)

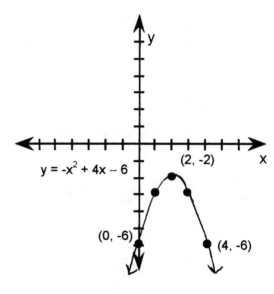

    g) D: all real numbers   R: $y \leq -2$

63. $y = -3x^2 + 14x - 8$

    a) $a = -3 < 0$, opens downward

    b) $x = \dfrac{7}{3}$ c) $\left(\dfrac{7}{3}, \dfrac{25}{3}\right)$ d) $(0, -8)$

    e) $\left(\dfrac{2}{3}, 0\right), (4, 0)$

    f)

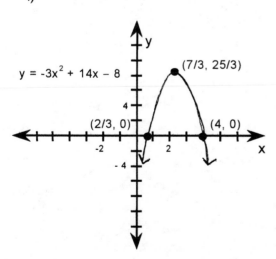

    g) D: all real numbers   R: $y \leq \dfrac{25}{3}$

65. $y = 3^x$

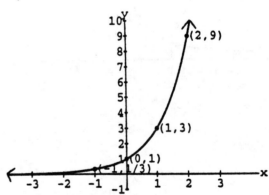

D: all real numbers   R: $y > 0$

67. $y = \left(\dfrac{1}{3}\right)^x$

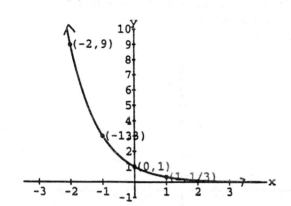

D: all real numbers   R: $y > 0$

69. $y = 2^x + 1$

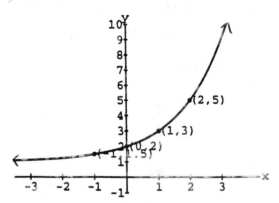

D: all real numbers   R: $y > 1$

71. $y = 4^x + 1$

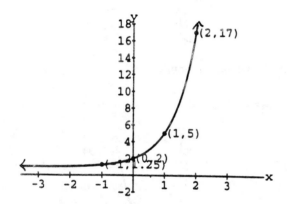

D: all real numbers   R: $y > 1$

73. $y = 3^{x-1}$

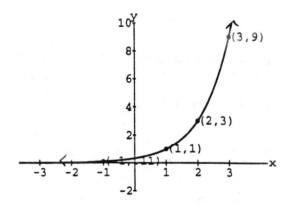

D: all real numbers   R: $y > 0$

75. $y = 4^{x+1}$

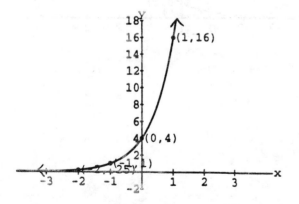

D: all real numbers   R: $y > 0$

77. $d(t) = 60t$

   a) $t = 3,\ d(3) = 60(3) = 180$ miles

   b) $t = 7,\ d(7) = 60(7) = 420$ miles

79. $T(A) = -0.02A^2 - 0.34A + 80,\ 0 \le A \le 15$

   a) $A = 5,\ T(5) = -0.02(5)^2 - 0.34(5) + 80$
$$= -0.5 - 1.7 + 80 = 77.8°F$$

   b) $A = 9,\ T(9) = -0.02(9)^2 - 0.34(9) + 80$
$$= -1.62 - 3.06 + 80 = 75.32°F$$

81. $P(x) = 4000(1.3)^{0.1x}$

   a) $x = 10,\ P(10) = 4000(1.3)^{0.1(10)}$
$$= 4000(1.3) = 5200 \text{ people}$$

   b) $x = 50,\ P(50) = 4000(1.3)^{0.1(50)}$
$$= 4000(3.71293)$$
$$= 14,851.72 \approx 14,852 \text{ people}$$

83. a) Yes, the average salary increased rapidly from 1960 to 1995.

   b) $\approx \$700,000$

85. $d = (21.9)(2)^{(20-x)/12}$

   a) $x = 19,\ d = (21.9)(2)^{(20-19)/12}$
$$= (21.9)(1.059463094) \approx 23.2 \text{ cm.}$$

   b) $x = 4,\ d = (21.9)(2)^{(20-4)/12}$
$$= (21.9)(2.519842099) \approx 55.2 \text{ cm.}$$

   c) $x = 0,\ d = (21.9)(2)^{(20-0)/12}$
$$= (21.9)(3.174802105) \approx 69.5 \text{ cm.}$$

87. $f(x) = -0.85x + 187$

   a) $f(20) = -0.85(20) + 187 = 170$ beats per minute

   b) $f(30) = -0.85(30) + 187 = 161.5 \approx 162$ beats per minute

   c) $f(50) = -0.85(50) + 187 = 144.5 \approx 145$ beats per minute

   d) $f(60) = -0.85(60) + 187 = 136$ beats per minute

   e) $-0.85x + 187 = 85$
$$-0.85x = -102$$
$$x = 120 \text{ years of age}$$

Review Exercises

1. $x = 4,\ x^2 + 7 = (4)^2 + 7 = 16 + 7 = 23$

2. $x = -3,\ -x^2 + 8 = -(-3)^2 + 8 = -9 + 8 = -1$

3. $x = 2$, $4x^2 - 2x + 5 = 4(2)^2 - 2(2) + 5$
$$= 16 - 4 + 5 = 17$$

4. $x = \dfrac{1}{2}$, $-x^2 + 7x - 3 = -\left(\dfrac{1}{2}\right)^2 + 7\left(\dfrac{1}{2}\right) - 3$
$$= -\dfrac{1}{4} + \dfrac{14}{4} - \dfrac{12}{4} = \dfrac{1}{4}$$

5. $x = -2$, $4x^3 - 7x^2 + 3x + 1$
$$= 4(-2)^3 - 7(-2)^2 + 3(-2) + 1$$
$$= -32 - 28 - 6 + 1 = -65$$

6. $x = 2$, $y = -1$, $4x^2 - 2xy + 3y^2$
$$= 4(2)^2 - 2(2)(-1) + 3(-1)^2$$
$$= 16 + 4 + 3 = 23$$

7. $2x + 5 - 8 - x = x - 3$

8. $3x + 4(x - 2) + 6x = 3x + 4x - 8 + 6x = 13x - 8$

9. $2(x - 4) + \dfrac{1}{2}(2x + 3) = 2x - 8 + x + \dfrac{3}{2}$
$$= 3x - \dfrac{16}{2} + \dfrac{3}{2} = 3x - \dfrac{13}{2}$$

10.
$$-2r - 8 = 20$$
$$-2r - 8 + 8 = 20 + 8$$
$$-2r = 28$$
$$\dfrac{-2r}{-2} = \dfrac{28}{-2}$$
$$r = -14$$

11.
$$3t + 8 = 6t - 13$$
$$3t - 3t + 8 = 6t - 3t - 13$$
$$8 = 3t - 13$$
$$8 + 13 = 3t - 13 + 13$$
$$21 = 3t$$
$$\dfrac{21}{3} = \dfrac{3t}{3}$$
$$7 = t$$

12.
$$\dfrac{x + 5}{6} = \dfrac{x - 3}{3}$$
$$3(x + 5) = 6(x - 3)$$
$$3x + 15 = 6x - 18$$
$$3x - 3x + 15 = 6x - 3x - 18$$
$$15 = 3x - 18$$
$$15 + 18 = 3x - 18 + 18$$
$$33 = 3x$$
$$\dfrac{33}{3} = \dfrac{3x}{3}$$
$$11 = x$$

13.
$$4(x - 2) = 3 + 5(x + 4)$$
$$4x - 8 = 3 + 5x + 20$$
$$4x - 8 = 5x + 23$$
$$4x - 4x - 8 = 5x - 4x + 23$$
$$-8 = x + 23$$
$$-8 - 23 = x + 23 - 23$$
$$-31 = x$$

14.
$$\dfrac{x}{3} + \dfrac{2}{5} = 4$$
$$15\left(\dfrac{x}{3} + \dfrac{2}{5}\right) = 15(4)$$
$$5x + 6 = 60$$
$$5x + 6 - 6 = 60 - 6$$
$$5x = 54$$
$$\dfrac{5x}{5} = \dfrac{54}{5}$$
$$x = \dfrac{54}{5}$$

15. $\dfrac{\frac{2}{1}}{\frac{1}{3}} = \dfrac{3}{x}$

$2x = 3\left(\dfrac{1}{3}\right)$

$2x = 1$

$\dfrac{2x}{2} = \dfrac{1}{2}$

$x = \dfrac{1}{2}$ cup

16. $1\,hr.\ 40\ min. = 100\,min.$

$\dfrac{120}{100} = \dfrac{450}{x}$

$120x = 100(450)$

$120x = 45,000$

$\dfrac{120x}{120} = \dfrac{45,000}{120}$

$x = 375\,mins.$ **or** $6\,hrs.\ 15\,mins.$

17. $A = lw$

$A = 13(8) = 104$

18. $V = 2\pi R^2 r^2$

$V = 2(3.14)(3)^2(1.75)^2$

$V = 2(3.14)(9)(3.0625)$

$V = 173.0925 \approx 173.1$

19. $Z = \dfrac{\bar{x} - \mu}{\dfrac{\sigma}{\sqrt{n}}}$

$2 = \dfrac{\bar{x} - 100}{\dfrac{3}{\sqrt{16}}}$

$\dfrac{2}{1} = \dfrac{\bar{x} - 100}{\dfrac{3}{4}}$

$2\left(\dfrac{3}{4}\right) = 1(\bar{x} - 100)$

$\dfrac{3}{2} = \bar{x} - 100$

$\dfrac{3}{2} + 100 = \bar{x} - 100 + 100$

$\dfrac{3}{2} + \dfrac{200}{2} = \bar{x}$

$\dfrac{203}{2} = \bar{x}$

$101.5 = \bar{x}$

20. $K = \dfrac{1}{2}mv^2$

$4500 = \dfrac{1}{2}m(30)^2$

$4500 = 450m$

$\dfrac{4500}{450} = \dfrac{450m}{450}$

$10 = m$

21. $4x - 6y = 12$

$4x - 4x - 6y = -4x + 12$

$-6y = -4x + 12$

$\dfrac{-6y}{-6} = \dfrac{-4x + 12}{-6}$

$y = \dfrac{-4x + 12}{-6} = \dfrac{-4}{-6}x + \dfrac{12}{-6} = \dfrac{2}{3}x - 2$

22. $5x + 6y = 18$

$5x - 5x + 6y = -5x + 18$

$6y = -5x + 18$

$\dfrac{6y}{6} = \dfrac{-5x + 18}{6}$

$y = \dfrac{-5x + 18}{6} = -\dfrac{5}{6}x + 3$

23.
$$2x - 3y + 52 = 30$$
$$2x - 2x - 3y + 52 = -2x + 30$$
$$-3y + 52 = -2x + 30$$
$$-3y + 52 - 52 = -2x + 30 - 52$$
$$-3y = -2x - 22$$
$$\frac{-3y}{-3} = \frac{-2x - 22}{-3}$$
$$y = \frac{-2x - 22}{-3} = \frac{2x + 22}{3} = \frac{2}{3}x + \frac{22}{3}$$

24.
$$-3x - 4y + 5z = 4$$
$$-3x + 3x - 4y + 5z = 3x + 4$$
$$-4y + 5z = 3x + 4$$
$$-4y + 5z - 5z = 3x - 5z + 4$$
$$-4y = 3x - 5z + 4$$
$$\frac{-4y}{-4} = \frac{3x - 5z + 4}{-4}$$
$$y = \frac{3x - 5z + 4}{-4} = \frac{-3x + 5z - 4}{4} = -\frac{3}{4}x + \frac{5}{4}z - 1$$

25. $A = lw$
$$\frac{A}{w} = \frac{lw}{w}$$
$$\frac{A}{w} = l$$

26. $P = 2l + 2w$
$$P - 2l = 2l - 2l + 2w$$
$$P - 2l = 2w$$
$$\frac{P - 2l}{2} = \frac{2w}{2}$$
$$\frac{P - 2l}{2} = w$$

27.
$$L = 2(wh + lh)$$
$$L = 2wh + 2lh$$
$$L - 2wh = 2wh - 2wh + 2lh$$
$$L - 2wh = 2lh$$
$$\frac{L - 2wh}{2h} = \frac{2lh}{2h}$$
$$\frac{L - 2wh}{2h} = l \text{ or } l = \frac{L}{2h} - w$$

28.
$$a_n = a_1 + (n-1)d$$
$$a_n - a_1 = a_1 - a_1 + (n-1)d$$
$$a_n - a_1 = (n-1)d$$
$$\frac{a_n - a_1}{n-1} = \frac{(n-1)d}{n-1}$$
$$\frac{a_n - a_1}{n-1} = d$$

29. $7 - 4x$

30. $5x - 3$

31. $10 + 3r$

32. $\frac{8}{q} - 11$

33. Let $x =$ the number
$3x = 3$ times a number
$12 - 3x = 12$ decreased by 3 times a number
$$12 - 3x = 21$$
$$12 - 12 - 3x = 21 - 12$$
$$-3x = 9$$
$$\frac{-3x}{-3} = \frac{9}{-3}$$
$$x = -3$$

34. Let $x =$ the number
$3x =$ the product of 3 and a number
$3x + 8 =$ the product of 3 and a number increased by 8
$x - 6 = 6$ less than the number
$$3x + 8 = x - 6$$
$$3x - x + 8 = x - x - 6$$
$$2x + 8 = -6$$
$$2x + 8 - 8 = -6 - 8$$
$$2x = -14$$
$$\frac{2x}{2} = \frac{-14}{2}$$
$$x = -7$$

35. Let $x =$ the number

$x - 4 =$ the difference of a number and 4

$5(x - 4) = 5$ times the difference of a number and 4

$5(x - 4) = 45$

$5x - 20 = 45$

$5x - 20 + 20 = 45 + 20$

$5x = 65$

$\dfrac{5x}{5} = \dfrac{65}{5}$

$x = 13$

36. Let $x =$ the number

$10x = 10$ times a number

$10x + 14 = 14$ more than 10 times a number

$x + 12 =$ the sum of a number and 12

$8(x + 12) = 8$ times the sum of a number and 12

$10x + 14 = 8(x + 12)$

$10x + 14 = 8x + 96$

$10x - 8x + 14 = 8x - 8x + 96$

$2x + 14 = 96$

$2x + 14 - 14 = 96 - 14$

$2x = 82$

$\dfrac{2x}{2} = \dfrac{82}{2}$

$x = 41$

37. Let $x =$ Marie's income

$\dfrac{1}{3}x =$ Wesley's income

$x + \dfrac{1}{3}x = 48{,}000$

$\dfrac{4}{3}x = 48{,}000$

$\dfrac{3}{4}\left(\dfrac{4}{3}x\right) = \dfrac{3}{4}(48{,}000)$

$x = \$36{,}000$ Marie's income

$\dfrac{1}{3}x = \dfrac{1}{3}(36{,}000) = \$12{,}000$ Wesley's income

38. Let $x =$ number of lawn chairs

$9.50x =$ variable cost per lawn chair

$9.50x + 15{,}000 = 95{,}000$

$9.50x + 15{,}000 - 15{,}000 = 95{,}000 - 15{,}000$

$9.50x = 80{,}000$

$\dfrac{9.50x}{9.50} = \dfrac{80{,}000}{9.50}$

$x = 8421.052632 \approx 8421$ lawn chairs

39. Let $x =$ profit at restaurant B

$x + 12{,}000 =$ profit at restaurant A

$x + x + 12{,}000 = 68{,}000$

$2x + 12{,}000 = 68{,}000$

$2x + 12{,}000 - 12{,}000 = 68{,}000 - 12{,}000$

$2x = 56{,}000$

$\dfrac{2x}{2} = \dfrac{56{,}000}{2}$

$x = \$28{,}000$ for restaurant B

$x + 12{,}000 = 28{,}000 + 12{,}000 = \$40{,}000$ for restaurant A

40. Let $x =$ the number of rental hours

$15x =$ rental cost per hour

$15x = 300$

$\dfrac{15x}{15} = \dfrac{300}{15}$

$x = 20$ hours

41. $R = \dfrac{k}{S^2}$

$8 = \dfrac{k}{(3)^2}$

$k = 9(8) = 72$

$R = \dfrac{72}{S^2}$

$R = \dfrac{72}{(6)^2} = \dfrac{72}{36} = 2$

42. $m = kn$

$80 = k(4)$

$k = \dfrac{80}{4} = 20$

$m = 20n$

$m = 20(12) = 240$

43. $W = \dfrac{kL}{A}$

$80 = \dfrac{k(100)}{20}$

$100k = 1600$

$k = \dfrac{1600}{100} = 16$

$W = \dfrac{16L}{A}$

$W = \dfrac{16(50)}{40} = \dfrac{800}{40} = 20$

44. $z = \dfrac{kxy}{r^2}$

$12 = \dfrac{k(20)(8)}{(8)^2}$

$160k = 768$

$k = \dfrac{768}{160} = 4.8$

$z = \dfrac{4.8xy}{r^2}$

$z = \dfrac{4.8(10)(80)}{(3)^2} = \dfrac{3840}{9} = 426.\overline{6} \approx 426.7$

45. $\dfrac{1 \; in.}{30 \; mi.} = \dfrac{x \; in.}{120 \; mi.}$

$30x = 120$

$\dfrac{30x}{30} = \dfrac{120}{30}$

$x = 4 \; in.$

46. $\dfrac{1 \; kWh}{\$0.162} = \dfrac{740 \; kWh}{x}$

$x = \$119.88$

47. $d = kt^2$

$16 = k(1)^2$

$k = 16$

$d = 16t^2$

$d = 16(5)^2 = 16(25) = 400$ ft.

48. $A = kr^2$

$78.5 = k(5)^2$

$k = \dfrac{78.5}{25} = 3.14$

$A = 3.14r^2$

$A = 3.14(8)^2 = 3.14(64) = 200.96$

49.
$$6 + 7x \geq -3x - 4$$
$$6 - 6 + 7x \geq -3x - 4 - 6$$
$$7x \geq -3x - 10$$
$$7x + 3x \geq -3x + 3x - 10$$
$$10x \geq -10$$
$$\frac{10x}{10} \geq \frac{-10}{10}$$
$$x \geq -1$$

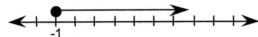

50.
$$3x + 7 \geq 5x + 9$$
$$3x - 5x + 7 \geq 5x - 5x + 9$$
$$-2x + 7 \geq 9$$
$$-2x + 7 - 7 \geq 9 - 7$$
$$-2x \geq 2$$
$$\frac{-2x}{-2} \leq \frac{2}{-2}$$
$$x \leq -1$$

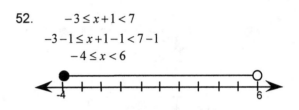

51.
$$3(x + 9) \leq 4x + 11$$
$$3x + 27 \leq 4x + 11$$
$$3x - 4x + 27 \leq 4x - 4x + 11$$
$$-x + 27 \leq 11$$
$$-x + 27 - 27 \leq 11 - 27$$
$$-x \leq -16$$
$$\frac{-x}{-1} \geq \frac{-16}{-1}$$
$$x \geq 16$$

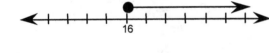

52.
$$-3 \leq x + 1 < 7$$
$$-3 - 1 \leq x + 1 - 1 < 7 - 1$$
$$-4 \leq x < 6$$

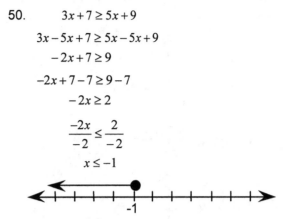

53.
$$2 + 7x > -12$$
$$2 - 2 + 7x > -12 - 2$$
$$7x > -14$$
$$\frac{7x}{7} > \frac{-14}{7}$$
$$x > -2$$

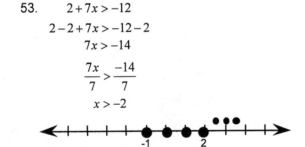

54.
$$5x + 13 \geq -22$$
$$5x + 13 - 13 \geq -22 - 13$$
$$5x \geq -35$$
$$\frac{5x}{5} \geq \frac{-35}{5}$$
$$x \geq -7$$

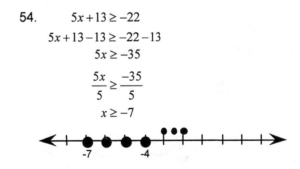

55. $-1 < x \leq 7$

56. $-8 \leq x + 2 \leq 7$
$$-8 - 2 \leq x + 2 - 2 \leq 7 - 2$$
$$-10 \leq x \leq 5$$

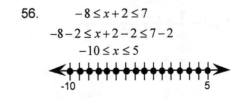

57. - 60.

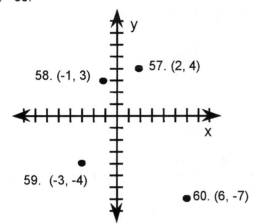

61.

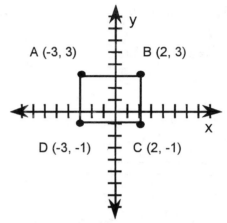

Area $= lw = 5(4) = 20$ square units

62.

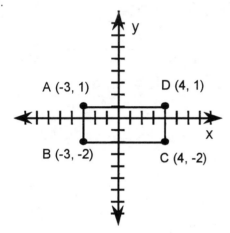

Area $= lw = 7(3) = 21$ square units

63. x - y = 4

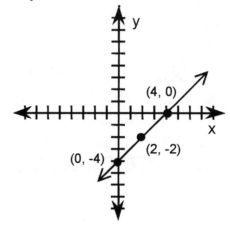

64. 2x + 3y = 12

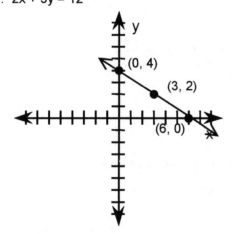

65. x = y

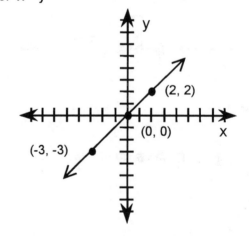

66. x = 3

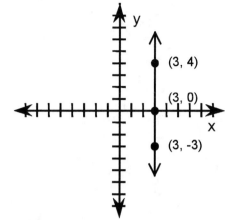

67. x + 4y = 8

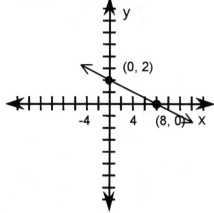

68. 3x - 2y = 6

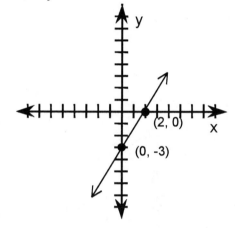

69. 4x - 3y = 12

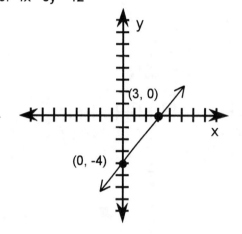

70. 2x + 3y = 9

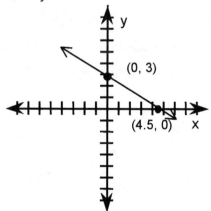

71. $m = \dfrac{2-3}{6-1} = -\dfrac{1}{5}$

72. $m = \dfrac{-4-(-1)}{5-3} = \dfrac{-4+1}{5-3} = -\dfrac{3}{2}$

73. $m = \dfrac{3-(-4)}{5-(-1)} = \dfrac{3+4}{5+1} = \dfrac{7}{6}$

74. $m = \dfrac{-2-2}{6-6} = \dfrac{-4}{0}$ Undefined

75. $y = 2x - 5$

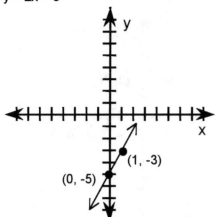

76. $2y - 4 = 3x$

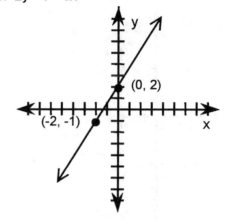

77. $2y + x = 8$

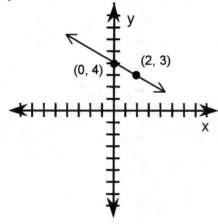

78. $y = -x - 1$

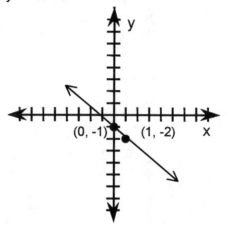

79. The y-intercept is 4, thus b = 4. Since the graph rises from left to right, the slope is positive. The change in y is 4 units while the change in x is 2. Thus, m, the slope is $\frac{4}{2}$ or 2. The equation is y = 2x + 4.

80. The y-intercept is 1, thus b = 1. Since the graph falls from left to right, the slope is negative. The change in y is 3 units while the change in x is 3. Thus, m, the slope is $\frac{-3}{3}$ or -1. The equation is y = -x + 1.

81. a)

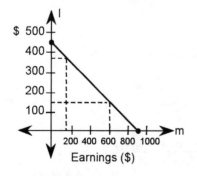

b)   About $160
c)   About $160

82. a)

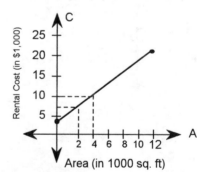

b)   About $6400
c)   About 4120 ft.^{2}

83. Graph 6x + 9y = 54. Since the original inequality is less than or equal to, a solid line is drawn. Since the point (0, 0) satisfies the inequality 6x + 9y ≤ 54, all points on the line and in the half-plane below the line 6x + 9y = 54 are in the solution set.

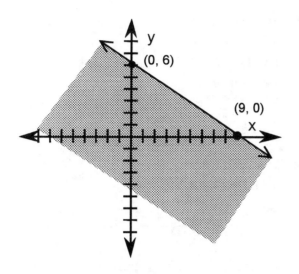

84. Graph 3x + 2y = 12. Since the original inequality is greater than or equal to, a solid line is drawn. Since the point (0, 0) does not satisfy the inequality 3x + 2y ≥ 12, all points in the half plane above the line 3x + 2y = 12 are in the solution set.

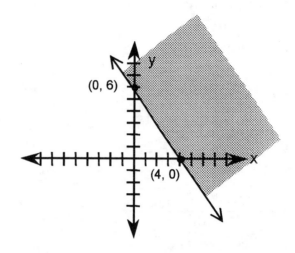

85. Graph 2x − 3y = 12. Since the original inequality is strictly greater than, a dashed line is drawn. Since the point (0, 0) does not satisfy the inequality 2x − 3y > 12, all points in the half-plane below the line 2x − 3y = 12 are in the solution set.

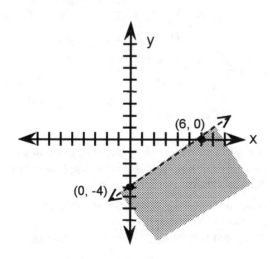

86. Graph -7x − 2y = 14. Since the original inequality is strictly less than, a dashed line is drawn. Since the point (0, 0) satisfies the inequality -7x − 2y < 14, all points in the half-plane to the right of the line -7x − 2y = 14 are in the solution set.

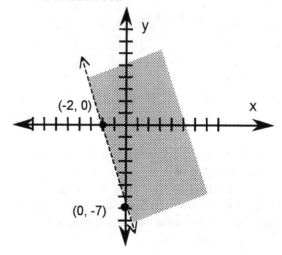

87. $x^2 + 9x + 18 = (x + 3)(x + 6)$

88. $x^2 + x - 20 = (x + 5)(x - 4)$

89. $x^2 - 10x + 24 = (x - 6)(x - 4)$

90. $x^2 - 9x + 20 = (x - 4)(x - 5)$

91. $2x^2 + x - 21 = (2x + 7)(x - 3)$

92. $3x^2 + 5x - 2 = (3x - 1)(x + 2)$

93. $x^2 + 5x + 6 = 0$

     $(x+2)(x+3) = 0$

     $x + 2 = 0$ or $x + 3 = 0$

     $x = -2$ $x = -3$

94. $x^2 - 6x = -5$

     $x^2 - 6x + 5 = 0$

     $(x-1)(x-5) = 0$

     $x - 1 = 0$ or $x - 5 = 0$

     $x = 1$ $x = 5$

95. $3x^2 - 17x + 10 = 0$

     $(3x - 2)(x - 5) = 0$

     $3x - 2 = 0$ or $x - 5 = 0$

     $3x = 2$ $x = 5$

     $x = \dfrac{2}{3}$

96. $3x^2 = -7x - 2$

     $3x^2 + 7x + 2 = 0$

     $(3x + 1)(x + 2) = 0$

     $3x + 1 = 0$ or $x + 2 = 0$

     $3x = -1$ $x = -2$

     $x = -\dfrac{1}{3}$

97. $x^2 - 3x - 7 = 0$

     $a = 1,\ b = -3,\ c = -7$

     $x = \dfrac{-(-3) \pm \sqrt{(-3)^2 - 4(1)(-7)}}{2(1)}$

     $x = \dfrac{3 \pm \sqrt{9 + 28}}{2} = \dfrac{3 \pm \sqrt{37}}{2}$

98. $x^2 - 3x + 2 = 0$

     $a = 1,\ b = -3,\ c = 2$

     $x = \dfrac{-(-3) \pm \sqrt{(-3)^2 - 4(1)(2)}}{2(1)}$

     $x = \dfrac{3 \pm \sqrt{9 - 8}}{2} = \dfrac{3 \pm \sqrt{1}}{2} = \dfrac{3 \pm 1}{2}$

     $x = \dfrac{4}{2} = 2$ or $x = \dfrac{2}{2} = 1$

99. $2x^2 - 3x + 4 = 0$

     $a = 2,\ b = -3,\ c = 4$

     $x = \dfrac{-(-3) \pm \sqrt{(-3)^2 - 4(2)(4)}}{2(2)}$

     $x = \dfrac{3 \pm \sqrt{9 - 32}}{4} = \dfrac{3 \pm \sqrt{-23}}{4}$

     No real solution

100. $2x^2 - x - 3 = 0$

     $a = 2,\ b = -1,\ c = -3$

     $x = \dfrac{-(-1) \pm \sqrt{(-1)^2 - 4(2)(-3)}}{2(2)}$

     $x = \dfrac{1 \pm \sqrt{1 + 24}}{4} = \dfrac{1 \pm \sqrt{25}}{4} = \dfrac{1 \pm 5}{4}$

     $x = \dfrac{6}{4} = \dfrac{3}{2}$ or $x = \dfrac{-4}{4} = -1$

101. Function since each value of x is paired with a unique value of y.

     D: x = -2, -1, 2, 3   R: y = -1, 0, 2

102. Not a function since it is possible to draw a vertical line that intersects the graph at more than one point.

103. Not a function since it is possible to draw a vertical line that intersects the graph at more than one point.

104. Function since each vertical line intersects the graph at only one point.

     D: all real numbers   R: all real numbers

105. $f(x) = 2x + 10,\ x = -3$

     $f(-3) = 2(-3) + 10 = -6 + 10 = 4$

106. $f(x) = -3x + 8,\ x = -2$

     $f(-2) = -3(-2) + 8 = 6 + 8 = 14$

107. $f(x) = 2x^2 - 3x + 4,\ x = 5$

     $f(5) = 2(5)^2 - 3(5) + 4 = 50 - 15 + 4 = 39$

108. $f(x) = -4x^2 + 7x + 9,\ x = 4$

     $f(4) = -4(4)^2 + 7(4) + 9 = -64 + 28 + 9 = -27$

109. $y = -x^2 - 4x + 21$
    a) $a = -1 < 0$, opens downward
    b) $x = -2$ c) $(-2, 25)$ d) $(0, 21)$
    e) $(-7, 0), (3, 0)$
    f)

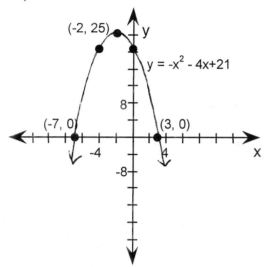

    g) D: all real numbers   R: $y \le 25$

110. $y = 3x^2 - 24x - 30$
    a) $a = 3 > 0$, opens upward
    b) $x = 4$ c) $(4, -78)$ d) $(0, -30)$
    e) $(4 - \sqrt{26}, 0), (4 + \sqrt{26}, 0)$
    f)

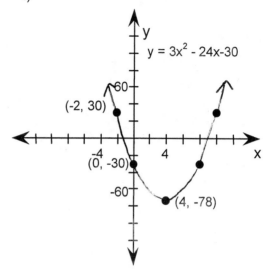

    g) D: all real numbers   R: $y \ge -78$

111. $y = 2^{2x}$

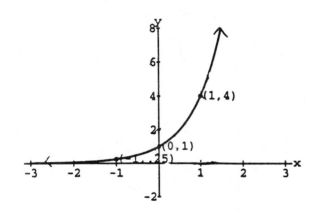

    D: all real numbers   R: $y > 0$

112. $y = \left(\dfrac{1}{2}\right)^x$

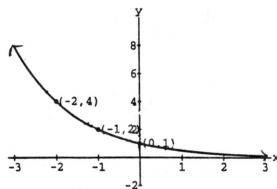

    D: all real numbers   R: $y > 0$

113. $m = 30 - 0.002n^2$, $n = 60$

$m = 30 - 0.002(60)^2 = 30 - 0.002(3600)$
$= 30 - 7.2 = 22.8$ miles per gallon

114. $n = 2a^2 - 80a + 5000$
    a) $a = 18$

$n = 2(18)^2 - 80(18) + 5000$
$= 648 - 1440 + 5000 = 4208$

    b) $a = 25$

$n = 2(25)^2 - 80(25) + 5000$
$= 1250 - 2000 + 5000 = 4250$

115. $P = 100(0.92)^x$, $x = 4.5$

$P = 100(0.92)^{4.5}$

$= 100(0.6871399881) = 68.71399881 \approx 68.7\%$

Chapter Test

1. $-3x^2 + 6x + 9$, $x = 2$

   $-3(2)^2 + 6(2) + 9 = -12 + 12 + 9 = 9$

2. $\quad 3x + 5 = 2(4x - 7)$

   $3x + 5 = 8x - 14$

   $3x - 8x + 5 = 8x - 8x - 14$

   $-5x + 5 = -14$

   $-5x + 5 - 5 = -14 - 5$

   $-5x = -19$

   $\dfrac{-5x}{-5} = \dfrac{-19}{-5}$

   $x = \dfrac{19}{5}$

3. $-2(x - 3) + 6x = 2x + 3(x - 4)$

   $-2x + 6 + 6x = 2x + 3x - 12$

   $4x + 6 = 5x - 12$

   $4x - 5x + 6 = 5x - 5x - 12$

   $-x + 6 = -12$

   $-x + 6 - 6 = -12 - 6$

   $-x = -18$

   $\dfrac{-x}{-1} = \dfrac{-18}{-1}$

   $x = 18$

4. Let $x =$ the number

   $3x =$ the product of a number and 3

   $3x - 10 =$ the product of a number and 3
   decreased by 10

   $3x - 10 = 11$

   $3x - 10 + 10 = 11 + 10$

   $3x = 21$

   $\dfrac{3x}{3} = \dfrac{21}{3}$

   $x = 7$

5. Let $x =$ number of items

   $4.35x + 60 =$ his cost

   $7.75x =$ his revenue

   $7.75x = 4.35x + 60$

   $7.75x - 4.35x = 4.35x - 4.35x + 60$

   $3.4x = 60$

   $\dfrac{3.4x}{3.4} = \dfrac{60}{3.4}$

   $x = 17.64705882 \approx 18$ units

6. $L = ah + bh + ch$; $a = 3$, $b = 4$, $c = 5$, $h = 7$

   $L = 3(7) + 4(7) + 5(7)$

   $= 21 + 28 + 35 = 84$

7.
$$5x - 8y = 17$$
$$5x - 5x - 8y = -5x + 17$$
$$-8y = -5x + 17$$
$$\frac{-8y}{-8} = \frac{-5x + 17}{-8}$$
$$y = \frac{-5x + 17}{-8} = \frac{5x - 17}{8} = \frac{5}{8}x - \frac{17}{8}$$

8.
$$L = \frac{kMN}{P}$$
$$12 = \frac{k(8)(3)}{2}$$
$$24k = 24$$
$$k = \frac{24}{24} = 1$$
$$L = \frac{(1)MN}{P}$$
$$L = \frac{(1)(10)(5)}{15} = \frac{50}{15} = 3.\overline{3} = 3\frac{1}{3}$$

9.
$$l = \frac{k}{w}$$
$$15 = \frac{k}{9}$$
$$k = 15(9) = 135$$
$$l = \frac{135}{w}$$
$$l = \frac{135}{20} = 6.75 \text{ ft.}$$

10.
$$-3x + 11 \le 5x + 35$$
$$-3x - 5x + 11 \le 5x - 5x + 35$$
$$-8x + 11 \le 35$$
$$-8x + 11 - 11 \le 35 - 11$$
$$-8x \le 24$$
$$\frac{-8x}{-8} \ge \frac{24}{-8}$$
$$x \ge -3$$

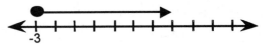

11. $m = \dfrac{-26 - 5}{10 - (-3)} = \dfrac{-26 - 5}{10 + 3} = -\dfrac{31}{13}$

12. y = 3x − 4

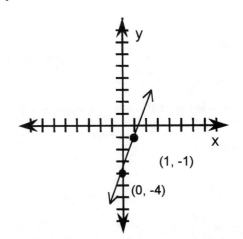

13. $2x - 3y = 15$

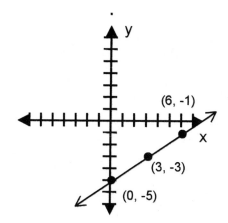

(6, -1)

(3, -3)

(0, -5)

14. Graph $3y = 5x - 12$. Since the original statement is greater than or equal to, a solid line is drawn. Since the point (0, 0) satisfies the inequality $3y \geq 5x - 12$, all points on the line and in the half-plane above the line

$3y = 5x - 12$ are in the solution set.

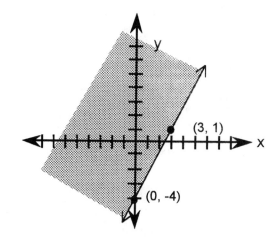

(3, 1)

(0, -4)

15. $x^2 - 3x = 28$

$x^2 - 3x - 28 = 0$

$(x - 7)(x + 4) = 0$

$x - 7 = 0$ or $x + 4 = 0$

$x = 7$ $\qquad x = -4$

16. $3x^2 + 2x = 8$

$3x^2 + 2x - 8 = 0$

$a = 3,\ b = 2,\ c = -8$

$x = \dfrac{-2 \pm \sqrt{(2)^2 - 4(3)(-8)}}{2(3)}$

$x = \dfrac{-2 \pm \sqrt{4 + 96}}{6} = \dfrac{-2 \pm \sqrt{100}}{6} = \dfrac{-2 \pm 10}{6}$

$x = \dfrac{8}{6} = \dfrac{4}{3}$ or $x = \dfrac{-12}{6} = -2$

17. Function since each vertical line intersects the graph at only one point.

18. $f(x) = -4x^2 - 11x + 5,\ x = -2$

$f(-2) = -4(-2)^2 - 11(-2) + 5$

$\qquad = -16 + 22 + 5 = 11$

19. $y = x^2 - 2x + 4$

  a) $a = 1 > 0$, opens upward

  b) $x = 1$ c) $(1, 3)$ d) $(0, 4)$

  e) no x-intercepts

  f)

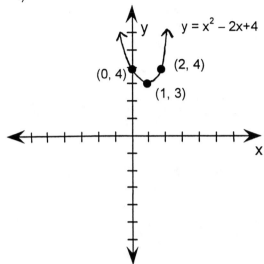

  g) D: all real numbers   R: $y \geq 3$

CHAPTER SEVEN

SYSTEMS OF LINEAR EQUATIONS AND INEQUALITIES

Exercise Set 7.1

1. Two or more linear equations form a system of linear equations.
3. A consistent system of equations is a system that has a solution.
5. An inconsistent system of equations is a system that has no solution.

7. To check if $(2, -1)$ is a solution, replace x with 2 and y with (-1) in each equation.

$x + 3y = -1$	$2x + y = 2$
$2 + 3(-1) = -1$	$2(2) + (-1) = 2$
$2 - 3 = -1$	$4 - 1 = 2$
$-1 = -1$ True	$3 = 2$ False

Since $(2, -1)$ does not satisfy both equations, it is not a solution.

9.

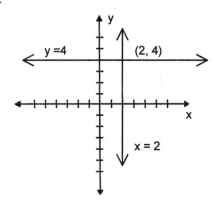

11.

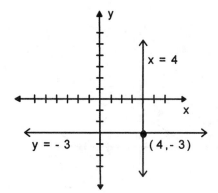

13.

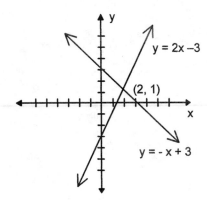

15.

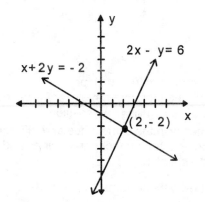

143

17.

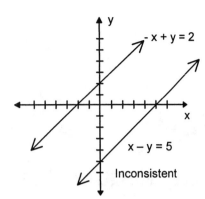

19.

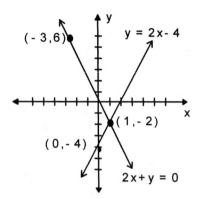

21.

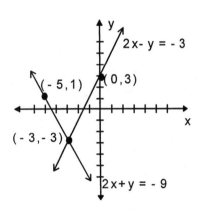

23.

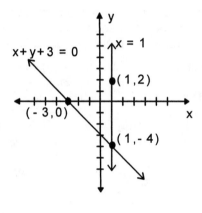

25.

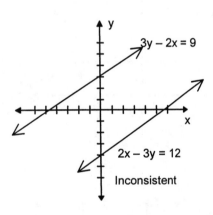

27.

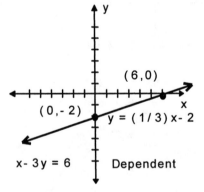

29.a)   Two lines with different slopes are not
        parallel, and therefore have exactly one point
        of intersection giving one solution.

   b)   Two lines with the same slope and different
        y- intercepts are distinct parallel lines and
        have no solution.

   c)   Two lines with the same slopes and
        y-intercepts have infinitely many solutions,
        each point on the line.

In problems 31 - 41, solve each equation for y and then compare using the answer from problem #29.

31. $y = -3x + 8$
    $y = -3x + 8$
    same slope, same y-intercept;
    Infinite number of solutions

33. $y = -(1/2)x + 3/2$
    $y = x - 3$
    different slopes; One solution

35. $y = -3x + 7$
    $y = -3x + 9$
    same slope, different y-intercepts;
    No solution

37. $y = -(1/4)x + 3$
    $y = (1/4)x - (3/4)$
    different slopes; One solution

39. $y = 2x + (4/3)$
    $y = 2x + (4/3)$
    same slope and y-intercept;
    Infinite number of solutions

41. $y = (12/5)x - (4/5)$
    $y = -(3/4)x + (3/2)$
    different slopes; One solution

43. $y = (2/5)x + 3$
    $y = (5/2)x + 1$
    $(2/5) \cdot (5/2) = 1 \neq -1$
    The lines are not perpendicular

45. $y = -2x + 3$
    $y = (1/2)x + 5/2$
    $-2 \cdot (1/2) = -(2/2) = -1$
    The lines are perpendicular.

47. a) Let c = cost
       let h = number of hours
       (Tom's): c = 60h + 200
       (Lawn Per.): c = 25h + 305

    b)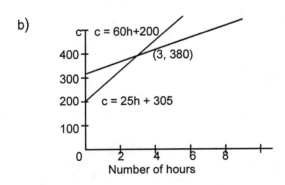

    c) From the graph, the point of intersection of the two lines is (3, 380) indicating 3 hours.

49. a) Let c = cost of printing
       let b = number of books
       (Sivle): c = 6b + 1600
       (Yelserp): c = 8b + 1200

    b)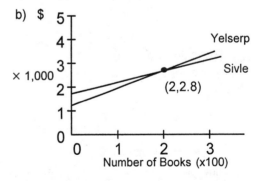

    c) From the graph, the point of intersection of the two lines is (200, 2800) indicating 200 books.

    d) Sivle: 6(100) + 1600 = $2200
       Yelserp: 8(100) + 1200 = $2000
       Yelserp is less expensive.

51. a) Let R = revenue, C = cost, and
        x = number of units.
        R = 165x
        C = 8400 + 95x

    c) Based on the graph, 120 units.
    d) P = R – C = 165x – (8400 + 95x)
         = 70x – 8400
    e) When x = 100, P = 70(100) – 8400 = – 1400
        A loss of $1400.
    f) P = 70x – 8400 = 1250
            70x = 9650
              x ≈ 138 units

b)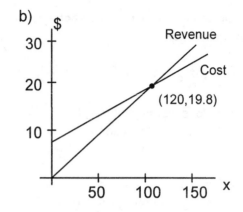

53. a) (1) s = 300 + 0.15v
         (2) s = 450
     b)

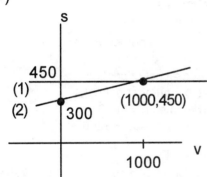

    c) $1000 sales volume.

55. a) one   b) three   c) six   d) ten

    e) number of equations: 2   3   4   5   6
       points of intersection: 1   1+2=3   3+3=6   6+4=10   10+5=15

Exercise Set 7.2

1. Write the equations with the variables on one side and the constants on the other side. If necessary
    multiply one or both equations by a constant(s) so that when the equations are added one of the variables
    will be eliminated. Solve for the remaining variable and then substitute that value into one of the original
    equations to solve for the other variable.

3. The system is inconsistent if the result is a false statement.

5. $y = x - 6$
$y = -x + 4$
Substitute $(x - 6)$ in place of y in the second equation.

$$\begin{aligned} x - 6 &= -x + 4 \quad \text{(solve for x)} \\ \underline{+\,x \qquad\quad +x} \\ 2x - 6 &= 4 \\ \underline{+\,6 \qquad +6} \\ 2x &= 10 \\ \frac{2x}{2} &= \frac{10}{2} \\ x &= 5 \end{aligned}$$

Now substitute 5 for x in the equation
$$\begin{aligned} y &= x - 6 \\ y &= 5 - 6 = -1 \end{aligned}$$
The solution is $(5, -1)$.

9. $y - x = 4$
$x - y = 3$
Solve the first equation for y.
$$\begin{aligned} y - x + x &= x + 4 \\ y &= x + 4 \end{aligned}$$
Substitute $(x + 4)$ in place of y in the second equation.
$$\begin{aligned} x - (x + 4) &= 3 \quad \text{(combine like terms)} \\ -4 &= 3 \quad \text{False} \end{aligned}$$
Since -4 does not equal 3, there is no solution to this system. The equations are inconsistent.

13. $y - 2x = 3$
$2y = 4x + 6$
Solve the first equation for y.
$$\begin{aligned} y - 2x + 2x &= 2x + 3 \\ y &= 2x + 3 \end{aligned}$$
Now substitute $(2x + 3)$ in place of y in the second equation.
$$\begin{aligned} 2(2x + 3) &= 4x + 6 \\ 4x + 6 &= 4x + 6 \\ 4x - 4x + 6 &= 4x - 4x + 6 \\ 6 &= 6 \end{aligned}$$
This statement is true for all values of x. The system is dependent.

7. $2x - 4y = 12$
$2x + y = -3$
Solve the second equation for y.
$y = -3 - 2x$
Substitute $(-3 - 2x)$ in place of y in the first equation.
$$\begin{aligned} 2x - 4(-3 - 2x) &= 12 \quad \text{(solve for x)} \\ 2x + 12 + 8x &= 12 \\ 10x + 12 &= 12 \\ 10x + 12 - 12 &= 12 - 12 \\ 10x &= 0 \\ x &= 0 \end{aligned}$$
Now substitute 0 in place of x in the equation
$y = -3 - 2x$.
$$\begin{aligned} y &= -3 - 2(0) \\ y &= -3 \end{aligned}$$
The solution is $(0, -3)$.

11. $x = 5y - 12$
$x - y = 0$
Substitute $(5y - 12)$ in place of x in the second equation.
$$\begin{aligned} 5y - 12 - y &= 0 \quad \text{(solve for y)} \\ 4y - 12 &= 0 \\ 4y &= 12 \quad \text{(div. by 4)} \\ y &= 3 \end{aligned}$$
Now substitute 3 for y in the second equation.
$$\begin{aligned} x - 3 &= 0 \\ x &= 3 \end{aligned}$$
The solution is $(3, 3)$.

15. $y = 2$
$y + x + 3 = 0$
Substitute 2 in place of y in the second equation.
$$\begin{aligned} 2 + x + 3 &= 0 \\ x + 5 &= 0 \\ x + 5 - 5 &= 0 - 5 \\ x &= -5 \end{aligned}$$
The solution is $(-5, 2)$.

17. $y + 3x - 4 = 0$
    $2x - y = 7$
    Solve the first equation for y.
    $$y + 3x - 4 = 0$$
    $$y = 4 - 3x$$
    Substitute $4 - 3x$ for y in the second eq.
    $$2x - (4 - 3x) = 7 \text{ (solve for x)}$$
    $$2x - 4 + 3x = 7$$
    $$5x = 11$$
    $$x = 11/5$$
    Substitute 11/5 for x in the second eq.
    $$2(11/5) - y = 7 \text{ (solve for y)}$$
    $$22/5 - y = 7$$
    $$-y = 13/5$$
    $$y = -13/5$$
    The solution is $(11/5, -13/5)$

19. $x = 2y + 3$
    $y = 3x - 1$
    Substitute $(3x - 1)$ in place of y in the first equation.
    $$x = 2(3x - 1) + 3$$
    $$x = 6x - 2 + 3$$
    $$x = 6x + 1$$
    $$x - 6x = 6x - 6x + 1$$
    $$-5x = 1$$
    $$\frac{-5x}{-5} = \frac{1}{-5}$$
    $$x = -1/5$$
    Substitute $-1/5$ in place of x in the second equation.
    $$y = 3(-1/5) - 1 = -3/5 - 5/5 = -8/5$$
    The solution is $(-1/5, -8/5)$.

21. $6x - y = 5$
    $y = 6x - 3$
    Substitute $(6x - 3)$ for y in the first equation.
    $$6x - (6x - 3) = 5$$
    $$6x - 6x + 3 = 5$$
    $$3 = 5 \text{ False}$$
    Since 3 does not equal 5, there is no solution to this system. The equations are inconsistent.

23. $4x + y = 9$
    $\underline{3x - y = 5}$ (add the equations)
    $$7x = 14$$
    $$x = 2$$
    Substitute 2 in place of x in the first equation.
    $$4(2) + y = 9 \text{ (solve for y)}$$
    $$8 + y = 9$$
    $$y = 1$$
    The solution is $(2, 1)$.

25. $-x + y = 5$
    $\underline{x + 3y = 3}$ (add the equations)
    $$4y = 8$$
    $$y = 2$$
    Substitute 2 in place of y in the 2nd equation.
    $$x + 3(2) = 3$$
    $$x + 6 = 3$$
    $$x = -3$$
    The solution is $(-3, 2)$.

27. $2x - y = -4$
    $-3x - y = 6$
    Multiplying the second equation by -1,
    $$2x - y = -4$$
    $\underline{3x + y = -6}$ (add the equations)
    $$5x = -10$$
    $$x = -2$$
    Substitute -2 in place of x in the first equation.
    $$2(-2) - y = -4$$
    $$-4 - y = -4$$
    $$-y = 0$$
    $$y = 0$$
    The solution is $(-2, 0)$.

29.
$$2x + y = 6$$
$$3x + y = 5$$
Multiplying the first equation by -1,
$$-2x - y = -6$$
$$\underline{3x + y = 5} \text{ (add the equations)}$$
$$x = -1$$
Substitute -1 in place of x in the first equation.
$$2(-1) + y = 6$$
$$-2 + y = 6$$
$$y = 8$$
The solution is $(-1, 8)$.

31. $2x + y = 11$
$x + 3y = 18$
Multiplying the second equation by -2,
$$2x + y = 11$$
$$\underline{-2x - 6y = -36} \text{ (add the equations)}$$
$$-5y = -25$$
$$y = 5$$
Substitute 5 in place of y in the 2nd equation.
$$x + 3(5) = 18$$
$$x + 15 = 18$$
$$x = 3$$
The solution is $(3, 5)$.

33.
$$3x - 4y = 11$$
$$3x + 5y = -7$$
Multiplying the first equation by (-1),
$$-3x + 4y = -11$$
$$\underline{3x + 5y = -7} \text{ (add the equations)}$$
$$9y = -18 \text{ (div. by 9)}$$
$$y = -2$$
Substitute -2 in place of y in the first equation.
$$3x - 4(-2) = 11$$
$$3x = 3$$
$$x = 1$$
The solution is $(1, -2)$.

35.
$$4x + y = 6$$
$$-8x - 2y = 13$$
Multiplying the first equation by 2,
$$8x + 2y = 12$$
$$\underline{-8x - 2y = 13} \text{ (add the equations)}$$
$$0 = 25 \quad \text{False}$$
Since this statement is not true for any values of x and y, the equations are inconsistent.

37.
$$7x + 8y = 11$$
$$5x + 6y = 7$$
Multiplying the first equation by (-5), and the second equation by (7).
$$-35x - 40y = -55$$
$$\underline{35x + 42y = 49} \text{ (add the equations)}$$
$$2y = -6 \text{ (div. by 2)}$$
$$y = -3$$
Substitute -3 in place of y in the first equation.
$$7x + 8(-3) = 11$$
$$7x - 24 = 11$$
$$7x = 35$$
$$x = 5$$
The solution is $(5, -3)$.

39. Let w = weekly salary
let s = amount of weekly sales
$$w = 300 + 0.04s$$
$$w = 0.16s$$
$$300 + 0.04s = 0.16s$$
$$300 = 0.12s$$
$$2500 = s$$
Thus, \$2,500 in weekly sales will result in equal salaries.

41. Let x = no. of games won
    y = no. of games tied.
    (1) $2x + 1y = 58$
    (2) $x = y + 23$
    Substitute y+23 for x in eq. (1)
    $2(y + 23) + y = 58$ (solve for y)
    $2y + 46 + y = 58$
    $3y = 12$
    $y = 4$
    Substitute 4 for y in equation (2).
    $x = 4 + 23$
    $x = 27$
    They won 27 games and tied 4 games.

43. Let x = no. of pounds of soybean meal
    y = no. of pounds of corn meal
    (1) $x + y = 300$
    (2) $0.16x + .07y = .10(300)$
    Solve equation (1) for y.
    $y = 300 - x$, sub.(300–x) for y in eq. (2)
    $0.16x + .07(300 - x) = 30$ (solve for x)
    $0.16x + 21 - 0.07x = 30$
    $0.09x = 9$
    $x = 100$
    Substitute 100 for x in eq. (1).
    $100 + y = 300$
    $y = 200$
    Mix 100 pounds of soybean meal with 200 pounds of corn meal.

45. Let c = monthly cost
    let x = number of copies
    Eco. Sales: $c = 18 + 0.02x$
    Office Sup.: $c = 24 + 0.015x$ (set eqs. equal)
    $18 + 0.02x = 24 + 0.015x$
    $0.005x = 6$
    $x = 1200$
    1200 copies per month

47. Let x = no. of pounds of nuts
    let y = no. of pounds of pretzels
    $x + y = 20$
    $3x + 1y = 30$
    $y = 30 - x$ (equation 1 solved for y)
    Substitute (20 – x) for y in the second equation.
    $3x + (20 - x) = 30$
    $3x + 20 - x = 30$
    $2x = 10$
    $x = 5$
    $y = 20 - 5 = 15$
    Mix 5 lbs. of the nuts with 15 lbs. of the pretzels.

49. Let a = number of grams of Mix A
    let b = number of grams of Mix B
    Protein: $0.10a + 0.20b = 20$
    Carbohydrates: $0.06a + 0.02b = 6$
    Multiplying the 2nd equation by (– 10),
    $-0.60a - 0.20b = -60$
    $\underline{0.10a + 0.20b = 20}$ (add)
    $-0.50a = -40$
    $a = 80$ grams of Mix A
    Substitute 80 in place of a in the first equation.
    $0.10(80) + 0.20b = 20$
    $8 + 0.20b = 20$
    $0.20b = 12$
    $b = 60$ grams of Mix B

51. Cassettes: $y = -29x + 450$
    Comp.discs $y = 57x + 150$
    $-29x + 450 = 57x + 150$
    $300 = 28x$
    $x = \dfrac{300}{86} \approx 3.5$
    Approx. 3.5 years after 1988 (in 1991).
    $y = 57(3.5) + 150 = 350$ million units.

53. (1) $\frac{1}{u} + \frac{2}{v} = 8$

    (2) $\frac{3}{u} - \frac{1}{v} = 3$

    Substitute x for $\frac{1}{u}$ and y for $\frac{1}{v}$.

    (1) $x + 2y = 8$
    (2) $3x - y = 3$

    Multiply eq. (2) by 2, then add.

    $\begin{array}{rl} x + 2y &= 8 \\ \underline{6x - 2y} &= \underline{6} \\ 7x &= 14 \end{array}$

    $x = 2$, thus $u = \frac{1}{2}$

    Substitute 2 for x in eq. (1).

    $\begin{array}{rl} 2 + 2y &= 8 \\ 2y &= 6 \end{array}$

    $y = 3$, thus $v = \frac{1}{3}$

    Answer: $\left(\frac{1}{2}, \frac{1}{3}\right)$

Exercise Set 7.3

1. A matrix is a rectangular array of elements.

3. A square matrix contains the same number of rows as columns.

5. a) Add numbers in the same positions to produce an entry in that position.

   b) $\begin{bmatrix} 5 & 3 & -1 \\ 0 & 2 & 4 \end{bmatrix} + \begin{bmatrix} 4 & 5 & 6 \\ -1 & 3 & 2 \end{bmatrix} = \begin{bmatrix} 5+4 & 3+5 & -1+6 \\ 0-1 & 2+3 & 4+2 \end{bmatrix} = \begin{bmatrix} 9 & 8 & 5 \\ -1 & 5 & 6 \end{bmatrix}$

7. a) The number of rows of the first matrix must be the same as the number of columns of the second matrix.

   b) The dimensions of the resulting matrix will have the same number of rows as the first matrix and the same number of columns as the second matrix. The product of a 2 × 2 with a 2 × 3 matrix will yield a 2 × 3 matrix.

9. a) $\begin{bmatrix} 1 & 0 \\ 0 & 1 \end{bmatrix}$ b) $\begin{bmatrix} 1 & 0 & 0 \\ 0 & 1 & 0 \\ 0 & 0 & 1 \end{bmatrix}$

11. $A + B = \begin{bmatrix} 2 & 7 \\ 1 & 6 \end{bmatrix} + \begin{bmatrix} -3 & -5 \\ 8 & 1 \end{bmatrix} = \begin{bmatrix} 2+(-3) & 7+(-5) \\ 1+8 & 6+1 \end{bmatrix} = \begin{bmatrix} -1 & 2 \\ 9 & 7 \end{bmatrix}$

13. $A + B = \begin{bmatrix} -1 & 0 \\ 0 & 4 \\ 6 & 2 \end{bmatrix} + \begin{bmatrix} 2 & 3 \\ 5 & 0 \\ 1 & -1 \end{bmatrix} = \begin{bmatrix} -1+2 & 0+3 \\ 0+5 & 4+0 \\ 6+1 & 2+(-1) \end{bmatrix} = \begin{bmatrix} 1 & 3 \\ 5 & 4 \\ 7 & 1 \end{bmatrix}$

15. $A - B = \begin{bmatrix} -2 & 5 \\ 9 & 1 \end{bmatrix} - \begin{bmatrix} 4 & -2 \\ -3 & 5 \end{bmatrix} = \begin{bmatrix} -2-4 & 5-(-2) \\ 9-(-3) & 1-5 \end{bmatrix} = \begin{bmatrix} -6 & 7 \\ 12 & -4 \end{bmatrix}$

17. $A - B = \begin{bmatrix} 5 & 3 & -1 \\ 7 & 4 & 2 \\ 6 & -1 & -5 \end{bmatrix} - \begin{bmatrix} 4 & 3 & 6 \\ -2 & -4 & 9 \\ 0 & -2 & 4 \end{bmatrix} = \begin{bmatrix} 5-4 & 3-3 & -1-6 \\ 7+2 & 4+4 & 2-9 \\ 6-0 & -1+2 & -5-4 \end{bmatrix} = \begin{bmatrix} 1 & 0 & -7 \\ 9 & 8 & -7 \\ 6 & 1 & -9 \end{bmatrix}$

19. $2B = 2\begin{bmatrix} 3 & 2 \\ 5 & 0 \end{bmatrix} = \begin{bmatrix} 2(3) & 2(2) \\ 2(5) & 2(0) \end{bmatrix} = \begin{bmatrix} 6 & 4 \\ 10 & 0 \end{bmatrix}$

21. $2B + 3C = 2\begin{bmatrix} 3 & 2 \\ 5 & 0 \end{bmatrix} + 3\begin{bmatrix} -2 & 3 \\ 4 & 0 \end{bmatrix} = \begin{bmatrix} 6 & 4 \\ 10 & 0 \end{bmatrix} + \begin{bmatrix} -6 & 9 \\ 12 & 0 \end{bmatrix} = \begin{bmatrix} 6-6 & 4+9 \\ 10+12 & 0+0 \end{bmatrix} = \begin{bmatrix} 0 & 13 \\ 22 & 0 \end{bmatrix}$

23. $3B - 2C = 3\begin{bmatrix} 3 & 2 \\ 5 & 0 \end{bmatrix} - 2\begin{bmatrix} -2 & 3 \\ 4 & 0 \end{bmatrix} = \begin{bmatrix} 9 & 6 \\ 15 & 0 \end{bmatrix} - \begin{bmatrix} -4 & 6 \\ 8 & 0 \end{bmatrix} = \begin{bmatrix} 9+4 & 6-6 \\ 15-8 & 0-0 \end{bmatrix} = \begin{bmatrix} 13 & 0 \\ 7 & 0 \end{bmatrix}$

25. $A \times B = \begin{bmatrix} 2 & 1 \\ 3 & 0 \end{bmatrix} \times \begin{bmatrix} 1 & 4 \\ 2 & 6 \end{bmatrix} = \begin{bmatrix} 2(1)+1(2) & 2(4)+1(6) \\ 3(1)+0(2) & 3(4)+0(6) \end{bmatrix} = \begin{bmatrix} 4 & 14 \\ 3 & 12 \end{bmatrix}$

27. $A \times B = \begin{bmatrix} 2 & 3 & -1 \\ 0 & 4 & 6 \end{bmatrix} \times \begin{bmatrix} 2 \\ 4 \\ 1 \end{bmatrix} = \begin{bmatrix} 2(2)+3(4)-1(1) \\ 0(2)+4(4)+6(1) \end{bmatrix} = \begin{bmatrix} 15 \\ 22 \end{bmatrix}$

29. $A \times B = \begin{bmatrix} 5 & 1 & 6 \\ -2 & 3 & 1 \\ 4 & 7 & 2 \end{bmatrix} \times \begin{bmatrix} 1 & 0 & 0 \\ 0 & 1 & 0 \\ 0 & 0 & 1 \end{bmatrix} = \begin{bmatrix} 5(1)+1(0)+6(0) & 5(0)+1(1)+6(0) & 5(0)+1(0)+6(1) \\ -2(1)+3(0)+1(0) & -2(0)+3(1)+1(0) & -2(0)+3(0)+1(1) \\ 4(1)+7(0)+2(0) & 4(0)+7(1)+2(0) & 4(0)+7(0)+2(1) \end{bmatrix} = \begin{bmatrix} 5 & 1 & 6 \\ -2 & 3 & 1 \\ 4 & 7 & 2 \end{bmatrix}$

31. $A + B = \begin{bmatrix} 1 & 2 & -2 \\ 3 & 0 & 4 \end{bmatrix} + \begin{bmatrix} 5 & 1 & 3 \\ 2 & -2 & 1 \end{bmatrix} = \begin{bmatrix} 1+5 & 2+1 & -2+3 \\ 3+2 & 0+(-2) & 4+1 \end{bmatrix} = \begin{bmatrix} 6 & 3 & 1 \\ 5 & -2 & 5 \end{bmatrix}$

A and B cannot be multiplied because the number of columns in A is not equal to the number of rows in B.

33. Matrices A and B cannot be added because they do not have the same dimensions.

$A \times B = \begin{bmatrix} 4 & 5 & 3 \\ 6 & 2 & 1 \end{bmatrix} \times \begin{bmatrix} 3 & 2 \\ 4 & 6 \\ -2 & 0 \end{bmatrix} = \begin{bmatrix} 4(3)+5(4)+3(-2) & 4(2)+5(6)+3(0) \\ 6(3)+2(4)+1(-2) & 6(2)+2(6)+1(0) \end{bmatrix} = \begin{bmatrix} 26 & 38 \\ 24 & 24 \end{bmatrix}$

35. A and B cannot be added because they do not have the same dimensions.

$A \times B = \begin{bmatrix} 1 & 2 \\ 3 & 4 \end{bmatrix} \times \begin{bmatrix} -3 \\ 2 \end{bmatrix} = \begin{bmatrix} 1(-3)+2(2) \\ 3(-3)+4(2) \end{bmatrix} = \begin{bmatrix} 1 \\ -1 \end{bmatrix}$

37. $A + B = \begin{bmatrix} 1 & 3 \\ 2 & -3 \end{bmatrix} + \begin{bmatrix} 4 & 5 \\ 6 & 2 \end{bmatrix} = \begin{bmatrix} 1+4 & 3+5 \\ 2+6 & -3+2 \end{bmatrix} = \begin{bmatrix} 5 & 8 \\ 8 & -1 \end{bmatrix}$

$B + A = \begin{bmatrix} 4 & 5 \\ 6 & 2 \end{bmatrix} + \begin{bmatrix} 1 & 3 \\ 2 & -3 \end{bmatrix} = \begin{bmatrix} 4+1 & 5+3 \\ 6+2 & 2+(-3) \end{bmatrix} = \begin{bmatrix} 5 & 8 \\ 8 & -1 \end{bmatrix}$ Thus $A + B = B + A$

39. $A + B = \begin{bmatrix} 0 & -1 \\ 3 & -4 \end{bmatrix} + \begin{bmatrix} 8 & 1 \\ 3 & -4 \end{bmatrix} = \begin{bmatrix} 0+8 & -1+1 \\ 3+3 & -4-4 \end{bmatrix} = \begin{bmatrix} 8 & 0 \\ 6 & -8 \end{bmatrix}$

$B + A = \begin{bmatrix} 8 & 1 \\ 3 & -4 \end{bmatrix} + \begin{bmatrix} 0 & -1 \\ 3 & -4 \end{bmatrix} = \begin{bmatrix} 8+0 & 1-1 \\ 3+3 & -4-4 \end{bmatrix} = \begin{bmatrix} 8 & 0 \\ 6 & -8 \end{bmatrix}$ Thus $A + B = B + A$.

41. $(A + B) + C = \left(\begin{bmatrix} 2 & 3 \\ 1 & 6 \end{bmatrix} + \begin{bmatrix} -1 & 4 \\ 5 & 0 \end{bmatrix} \right) + \begin{bmatrix} 3 & 4 \\ -2 & 7 \end{bmatrix} = \begin{bmatrix} 1 & 7 \\ 6 & 6 \end{bmatrix} + \begin{bmatrix} 3 & 4 \\ -2 & 7 \end{bmatrix} = \begin{bmatrix} 4 & 11 \\ 4 & 13 \end{bmatrix}$

$A + (B + C) = \begin{bmatrix} 2 & 3 \\ 1 & 6 \end{bmatrix} + \left(\begin{bmatrix} -1 & 4 \\ 5 & 0 \end{bmatrix} + \begin{bmatrix} 3 & 4 \\ -2 & 7 \end{bmatrix} \right) = \begin{bmatrix} 2 & 3 \\ 1 & 6 \end{bmatrix} + \begin{bmatrix} 2 & 8 \\ 3 & 7 \end{bmatrix} = \begin{bmatrix} 4 & 11 \\ 4 & 13 \end{bmatrix}$

Thus, $(A + B) + C = A + (B + C)$.

43. $(A + B) + C = \left(\begin{bmatrix} 7 & 4 \\ 9 & -36 \end{bmatrix} + \begin{bmatrix} 5 & 6 \\ -1 & -4 \end{bmatrix} \right) + \begin{bmatrix} -7 & -5 \\ -1 & 3 \end{bmatrix} = \begin{bmatrix} 12 & 10 \\ 8 & -40 \end{bmatrix} + \begin{bmatrix} -7 & -5 \\ -1 & 3 \end{bmatrix} = \begin{bmatrix} 5 & 5 \\ 7 & -37 \end{bmatrix}$

$A + (B + C) = \begin{bmatrix} 7 & 4 \\ 9 & -36 \end{bmatrix} + \left(\begin{bmatrix} 5 & 6 \\ -1 & -4 \end{bmatrix} + \begin{bmatrix} -7 & -5 \\ -1 & 3 \end{bmatrix} \right) = \begin{bmatrix} 7 & 4 \\ 9 & -36 \end{bmatrix} + \begin{bmatrix} -2 & 1 \\ -2 & -1 \end{bmatrix} = \begin{bmatrix} 5 & 5 \\ 7 & -37 \end{bmatrix}$

Thus, $(A + B) + C = A + (B + C)$.

45. $A \times B = \begin{bmatrix} 2 & -1 \\ 4 & -3 \end{bmatrix} \times \begin{bmatrix} 2 & 4 \\ -1 & -3 \end{bmatrix} = \begin{bmatrix} 2(2)+(-1)(-1) & 2(4)+(-1)(-3) \\ 4(2)+(-3)(-1) & 4(4)+(-3)(-3) \end{bmatrix} = \begin{bmatrix} 5 & 11 \\ 11 & 25 \end{bmatrix}$

$B \times A = \begin{bmatrix} 2 & 4 \\ -1 & -3 \end{bmatrix} \times \begin{bmatrix} 2 & -1 \\ 4 & -3 \end{bmatrix} = \begin{bmatrix} 2(2)+4(4) & 2(-1)+4(-3) \\ -1(2)+(-3)(4) & (-1)(-1)+(-3)(-3) \end{bmatrix} = \begin{bmatrix} 20 & -14 \\ -14 & 10 \end{bmatrix}$

Thus, $A \times B \neq B \times A$.

47. $A \times B = \begin{bmatrix} 4 & 2 \\ 1 & -3 \end{bmatrix} \times \begin{bmatrix} 2 & 4 \\ -3 & 1 \end{bmatrix} = \begin{bmatrix} 4(2)+2(-3) & 4(4)+2(1) \\ 1(2)+(-3)(-3) & 1(4)+(-3)(1) \end{bmatrix} = \begin{bmatrix} 2 & 18 \\ 11 & 1 \end{bmatrix}$

$B \times A = \begin{bmatrix} 2 & 4 \\ -3 & 1 \end{bmatrix} \times \begin{bmatrix} 4 & 2 \\ 1 & -3 \end{bmatrix} = \begin{bmatrix} 2(4)+4(1) & 2(2)+4(-3) \\ -3(4)+1(1) & -3(2)+1(-3) \end{bmatrix} = \begin{bmatrix} 12 & -8 \\ -11 & -9 \end{bmatrix}$

Thus, $A \times B \neq B \times A$.

49. Since $B = I$, (the identity matrix), and $A \times I = I \times A = A$ we can conclude that $A \times B = B \times A$.

51. $(A \times B) \times C = \left(\begin{bmatrix} 1 & 2 \\ 4 & 0 \end{bmatrix} \begin{bmatrix} 2 & 1 \\ 3 & 0 \end{bmatrix} \right) \begin{bmatrix} 4 & 2 \\ 3 & 1 \end{bmatrix} = \begin{bmatrix} 1(2)+2(3) & 1(1)+2(0) \\ 4(2)+0(3) & 4(1)+0(0) \end{bmatrix} \begin{bmatrix} 4 & 2 \\ 3 & 1 \end{bmatrix}$

$= \begin{bmatrix} 8 & 1 \\ 8 & 4 \end{bmatrix} \begin{bmatrix} 4 & 2 \\ 3 & 1 \end{bmatrix} = \begin{bmatrix} 8(4)+1(3) & 8(2)+1(1) \\ 8(4)+4(3) & 8(2)+4(1) \end{bmatrix} = \begin{bmatrix} 35 & 17 \\ 44 & 20 \end{bmatrix}$

$A \times (B \times C) = \begin{bmatrix} 1 & 2 \\ 4 & 0 \end{bmatrix} \left(\begin{bmatrix} 2 & 1 \\ 3 & 0 \end{bmatrix} \begin{bmatrix} 4 & 2 \\ 3 & 1 \end{bmatrix} \right) = \begin{bmatrix} 1 & 2 \\ 4 & 0 \end{bmatrix} \begin{bmatrix} 2(4)+1(3) & 2(2)+1(1) \\ 3(4)+0(3) & 3(2)+0(1) \end{bmatrix}$

$= \begin{bmatrix} 1 & 2 \\ 4 & 0 \end{bmatrix} \begin{bmatrix} 11 & 5 \\ 12 & 6 \end{bmatrix} = \begin{bmatrix} 1(11)+2(12) & 1(5)+2(6) \\ 4(11)+0(12) & 4(5)+0(6) \end{bmatrix} = \begin{bmatrix} 35 & 17 \\ 44 & 20 \end{bmatrix}$

53. $(A \times B) \times C = \left(\begin{bmatrix} 4 & 3 \\ -6 & 2 \end{bmatrix} \begin{bmatrix} 1 & 2 \\ 0 & 1 \end{bmatrix} \right) \begin{bmatrix} 4 & 3 \\ 0 & -2 \end{bmatrix} = \begin{bmatrix} 4(1)+3(0) & 4(2)+3(1) \\ -6(1)+2(0) & -6(2)+2(1) \end{bmatrix} \begin{bmatrix} 4 & 3 \\ 0 & -2 \end{bmatrix}$

$= \begin{bmatrix} 4 & 11 \\ -6 & -10 \end{bmatrix} \begin{bmatrix} 4 & 3 \\ 0 & -2 \end{bmatrix} = \begin{bmatrix} 4(4)+11(0) & 4(3)+11(-2) \\ -6(4)-10(2) & -6(3)-10(-2) \end{bmatrix} = \begin{bmatrix} 16 & -10 \\ -24 & 2 \end{bmatrix}$

$A \times (B \times C) = \begin{bmatrix} 4 & 3 \\ -6 & 2 \end{bmatrix} \left(\begin{bmatrix} 1 & 2 \\ 0 & 1 \end{bmatrix} \begin{bmatrix} 4 & 3 \\ 0 & -2 \end{bmatrix} \right) = \begin{bmatrix} 4 & 3 \\ -6 & 2 \end{bmatrix} \begin{bmatrix} 1(4)+2(0) & 1(3)+2(-2) \\ 0(4)+1(0) & 0(3)+1(-2) \end{bmatrix}$

$= \begin{bmatrix} 4 & 3 \\ -6 & 2 \end{bmatrix} \begin{bmatrix} 4 & -1 \\ 0 & -2 \end{bmatrix} = \begin{bmatrix} 4(4)+3(0) & 4(-1)+3(-2) \\ -6(4)+2(0) & -6(-1)+2(-2) \end{bmatrix} = \begin{bmatrix} 16 & -10 \\ -24 & 2 \end{bmatrix}$

55. $(A \times B) \times C = \left(\begin{bmatrix} 3 & 4 \\ -1 & -2 \end{bmatrix} \begin{bmatrix} 0 & 1 \\ 1 & 0 \end{bmatrix} \right) \begin{bmatrix} 2 & 0 \\ 3 & 0 \end{bmatrix} = \begin{bmatrix} 3(0)+4(1) & 3(1)+4(0) \\ -1(0)-2(1) & -1(1)-2(0) \end{bmatrix} \begin{bmatrix} 2 & 0 \\ 3 & 0 \end{bmatrix}$

$= \begin{bmatrix} 4 & 3 \\ -2 & -1 \end{bmatrix} \begin{bmatrix} 2 & 0 \\ 3 & 0 \end{bmatrix} = \begin{bmatrix} 4(2)+3(3) & 4(0)+3(0) \\ -2(2)-1(3) & -2(0)-1(0) \end{bmatrix} = \begin{bmatrix} 17 & 0 \\ -7 & 0 \end{bmatrix}$

$A \times (B \times C) = \begin{bmatrix} 3 & 4 \\ -1 & -2 \end{bmatrix} \left(\begin{bmatrix} 0 & 1 \\ 1 & 0 \end{bmatrix} \begin{bmatrix} 2 & 0 \\ 3 & 0 \end{bmatrix} \right) = \begin{bmatrix} 3 & 4 \\ -1 & -2 \end{bmatrix} \begin{bmatrix} 0(2)+1(3) & 0(0)+1(0) \\ 1(2)+0(3) & 1(0)+0(0) \end{bmatrix}$

$= \begin{bmatrix} 3 & 4 \\ -1 & -2 \end{bmatrix} \begin{bmatrix} 3 & 0 \\ 2 & 0 \end{bmatrix} = \begin{bmatrix} 3(3)+4(2) & 3(0)+4(0) \\ -1(3)-2(2) & -1(0)-2(0) \end{bmatrix} = \begin{bmatrix} 17 & 0 \\ -7 & 0 \end{bmatrix}$

57. $A \times B = \begin{bmatrix} 2 & 2 & .5 & 1 \\ 3 & 2 & 1 & 2 \\ 0 & 1 & 0 & 3 \\ .5 & 1 & 0 & 0 \end{bmatrix} \begin{bmatrix} 10 & 12 \\ 5 & 8 \\ 8 & 8 \\ 4 & 6 \end{bmatrix} = \begin{bmatrix} 2 \cdot 10 + 2 \cdot 5 + .5 \cdot 8 + 1 \cdot 4 & 2 \cdot 12 + 2 \cdot 8 + .5 \cdot 8 + 1 \cdot 6 \\ 3 \cdot 10 + 2 \cdot 5 + 1 \cdot 8 + 2 \cdot 4 & 3 \cdot 12 + 2 \cdot 8 + 1 \cdot 8 + 2 \cdot 6 \\ 0 \cdot 10 + 1 \cdot 5 + 0 \cdot 8 + 3 \cdot 4 & 0 \cdot 12 + 1 \cdot 8 + 0 \cdot 8 + 3 \cdot 6 \\ .5 \cdot 10 + 1 \cdot 5 + 0 \cdot 8 + 0 \cdot 4 & .5 \cdot 12 + 1 \cdot 8 + 0 \cdot 8 + 0 \cdot 6 \end{bmatrix} = \begin{bmatrix} 38 & 50 \\ 56 & 72 \\ 17 & 26 \\ 10 & 14 \end{bmatrix}$

59. $C(A \times B) = \begin{bmatrix} 40 & 30 & 12 & 20 \end{bmatrix} \begin{bmatrix} 38 & 50 \\ 56 & 72 \\ 17 & 26 \\ 10 & 14 \end{bmatrix} = \begin{bmatrix} 3604 & 4752 \end{bmatrix}$ cents or small \$36.04, lg. \$47.52

61. $A + B = \begin{bmatrix} 6 & 3 \\ 4 & -2 \end{bmatrix} + \begin{bmatrix} -6 & -3 \\ -2 & -4 \end{bmatrix} = \begin{bmatrix} 6+(-6) & 3+(-3) \\ 4+(-2) & -2+(-4) \end{bmatrix} = \begin{bmatrix} 0 & 0 \\ 2 & -6 \end{bmatrix}$

Since $A+B \neq I$ where I is the additive identity matrix, A and B are not additive inverses.

63. $A \times B = \begin{bmatrix} 5 & -2 \\ -2 & 1 \end{bmatrix}\begin{bmatrix} 1 & 2 \\ 2 & 5 \end{bmatrix} = \begin{bmatrix} 5(1)-2(2) & 5(2)-2(5) \\ -2(1)+1(2) & -2(2)+1(5) \end{bmatrix} = \begin{bmatrix} 1 & 0 \\ 0 & 1 \end{bmatrix}$

$B \times A = \begin{bmatrix} 1 & 2 \\ 2 & 5 \end{bmatrix}\begin{bmatrix} 5 & -2 \\ -2 & 1 \end{bmatrix} = \begin{bmatrix} 1(5)+2(-2) & 1(-2)+2(1) \\ 2(5)+5(-2) & 2(-2)+5(1) \end{bmatrix} = \begin{bmatrix} 1 & 0 \\ 0 & 1 \end{bmatrix}$

Thus, A and B are multiplicative inverses.

65. False. Let A = [1 3] and B = [2 1]. Then A − B = [−1 2] and B − A = [1 −2] ≠ A− B.

67. a) 1.4(14) + 0.7(10) + 0.3(7) = $28.70
    b) 2.7(12) + 2.8(9) + 0.5(5) = $60.10

              Ames Bay
    c) $L \times C = \begin{bmatrix} 28.7 & 24.6 \\ 41.3 & 35.7 \\ 69.3 & 60.1 \end{bmatrix}$ small medium large

    This array shows the total cost of each boat at each plant.

Exercise Set 7.4

1. a) An augmented matrix is a matrix formed with the coefficients of the variables and the constants. The coefficients are separated from the constants by a vertical bar.

   b) $\begin{bmatrix} 1 & 3 & | & 7 \\ 2 & -1 & | & 4 \end{bmatrix}$

3. If you obtain an augmented matrix in which a 0 appears across an entire row, the system of equations is dependent.

5. $\begin{bmatrix} 1 & 1 & | & 3 \\ 2 & -1 & | & 9 \end{bmatrix} \underset{(r_2 - 2r_1)}{=} \begin{bmatrix} 1 & 1 & | & 3 \\ 0 & -3 & | & 3 \end{bmatrix} \underset{(r_2 \div (-3))}{=} \begin{bmatrix} 1 & 1 & | & 3 \\ 0 & 1 & | & -1 \end{bmatrix} \underset{=}{(r_1 - r_2)} \begin{bmatrix} 1 & 0 & | & 4 \\ 0 & 1 & | & -1 \end{bmatrix}$

   The solution is (4,−1).

7. $\begin{bmatrix} 1 & 2 & | & 4 \\ 2 & -1 & | & 3 \end{bmatrix} \underset{(r_2 - 2r_1)}{=} \begin{bmatrix} 1 & 2 & | & 4 \\ 0 & -5 & | & -5 \end{bmatrix} \underset{(r_2 \div (-5))}{=} \begin{bmatrix} 1 & 2 & | & 4 \\ 0 & 1 & | & 1 \end{bmatrix} \underset{=}{(r_1 - 2r_2)} \begin{bmatrix} 1 & 0 & | & 2 \\ 0 & 1 & | & 1 \end{bmatrix}$

   The solution is (2,1).

9. $\begin{bmatrix} 2 & -5 & | & -6 \\ -4 & 10 & | & 12 \end{bmatrix} \underset{(r_2 + 2r_1)}{=} \begin{bmatrix} 2 & -5 & | & -6 \\ 0 & 0 & | & 0 \end{bmatrix} \Rightarrow$ Dependent system.

   The solution is all points on the line 2x − 5y = − 6.

11. $\begin{bmatrix} 1 & 3 & | & 1 \\ -2 & 1 & | & 5 \end{bmatrix} \underset{(r_2 + 2r_1)}{=} \begin{bmatrix} 1 & 3 & | & 1 \\ 0 & 7 & | & 7 \end{bmatrix} \underset{(r_2 \div 7)}{=} \begin{bmatrix} 1 & 3 & | & 1 \\ 0 & 1 & | & 1 \end{bmatrix} \underset{=}{(r_1 - 3r_2)} \begin{bmatrix} 1 & 0 & | & -2 \\ 0 & 1 & | & 1 \end{bmatrix}$

    The solution is (− 2,1).

13. $\begin{bmatrix} 2 & -4 & | & 0 \\ 1 & -3 & | & -1 \end{bmatrix} \underset{=}{(r_1 \div 2)} \begin{bmatrix} 1 & -2 & | & 0 \\ 1 & -3 & | & -1 \end{bmatrix} \underset{(r_2 - r_1)}{=} \begin{bmatrix} 1 & -2 & | & 0 \\ 0 & -1 & | & -1 \end{bmatrix} \underset{(r_2 \div (-1))}{=} \begin{bmatrix} 1 & -2 & | & 0 \\ 0 & 1 & | & 1 \end{bmatrix} \underset{=}{(r_1 + 2r_2)} \begin{bmatrix} 1 & 0 & | & 2 \\ 0 & 1 & | & 1 \end{bmatrix}$

    The solution is (2, 1).

15. $\begin{bmatrix} -3 & 6 & | & 5 \\ 2 & -4 & | & 8 \end{bmatrix} (r_1 \div (-3)) \begin{bmatrix} 1 & -2 & | & \frac{-5}{3} \\ 2 & -4 & | & 8 \end{bmatrix} (r_2 - 2r_1) \begin{bmatrix} 1 & -2 & | & \frac{-5}{3} \\ 0 & 0 & | & \frac{34}{3} \end{bmatrix} \Rightarrow$ Inconsistent system.

No solution.

17. $\begin{bmatrix} 2 & 1 & | & 11 \\ 1 & 3 & | & 18 \end{bmatrix} (r_1 \div 2) \begin{bmatrix} 1 & \frac{1}{2} & | & \frac{11}{2} \\ 1 & 3 & | & 18 \end{bmatrix} (r_2 - r_1) \begin{bmatrix} 1 & \frac{1}{2} & | & \frac{11}{2} \\ 0 & \frac{5}{2} & | & \frac{25}{2} \end{bmatrix} (\frac{2}{5}r_2) \begin{bmatrix} 1 & \frac{1}{2} & | & \frac{11}{2} \\ 0 & 1 & | & 5 \end{bmatrix} (r_1 - \frac{1}{2}r_2) \begin{bmatrix} 1 & 0 & | & 3 \\ 0 & 1 & | & 5 \end{bmatrix}$

The solution is (3, 5)

19. Let x = cost of poster board $4x + 2y = 8$
    y = cost of a marker pen $8x + 5y = 18$

$\begin{bmatrix} 4 & 2 & | & 8 \\ 8 & 5 & | & 18 \end{bmatrix} (r_1 \div 4) \begin{bmatrix} 1 & \frac{1}{2} & | & 2 \\ 8 & 5 & | & 18 \end{bmatrix} (r_2 - 8r_1) \begin{bmatrix} 1 & \frac{1}{2} & | & 2 \\ 0 & 1 & | & 2 \end{bmatrix} (r_1 - \frac{1}{2}r_2) \begin{bmatrix} 1 & 0 & | & 1 \\ 0 & 1 & | & 2 \end{bmatrix}$ The solution is (1,2).

Poster board: $1; markers: $2.

21. Let x = cost per pound of cherries $2x + 3y = 23$
    y = cost per pound of mints $1x + 2y = 14$

$\begin{bmatrix} 2 & 3 & | & 23 \\ 1 & 2 & | & 14 \end{bmatrix} = \begin{bmatrix} 1 & \frac{3}{2} & | & \frac{23}{2} \\ 1 & 2 & | & 14 \end{bmatrix} = \begin{bmatrix} 1 & \frac{3}{2} & | & \frac{23}{2} \\ 0 & \frac{1}{2} & | & \frac{5}{2} \end{bmatrix} = \begin{bmatrix} 1 & \frac{3}{2} & | & \frac{23}{2} \\ 0 & 1 & | & 5 \end{bmatrix} = \begin{bmatrix} 1 & 0 & | & 4 \\ 0 & 1 & | & 5 \end{bmatrix}$

The cherries are $4 per pound and the mints are $5 per pound.

23. $\left. \begin{array}{r} 1.5x + 2y = 337.5 \\ x + y = 200 \end{array} \right\} \Rightarrow \begin{bmatrix} 1.5 & 2 & | & 337.5 \\ 1 & 1 & | & 200 \end{bmatrix} = \begin{bmatrix} 1 & 1.\overline{33} & | & 225 \\ 1 & 1 & | & 200 \end{bmatrix} = \begin{bmatrix} 1 & 1.\overline{33} & | & 225 \\ 1 & 1 & | & 200 \end{bmatrix} = \begin{bmatrix} 1 & 1.\overline{33} & | & 225 \\ 0 & -.\overline{33} & | & -25 \end{bmatrix}$

$= \begin{bmatrix} 1 & 1.\overline{33} & | & 225 \\ 0 & 1 & | & 75 \end{bmatrix} = \begin{bmatrix} 1 & 0 & | & 125 \\ 0 & 1 & | & 75 \end{bmatrix}$

The solution is 125 @ $1.50 and 75 @ $2.00.

Exercise Set 7.5

1. The solution set of a system of linear inequalities is the set of points that satisfy all inequalities in the system.

3.

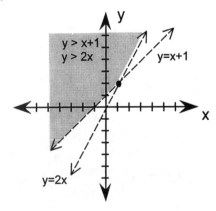

5.

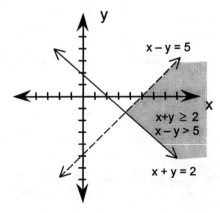

7.

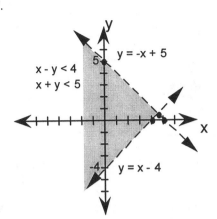

9.

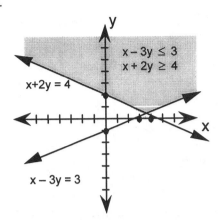

11.

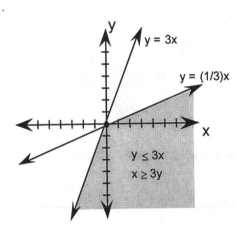

13.

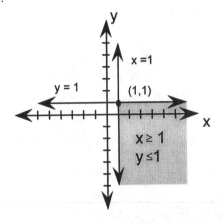

15.

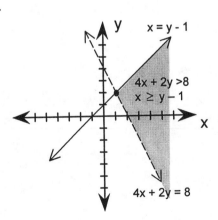

17.

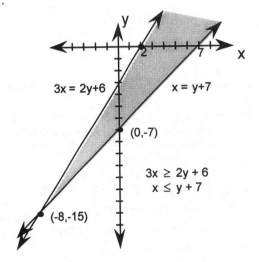

19. a) $x + y < 500$
    $x \geq 150$
    $y \geq 150$

    b)
    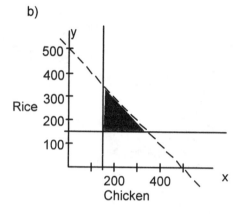

    c) (220, 220) means 220 calories of chicken and 220 calories of rice, or approx. 3.7 oz. of chicken and 8.8 oz. of rice.

21. a) No, if the lines are parallel there may not be a solution to the system.
    b) Example: $y \geq x$
    $y \leq x - 2$
    This system has no solution.

    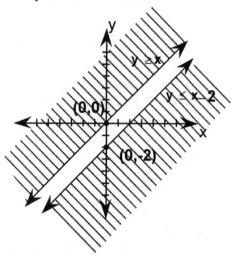

23. No. Every line divides the plane into two halves only one of which can be part of the solution. Therefore, the points in the other half cannot satisfy both inequalities and so do not solve the system.
    Example: $y \geq x$
    $x \geq 2$

    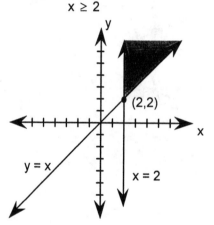

Exercise Set 7.6

1. Constraints are restrictions that are represented as linear inequalities.
3. Vertices.
5. If a linear equation of the form $K = Ax + By$ is evaluated at each point in a closed polygonal region, the maximum and minimum values of the equation occur at a corner.

7. At (0, 0), $K = 3(0) + 4(0) = 0$
   At (0, 4), $K = 3(0) + 4(4) = 16$
   At (2, 3), $K = 3(2) + 4(3) = 18$
   At (5, 0), $K = 3(5) + 4(0) = 15$

   The maximum value is 18 at (2, 3);
   minimum value is 0 at (0, 0).

9. a)

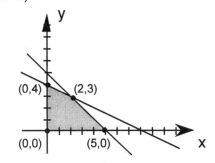

b) P = 3x + 5y
    At (0,0), P = 3(0) + 5(0) = 0
    At (0,4), P = 3(0) + 5(4) = 20
    At (2,3), P = 3(2) + 5(3) = 21
    At (5,0), P = 3(5) + 5(0) = 15
    Max. profit is 21 at (2,3)
    Min. profit is 0 at (0,0)

13. a)

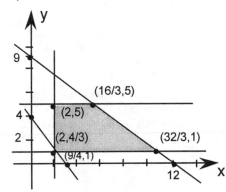

b) P = 2.20x + 1.65y
    At (2,4/3), P= 2.20(2)+1.65(4/3) = 6.60
    At (2,5), P= 2.20(2)+1.65(5) = 12.65
    At (16/3,5), P=2.20(16/3)+1.65(5) = 19.98
    At (32/3,1), P=2.20(32/3)+1.65(1) = 25.12
    At (9/4,1), P=2.20(9/4)+1.65(1) = 6.60
    Max. profit is 25.12 at (32/3,1)
    Min. profit is 6.60 at (2,4/3), (9/4,1)

11. a)

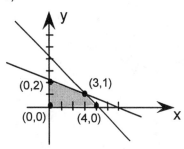

b) P = 7x + 6y
    At (0,0), P = 7(0) + 6(0) = 0
    At (0,2), P = 7(0) + 6(2) = 12
    At (3,1), P = 7(3) + 6(1) = 27
    At (4,0), P = 7(4) + 6(0) = 28
    Max. profit is 28 at (4,0)
    Min. profit is 0 at (0,0)

15. a) Let x = number of skateboards
         y = number of in-line skates
         x + y ≤ 20
         x ≥ 3
         x ≤ 6
         y ≥ 2
    b) P = 25x + 20y
    c)

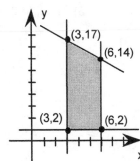

    d) (3,2) (3,17) (6,14) (6,2)
    e) At (3,2), P = 25(3) + 20(2) = 115
        At (3,17), P = 25(3) + 20(17) = 415
        At (6,14), P = 25(6) + 20(14) = 430
        At (6,2), P = 25(6) + 20(2) = 190
        Six skateboards and 14 pairs of in-line skates.
    f) Max. profit = $430.

17. a) Let x = no. of cups of Trimfit.
       y = no. of cups of Usave.
    constraints: $60x + 50y \geq 300$ cal.
                 $8x + 20y \geq 80$ A
                 $6x + 30y \geq 90$ C

    b) $C = 0.25x + 0.32y$

    c)

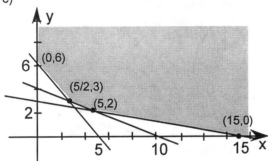

    d) (0,6), (5/2,3), (5,2) (15,0)

    e) $C = .25x + .32y$
       At (0,6) $C = .25(0) + .32(6) = 1.92$
       At (5/2,3) $C = .25(5/2) + .32(3) = 1.59$
       At (5,2) $C = .25(5) + .32(2) = 1.89$
       At (15,0) $C = .25(15) + .32(0) = 3.75$
       2.5 cups of Trimfit and 3 cups of Usave.

    f) Min. cost is $1.59

19. Let x = no. of 4-cylinder engines
       y = no. of 6 cylinder engines
    The vertices are: (0,0), (0,8), (2,7), (6,3), (8,0).
    $P = 150x + 250y$
    Max. profit is $2050 at (2,7)

    constraints: $x \geq 0$, $y \geq 0$
                  $x + y \leq 9$ for cleaning
                  $3x + 2y \leq 24$ for testing
                  $5x + 10y \leq 80$ for overhauling

Review Exercises

1.

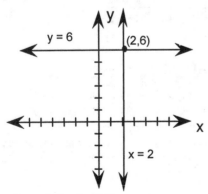

The solution is (2,6).

2.

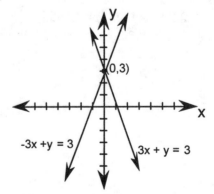

The solution is (0,3).

3.

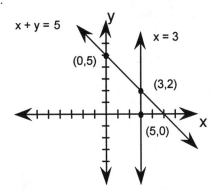

x + y = 5   x = 3
(0,5)
(3,2)
(5,0)

The solution is (3,2).

5. y = (2/3)x + 5
y = (2/3)x + 5
Same slope and y-intercept.
Infinitely many solutions.

7. 6y − 2x = 20 becomes y = (1/3)x + 10/3
4y + 2x = 10 becomes y = − (1/2)x + 5/2
Different slopes. One solution.

9. x − 2y = 1
2x + y = 7
Solve the first equation for x.
x = 2y + 1
Substitute (2y + 1) in place of x in the second equation.
$$2(2y + 1) + y = 7 \quad (\text{solve for } y)$$
$$4y + 2 + y = 7$$
$$5y + 2 = 7$$
$$5y = 5$$
$$y = 1$$
Substitute 1 in place of y in the equation
x = 2y + 1.
x = 2(1) + 1 = 2 + 1 = 3
The solution is (3,1).

11. 2x − y = 4
3x − y = 2
Solve for y in the first equation.
$$2x − 2x − y = − 2x + 4$$
$$− y = − 2x + 4$$
$$y = 2x − 4$$
Substitute 2x − 4 in place of y in the second equation.
$$3x − (2x − 4) = 2 \quad (\text{solve for } x)$$
$$3x − 2x + 4 = 2$$
$$x + 4 = 2$$
$$x = −2$$
Substitute − 2 in place of x in the equation
y = 2x − 4.
y = 2(− 2) − 4 = − 4 − 4 = −8
The solution is (− 2, − 8).

4.

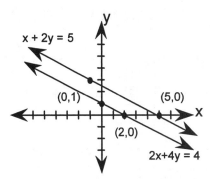

x + 2y = 5
(0,1)   (5,0)
(2,0)
2x+4y = 4

Inconsistent

6. y = (2/3)x + 5
y = (2/3)x − 8/3
Same slope but different
y-intercepts. No solution.

8. y = (1/2)x − 2
y = 2x + 6
Different slopes. One solution.

10. x + 2y = − 11
y = 2x − 3
Substitute (2x − 3) in place of y in the first equation.
$$x + 2(2x − 3) = − 11 \quad (\text{solve for } x)$$
$$x + 4x − 6 = − 11$$
$$5x − 6 = − 11$$
$$5x = − 5$$
$$x = − 1$$
Substitute (− 1) in place of x in the second equation.
y = 2(− 1) − 3 = − 2− 3 = − 5
The solution is (− 1,− 5).

12. 3x + y = 1
3y = − 9x − 4
Solve the first equation for y.
y = − 3x + 1
Substitute (− 3x + 1) in place of y in the second equation.
$$3(− 3x + 1) = − 9x − 4 \quad (\text{solve for } x)$$
$$− 9x + 3 = − 9x − 4$$
$$3 = − 4 \quad \text{False}$$
Since 3 does not equal − 4 we can conclude that there is no solution to this system. The equations are inconsistent.

13.
$$(1) \quad -x + \ y \ = 12$$
$$(2) \quad \underline{x + 2y \ = -3} \ \text{(add)}$$
$$3y \ = 9$$
$$y \ = 3$$
Substitute 3 in place of y in the first equation.
$$-x + 3 \ = 12$$
$$-x \ = 9$$
$$x \ = -9$$
The solution is (– 9,3).

14.
$$(1) \quad 2x + y = 2$$
$$(2) \quad \underline{-3x - y = 5} \ \text{(add)}$$
$$-x = 7$$
$$x = -7$$
Substitute (– 7) in place of x in the first equation.
$$2(-7) + y \ = 2$$
$$-14 + y \ = 2$$
$$y \ = 16$$
The solution is (– 7, 16).

15.
$$(1) \ x + y \ = 2$$
$$(2) \ x + 3y \ = -2$$
Multiply the first equation by –1.
$$-x - y \ = -2$$
$$\underline{x + 3y \ = -2} \ \text{(add)}$$
$$2y \ = -4$$
$$y \ = -2$$
Substitute (–2) for y in equation (2).
$$x + 3(-2) \ = -2$$
$$x - 6 \ = -2$$
$$x \ = 4$$
The solution is (4,–2).

16.
$$(1) \ 3x + 4y \ = 6$$
$$(2) \ 2x - 3y \ = 4$$
Multiply the first equation by 2, and the second equation by – 3.
$$6x + 8y \ = 12$$
$$\underline{-6x + 9y \ = -12} \ \text{(add)}$$
$$17y \ = 0$$
$$y \ = 0$$
Substitute 0 for y in the first equation.
$$3x + 4(0) \ = 6$$
$$3x \ = 6 \ \text{or} \ x = 2$$
The solution is (2,0).

17.
$$(1) \ 3x + 5y \ = 15$$
$$(2) \ 2x + 4y \ = 0$$
Multiply the first equation by 2, and the second equation by (– 3).
$$6x + 10y \ = 30$$
$$\underline{-6x - 12y \ = 0} \ \text{(add)}$$
$$-2y \ = 30$$
$$y \ = -15$$
Substitute (– 15) for y in the second equation.
$$2x + 4(-15) \ = 0$$
$$2x - 60 \ = 0$$
$$2x \ = 60 \ \text{or} \ x = 30$$
The solution is (30,– 15).

18.
$$3x + \ y \ = \ 6$$
$$-6x - 2y \ = -12$$
Multiply the first equation by 2.
$$6x + 2y \ = \ 12$$
$$\underline{6x - 2y \ = -12} \ \text{(add)}$$
$$0 \ = 0$$
The system of equations is dependent.

19. $A + B = \begin{bmatrix} 1 & -3 \\ 2 & 4 \end{bmatrix} + \begin{bmatrix} -2 & -5 \\ 6 & 3 \end{bmatrix} = \begin{bmatrix} 1+(-2) & -3+(-5) \\ 2+6 & 4+3 \end{bmatrix} = \begin{bmatrix} -1 & -8 \\ 8 & 7 \end{bmatrix}$

20. $A - B = \begin{bmatrix} 1 & -3 \\ 2 & 4 \end{bmatrix} - \begin{bmatrix} -2 & -5 \\ 6 & 3 \end{bmatrix} = \begin{bmatrix} 1-(-2) & -3-(-5) \\ 2-6 & 4-3 \end{bmatrix} = \begin{bmatrix} 3 & 2 \\ -4 & 1 \end{bmatrix}$

21. $2A = 2\begin{bmatrix} 1 & -3 \\ 2 & 4 \end{bmatrix} = \begin{bmatrix} 2(1) & 2(-3) \\ 2(2) & 2(4) \end{bmatrix} = \begin{bmatrix} 2 & -6 \\ 4 & 8 \end{bmatrix}$

22. $3A - 2B = 3\begin{bmatrix} 1 & -3 \\ 2 & 4 \end{bmatrix} - 2\begin{bmatrix} -2 & -5 \\ 6 & 3 \end{bmatrix} = \begin{bmatrix} 3 & -9 \\ 6 & 12 \end{bmatrix} - \begin{bmatrix} -4 & -10 \\ 12 & 6 \end{bmatrix} = \begin{bmatrix} 3-(-4) & -9-(-10) \\ 6-12 & 12-6 \end{bmatrix} = \begin{bmatrix} 7 & 1 \\ -6 & 6 \end{bmatrix}$

23. $A \times B = \begin{bmatrix} 1 & -3 \\ 2 & 4 \end{bmatrix} \times \begin{bmatrix} -2 & -5 \\ 6 & 3 \end{bmatrix} = \begin{bmatrix} 1(-2)+(-3)6 & 1(-5)+(-3)3 \\ 2(-2)+4(6) & 2(-5)+4(3) \end{bmatrix} = \begin{bmatrix} -20 & -14 \\ 20 & 2 \end{bmatrix}$

24. $B \times A = \begin{bmatrix} -2 & -5 \\ 6 & 3 \end{bmatrix} \times \begin{bmatrix} 1 & -3 \\ 2 & 4 \end{bmatrix} = \begin{bmatrix} (-2)1+(-5)2 & (-2)(-3)+(-5)4 \\ 6(1)+3(2) & 6(-3)+3(4) \end{bmatrix} = \begin{bmatrix} -12 & -14 \\ 12 & -6 \end{bmatrix}$

25. $\begin{bmatrix} 1 & 2 & | & 4 \\ 1 & 1 & | & 2 \end{bmatrix} \begin{matrix} = \\ (r_2 - r_1) \end{matrix} \begin{bmatrix} 1 & 2 & | & 4 \\ 0 & -1 & | & -2 \end{bmatrix} \begin{matrix} (r_1 - 2r_2) \\ (-1)r_2 \end{matrix} = \begin{bmatrix} 1 & 0 & | & 0 \\ 0 & 1 & | & 2 \end{bmatrix}$ The solution is (0, 2).

26. $\begin{bmatrix} -1 & 1 & | & 4 \\ 1 & 2 & | & 2 \end{bmatrix} = \begin{bmatrix} 1 & -1 & | & -4 \\ 0 & 3 & | & 6 \end{bmatrix} = \begin{bmatrix} 1 & 0 & | & -2 \\ 0 & 1 & | & 2 \end{bmatrix}$ The solution is (– 2, 2).

27. $\begin{bmatrix} 2 & 1 & | & 3 \\ 3 & -1 & | & 12 \end{bmatrix} \begin{matrix} (r_1 \div 2) \\ = \end{matrix} \begin{bmatrix} 1 & \frac{1}{2} & | & \frac{3}{2} \\ 3 & -1 & | & 12 \end{bmatrix} \begin{matrix} = \\ (r_2 - 3r_1) \end{matrix} \begin{bmatrix} 1 & \frac{1}{2} & | & \frac{3}{2} \\ 0 & -\frac{5}{2} & | & \frac{15}{2} \end{bmatrix} \begin{matrix} \\ (-\frac{2}{5}r_2) \end{matrix} \begin{bmatrix} 1 & \frac{1}{2} & | & \frac{3}{2} \\ 0 & 1 & | & -3 \end{bmatrix} \begin{matrix} (-\frac{1}{2}r_2 + r_1) \\ = \end{matrix} \begin{bmatrix} 1 & 0 & | & 3 \\ 0 & 1 & | & -3 \end{bmatrix}$

The solution is (3,– 3).

28. $\begin{bmatrix} 2 & 3 & | & 2 \\ 4 & -9 & | & 4 \end{bmatrix} = \begin{bmatrix} 1 & \frac{3}{2} & | & 1 \\ 0 & -15 & | & 0 \end{bmatrix} = \begin{bmatrix} 1 & \frac{3}{2} & | & 1 \\ 0 & 1 & | & 0 \end{bmatrix} = \begin{bmatrix} 1 & 0 & | & 1 \\ 0 & 1 & | & 0 \end{bmatrix}$ The solution is (1,0)

29. $\begin{bmatrix} 1 & 3 & | & 3 \\ 3 & -2 & | & 2 \end{bmatrix} = \begin{bmatrix} 1 & 3 & | & 3 \\ 0 & -11 & | & -7 \end{bmatrix} = \begin{bmatrix} 1 & 3 & | & 3 \\ 0 & 1 & | & \frac{7}{11} \end{bmatrix} = \begin{bmatrix} 1 & 0 & | & \frac{12}{11} \\ 0 & 1 & | & \frac{7}{11} \end{bmatrix}$ The solution is $\left(\dfrac{12}{11}, \dfrac{7}{11} \right)$

30. $\begin{bmatrix} 3 & -6 & | & 3 \\ 4 & 5 & | & 17 \end{bmatrix} = \begin{bmatrix} 1 & -2 & | & 1 \\ 0 & 13 & | & 13 \end{bmatrix} = \begin{bmatrix} 1 & -2 & | & 1 \\ 0 & 1 & | & 1 \end{bmatrix} = \begin{bmatrix} 1 & 0 & | & 3 \\ 0 & 1 & | & 1 \end{bmatrix}$ The solution is (3,1)

31. a) Let C = total cost for parking
      x = number of additional hours
      All-Day: C = 5 + 0.50x
      Sav-A-Lot: C = 4.25 + 0.75x
        5 + 0.50x = 4.25 + 0.75x
            0.75 = 0.25x
              3 = x
    The total cost will be the same after 3 additional hours or 4 hours total.
    b) After 5 hours or x = 4 additional hours:
        All-Day: C = 5 + 0.50(4) = $7.00
        Sav-A-Lot: C = 4.25 + 0.75(4) = $7.25
    All-Day would be less expensive.

32. Let s = liters of 80% acid solution
      let w = liters of 50% acid solution
                    s + w = 100
          0.80s + 0.50w = 100(0.75)
          0.80s + 0.50w = 75
                      s = 100 – w
      0.80(100 – w) + 0.50w = 75
        80 – 0.80w + 0.50w = 75
                  – 0.30w = – 5
      w = – 5/(– 0.30) = 16 2/3 liters
      s = 100 – 16 2/3 = 83 1/3 liters

33. Let s = salary
    r = commission rate
    (1) s + 4000r = 660
    (2) s + 6000r = 740 (subtract 1 from 2)
          2000r = 80
              r = 80/2000
              r = 0.04
Substitute 0.04 for r in eq. 1.
s = 660 − 4000(.04)
s = 500
His salary is 500 per week and his commission rate is 4%.

34. Let x = number of quarters
    let y = number of dimes
          x + y = 40
          .25x + .10y = 5.50
Solve the first equation for y.
y = 40 − x
Substitute (40 − x) in place of y in the second equation.
.25x + .10(40 − x) = 5.50
.25x + 4.00 − .10x = 5.50
    .15x + 4.00 = 5.50
        .15x = 1.50 or x = 10
Substitute 10 in place of x in the equation
y = 40 − x.
y = 40 − 10 = 30
Cheryl has 10 quarters and 30 dimes.

35. Let c = total cost
    x = no. of months to operate
a) model 1600A: c = 950 + 32x
   model 6070B: c = 1275 + 22x
        950 + 32x = 1275 + 22x
            10x = 325
              x = 32.5 months
After 32.5 months of operation the total cost of the units will be equal.

b) After 32.5 months or 2.7 years, the most cost effective unit is the unit with the lower per month to operate cost. Thus model 6070B is the better deal in the long run.

36.

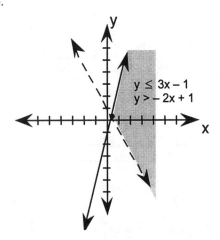

$y \leq 3x - 1$
$y > -2x + 1$

37.

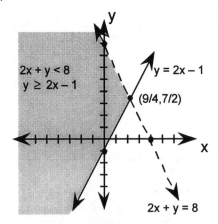

$2x + y < 8$
$y \geq 2x - 1$

$y = 2x - 1$

(9/4, 7/2)

$2x + y = 8$

38.

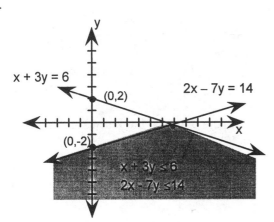

40. P = 6x + 5y
At (0,0), P = 6(0) + 5(0) = 0
At (0,10), P = 6(0) + 5(10) = 50
At (9,0), P = 6(9) + 5(0) = 54

The maximum profit is $54 at (9,0).

39.

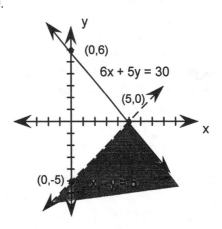

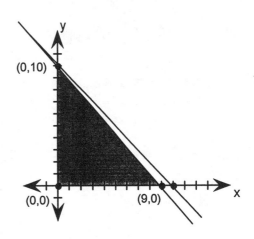

Chapter Test

1. If the lines do not intersect (parallel) the system of equations is inconsistent. The system of equations is consistent if the lines intersect only once. If both equations represent the same line then the system of equations is dependent.

2.

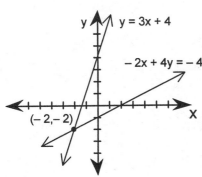

The solution is (− 2,− 2).

3. Write each equation in slope intercept form, then compare slopes and intercepts.

4x + 5y = 6	− 3x + 5y = 13
5y = − 4x + 6	5y = 3x + 13
y = − (4/5)x + 6/5	y = (3/5)x + 13/5

The slopes are different so there is only one solution.

4.
$$x - y = 5$$
$$2x + 3y = -5$$
Solve the first equation for x.
$$x = y + 5$$
Substitute $(y + 5)$ for x in the second equation.
$$2(y + 5) + 3y = -5 \text{ (solve for y)}$$
$$2y + 10 + 3y = -5$$
$$5y + 10 = -5$$
$$5y = -15$$
$$y = -3$$
Substitute (-3) for y in the equation $x = y + 5$.
$$x = -3 + 5 = 2$$
The solution is $(2, -3)$.

5.
$$y = 4x + 6$$
$$y = 2x + 18$$
Substitute $(4x + 6)$ in place of y in the second equation.
$$4x + 6 = 2x + 18 \text{ (solve for x)}$$
$$2x = 12$$
$$x = 6$$
Substitute 6 for x in the first equation.
$$y = 4(6) + 6 = 24 + 6 = 30$$
The solution is $(6, 30)$.

6.
$$x - y = 4$$
$$\underline{2x + y = 5} \text{ (add)}$$
$$3x = 9$$
$$x = 3$$
Substitute 3 for x in the 2nd equation.
$$2(3) + y = 5$$
$$6 + y = 5$$
$$y = -1$$
The solution is $(3, -1)$.

7.
$$4x + 3y = 5$$
$$2x + 4y = 10$$
Multiply the second equation by (-2).
$$4x + 3y = 5$$
$$\underline{-4x - 8y = -20} \text{ (add)}$$
$$-5y = -15$$
$$y = 3$$
Substitute 3 for y in the first equation.
$$4x + 3(3) = 5$$
$$4x + 9 = 5$$
$$4x = -4 \text{ or } x = -1$$
The solution is $(-1, 3)$.

8.
$$2x + 3y = 4$$
$$6x + 4y = 7$$
Multiply the first equation by -3.
$$-6x - 9y = -12$$
$$\underline{6x + 4y = 7}$$
$$-5y = -5$$
$$y = 1$$
Substitute 1 for y in the first equation.
$$2x + 3(1) = 4 \text{ (solve for x)}$$
$$2x = 1$$
$$x = 1/2$$
The solution is $(1/2, 1)$.

9.
$$\left. \begin{array}{l} x + 3y = 4 \\ 5x + 7y = 4 \end{array} \right\} \begin{bmatrix} 1 & 3 & | & 4 \\ 5 & 7 & | & 4 \end{bmatrix} \underset{(-5r_1 + r_2)}{=} \begin{bmatrix} 1 & 3 & | & 4 \\ 0 & -8 & | & -16 \end{bmatrix} \underset{(r_2 \div (-8))}{=} \begin{bmatrix} 1 & 3 & | & 4 \\ 0 & 1 & | & 2 \end{bmatrix} \underset{=}{(r_1 - 3r_2)} \begin{bmatrix} 1 & 0 & | & -2 \\ 0 & 1 & | & 2 \end{bmatrix}$$
The solution is $(-2, 2)$.

10. $A + B = \begin{bmatrix} 2 & -5 \\ 4 & 6 \end{bmatrix} + \begin{bmatrix} -1 & 3 \\ 2 & 5 \end{bmatrix} = \begin{bmatrix} 2 + (-1) & -5 + 3 \\ 4 + 2 & 6 + 5 \end{bmatrix} = \begin{bmatrix} 1 & -2 \\ 6 & 11 \end{bmatrix}$

11. $3A - B = 3\begin{bmatrix} 2 & -5 \\ 4 & 6 \end{bmatrix} - \begin{bmatrix} -1 & 3 \\ 2 & 5 \end{bmatrix} = \begin{bmatrix} 3(2) - (-1) & 3(-5) - 3 \\ 3(4) - 2 & 3(6) - 5 \end{bmatrix} = \begin{bmatrix} 7 & -18 \\ 10 & 13 \end{bmatrix}$

12. $A \times B = \begin{bmatrix} 2 & -5 \\ 4 & 6 \end{bmatrix} \times \begin{bmatrix} -1 & 3 \\ 2 & 5 \end{bmatrix} = \begin{bmatrix} 2(-1) + (-5)(2) & 2(3) + (-5)(5) \\ 4(-1) + (6)(2) & 4(3) + (6)(5) \end{bmatrix} = \begin{bmatrix} -12 & -19 \\ 8 & 42 \end{bmatrix}$

13.

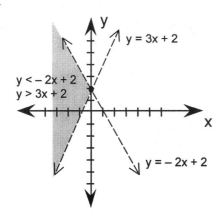

$y = 3x + 2$

$y < -2x + 2$
$y > 3x + 2$

$y = -2x + 2$

14. Let x = lb of $6.00 coffee
    let y = lb of $7.50 coffee
    x + y = 30
    6x + 7.5y = 7.00(30)
    Solve the first equation for y.
    y = 30 − x
    Substitute (30 − x) for y in the second equation.
    $\quad\quad 6x + 7.5(30 - x) \ = 210$
    $\quad\quad 6x + 225 - 7.5x \ = 210$
    $\quad\quad\quad\quad\quad -1.5x \ = -15$
    $\quad\quad\quad\quad\quad\quad\ \ x \ = 10$
    Substitute 10 for x in the equation y = 30 − x.
    y = 30 − 10 = 20
    Mix 10 lb of the $6.00 coffee with 20 lb of the $7.50 coffee.

15. Let x = no. of one bedroom units
    let y = no. of two bedroom units
    x + y = 20
    425x + 500y = 9100
    Solve the first equation for x.
    x = 20 − y
    Substitute (20 − y) for x in the second equation.
    $\quad 425(20 - y) + 500y \ = 9100$
    $\quad\quad\quad\quad\quad\quad\ \ 75y \ = 600$
    $\quad\quad\quad\quad\quad\quad\quad\ \ y \ = 8$
    Substitute 8 for y in the first equation.
    $\quad\quad\quad\quad x + 8 \ = 20$
    $\quad\quad\quad\quad\quad\ \ x \ = 12$
    The building has 12 one bedroom and 8 two bedroom apartments.

16. a)

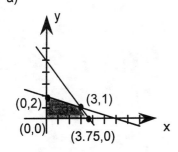

(0,2)
(0,0)
(3,1)
(3.75,0)

b) P = 2x + 3y
    At (0,0) P = 2(0) + 3(0) = 0
    At (0,2) P = 2(0) + 3(2) = 6
    At (3,1) P = 2(3) + 3(1) = 9
    At (3.75,0) P = 2(3.75) + 3(0) = 7.50
    Max. is 9 at (3,1)
    Min. is 0 at (0,0)

CHAPTER EIGHT

THE METRIC SYSTEM

Exercise Set 8.1

1. The metric system.

3. It is the worldwide accepted standard of measurement. There is only 1 basic unit of measurement for each quantity. It is based on the number 10 which makes many calculations easier.

5. a) Move the decimal point one place for each change in unit of measure.

   b) $497.2 \text{ cm} = \dfrac{497.2}{100} \text{ m} = 4.972 \text{ m} = \dfrac{4.972}{1000} \text{ km} = 0.004972 \text{ km}$

   c) $30.8 \text{ hm} = (30.8)(1000) \text{ dm} = 30800 \text{ dm}$

7. Student activity

9. a) 100 times greater   b) 1 dam = 100 dm   c) 1dm = 0.01 dam

11. 2 pounds   13. 5 grams   15. b   17. d

19. e   21. decigram   23. gram   25. dekaliter

27. centimeter   29. degree Celsius

31. a) 10 liters   b) $\dfrac{1}{100}$ liter   c) $\dfrac{1}{1000}$ liter

   d) $\dfrac{1}{10}$ liter   e) 1000 liters   f) 100 liters

33. mg, 0.001 g   35. dg, 0.1 g   37. hg, 100 g

39. Max. load 320 kg = (320 × 1,000) g = 320 000 g

41. 9 m = (9 × 100) cm = 900 cm

43. 15.7 hg = (15.7 × 100) g = 1 570 g

45. 242.6 cm = (242.6)(0.0001) hm = 0.02426 hm   47. 974 g = (974)(0.01) hg = 9.74 hg

49. 1.34 hm = (1.34)(10000) cm = 13 400 cm   51. 8.3 m = 830 cm

53. 895 l = 895 000 ml   55. 130 cm = 0.013 hm

57. 8 472 ml = 0.8472 dal

59. 514 hm = 51400 m; 62 km = 62 000 m   61. 420 cl = 4.3 l; 0.045 kl = 45 l
    680 m, 514 hm, 62 km   420 cl, 4.3 l, 0.045 kl

63. 0.032 kl = 32 l;   460 dl = 46 l;   48 000 cl = 480 l
     0.032 kl, 460 dl, 48 000 cl

65. The side with the 5 kg weight would go down.   5 kg = 5(2.2 lbs.) = 11 lbs.
67. The pump that removes 1 dal of water per min. 1 dekaliter is more than 1 deciliter.

69. a) Perimeter= 2l + 2w= 2(74) + 2(99)= 346 cm   b) 346 cm = (346 × 1000) mm = 346 000 mm

71. a) 14 × 250 mg = 3 500 mg per week   b) 3 500 mg = 3.5 g

73. a) $\dfrac{1200 \text{ km}}{187 \text{ l}}$ = 6.417 km/l   b) 6.417 km/l = 6 417 m/l

75. 3 × 2 l = 6 l of soda;   6 l = 6000 ml; $\dfrac{6000}{12}$ = 500 ml per person

77. $0.96 per l × 24.3 l = $23.33
79. 1000 meters
81. 1×10^{24} picoliters
83. 288 mg = 0.288 g, 0.8 ÷ 0.288 = 2.8 cups
85. 1.6 mg = 0.0016 g, 0.8 ÷ 0.016 = 500, 500 × 49 = 24500 g

87. 9 dam   89. 4 dm   91. 2 dam

Exercise Set 8.2

1. length   3. area   5. volume   7. volume
9. area   11. volume   13. answers will vary   15. answers will vary
17. answers will vary   19. A cubic decimeter   21. cubic centimeter   23. 2.5 acres
25. meters or cm   27. kilometers   29. centimeters   31. millimeters
33. centimeters   35. cm or mm   37. student activity   39. (a)
41. (a)   43. (b)   45. (c)   47. student activity
49. student activity   51. student activity   53. cm or km   55. meter
57. centimeter   59. square meters

61. square millimeters or square centimeters
63. square meters or hectares
65. square millimeters or square centimeters
67. square centimeters

69. (a)   71. (a)   73. (c)   75. (a)
77. student activity   79. student activity   81. student activity   83. kiloliters
85. milliliters   87. liters or milliliters   89. cubic meters   91. liters
93. (c)   95. (c)   97. (b)   99. (b)
101. b) v = 2 × 1.5 × 0.25 = 0.75 m³   103. b) v = $\pi r^2 h$ ≈ 3.14 × (0.5)² × 10 = 7.85 cm³
105. long side = 4 cm, short side = 1.8 cm,   107. A = l • w;
      height = 1.5 cm;   matted area = total area – picture area
      P = sum of all sides = 4+4+1.8+1.8 = 11.6 cm   = (82 × 62) – (50 × 42)
      A = base × height = 4 × 1.5 = 6 cm²   = 5084 – 2100 = 2984 cm²

109. a) $A = l \cdot w = 1.4 \times 3.75 = 5.25$ km^2
     b) $5.25 \times 100 = 525$ ha

111. a) $V = lwh$, $l = 18$ m, $w = 10$ m , $h = 2.5$ m,
     $V = (18)(10)(2.5) = 450$ m^3
     b) 450 m$^3 = 450$ kl

113. Total Surface Area of 4 walls = $2lh + 2wh = 2(20)(6) + 2(12)(6) = 384$ m^2

Liters for first coat = $(384 \text{ m}^2)(\dfrac{1 \text{ l}}{10 \text{ m}^2}) = 38.4$ l

Liters for second coat = $(384 \text{ m}^2)(\dfrac{1 \text{ l}}{15 \text{ m}^2}) = 25.6$ l

Total liters = $38.4 + 25.6 = 64$ l
Total cost = $(64)(\$4.75) = \$304$

115. $100^2 = 10,000$ times larger

117. $10^3 = 1000$ times larger

119. $1\ 000\ 000$ mm^2

121. 100 hm^2

123. $10\ 000$ mm^2

125. $1\ 000\ 000$ cm^3

127. 620 l

129. 76 m^3

131. 6.7 kl $= 6.7$ m$^3 = (6.7 \times 10^3)$ dm$^3 = 6\ 700$ dm^3

133. a) 1 sq mi $= 1$ mi$^2 \times (5280)^2 \dfrac{ft^2}{mi^2} = 27{,}878{,}400$ ft^2

$27{,}878{,}400$ ft$^2 \times (12)^2 \dfrac{in^2}{ft^2} = 4{,}014{,}489{,}600$ in^2

b) It is easier to convert in the metric system because it is a base 10 system.

Exercise Set 8.3

1. kilogram
3. 5 g
5. approx. 35° C
7. Answers will vary
9. kilograms or grams
11. grams
13. grams
15. metric tonnes
17. grams
19. (b)
21. (c)
23. (b)
25. Answers will vary
27. Answers will vary
29. (c)
31. (b)
33. (b)
35. (c)

37. $F = \dfrac{9}{5}(20) + 32 = 36 + 32 = 68^\circ$ F

39. $C = \dfrac{5}{9}(92 - 32) = \dfrac{5}{9}(60) = 33.3^\circ$ C

41. $C = \dfrac{5}{9}(350 - 32) = \dfrac{5}{9}(318) = 176.7^\circ$ C

43. $F = \dfrac{9}{5}(37) + 32 = 66.6 + 32 = 98.6^\circ$ F

45. $C = \dfrac{5}{9}(13 - 32) = \dfrac{5}{9}(-19) = -10.6^\circ$ C

47. $F = \dfrac{9}{5}(45) + 32 = 81 + 32 = 113^\circ$ F

49. $C = \dfrac{5}{9}(113 - 32) = \dfrac{5}{9}(81) = 45^\circ$ C

51. $F = \dfrac{9}{5}(22) + 32 = 39.6 + 32 = 71.6° \, F$

53. $F = \dfrac{9}{5}(15.6) + 32 = 28.1 + 32 = 60.1° \, F$

55. low: $F = \dfrac{9}{5}(17.8) + 32 = 32 + 32 = 64° \, F$

     high: $F = \dfrac{9}{5}(23.5) + 32 = 42.3 + 32 = 74.3° \, F$

57. cost = $4.5 \times 0.70 = \$3.15$

59. total mass = 45 g + 29 g + 370 ml = 45 g + 29 g + 370 g = 444 g

61. a) V = lwh, l = 16 m, w = 12 m, h = 12 m, V = 16(12)(12) = 2304 m^3

     b) 2304 m^3 = 2304 kl

     c) 2304 kl = 2304 t

63. $3.6 \, kg = 3.6 \, kg \times \dfrac{1 \, t}{1000 \, kg} = 0.0036 \, t$

65. $42.6 \, t = 42.6 \, t \times \dfrac{1000 \, kg}{1 \, t} = 42\ 600 \, kg = 42\ 600\ 000 \, g$

67. Yes, $78° \, F = \dfrac{5}{9}(78 - 32) \approx 25.6° \, C,$ not $20° \, C$

69. a) V = lwh, l = 1 yd = 3 ft, w = 15 in = 1.25 ft, h = 1.5 ft; V = (3)(1.25)(1.5) = 5.625 cubic feet

     b) $5.625 \, ft^3 \times 62.5 \dfrac{lbs}{ft^3} = 351.6 \, lb$

     c) $351.6 \, lb \times \dfrac{1 \, gal}{8.3 \, lb} = 42.4 \, gal$

Exercise Set 8.4

1. **Dimensional analysis** is a procedure used to convert from one unit of measurement to a different unit of measurement.

3. $\dfrac{60 \, seconds}{1 \, minute}$ or $\dfrac{1 \, minute}{60 \, seconds}$ because $60 \, seconds = 1 \, minute$

5. $\dfrac{1 \, lb}{0.45 \, kg}$ Since we need to eliminate kilograms, kg must appear in the denominator. Since we need to convert to pounds, lb must appear in the numerator.

7. $\dfrac{0.8 \, m^2}{1 \, yd^2}$ Since we need to eliminate square yards, yd^2 must appear in the denominator. Since we need to convert to square meters, m^2 must appear in the numerator.

9. $147 \, km = \left(147 \, km\right)\left(\dfrac{1 \, mi}{1.6 \, km}\right) = 91.875 \, mi$

11. $4.2 \, ft = \left(4.2 \, ft\right)\left(\dfrac{30 \, cm}{1 \, ft}\right)\left(\dfrac{1 \, m}{100 \, cm}\right) = 1.26 \, m$

13. $15\,yd^2 = \left(15\,yd^2\right)\left(\dfrac{0.8\,m^2}{1\,yd^2}\right) = 12\,m^2$

15. $39\,mi = \left(39\,mi\right)\left(\dfrac{1.6\,km}{1\,mi}\right) = 62.4\,km$

17. $675\,ha = \left(675\,ha\right)\left(\dfrac{1\,acre}{0.4\,ha}\right) = 1687.5\,acres$

19. $10.4\,c = \left(10.4\,c\right)\left(\dfrac{0.24\,l}{1\,c}\right) = 2.496\,l$

21. $45.6\,ml = \left(45.6\,ml\right)\left(\dfrac{1\,fl\,oz}{30\,ml}\right) = 1.52\,fl\,oz$

23. $120\,lb = \left(120\,lb\right)\left(\dfrac{0.45\,kg}{1\,lb}\right) = 54\,kg$

25. $28\,grams, 0.45\,kilogram$

27. $2.54\,centimeters, 1.6\,kilometers$

29. $5\,ft = \left(5\,ft\right)\left(\dfrac{12\,in}{1\,ft}\right)\left(\dfrac{2.54\,cm}{1\,in}\right) = 152.4\,cm$

 $2\,in = \left(2\,in\right)\left(\dfrac{2.54\,cm}{1\,in}\right) = 5.08\,cm$

 $152.4\,cm + 5.08\,cm = 157.48\,centimeters$

 $157.48\,cm = \left(157.48\,cm\right)\left(\dfrac{1\,m}{100\,cm}\right) = 1.5748 \approx 1.57\,meters$

31. $10\,yd = \left(10\,yd\right)\left(\dfrac{0.9\,m}{1\,yd}\right) = 9\,meters$

33. $505\,m = \left(505\,m\right)\left(\dfrac{1\,yd}{0.9\,m}\right) = 561.\overline{1} \approx 561.11\,yd$

35. $344\,m = \left(344\,m\right)\left(\dfrac{100\,cm}{1\,m}\right)\left(\dfrac{1\,ft}{30\,cm}\right) = 1146.\overline{6} \approx 1146.67\,ft$

37. $18\,km = \left(18\,km\right)\left(\dfrac{1\,mi}{1.6\,km}\right) = 11.25\,mi$

39. $\left(6\,yd\right)\left(9\,yd\right) = 54\,yd^2$

 $54\,yd^2 = \left(54\,yd^2\right)\left(\dfrac{0.8\,m^2}{1\,yd^2}\right) = 43.2\,m^2$

41. $70\,mi = \left(70\,mi\right)\left(\dfrac{1.6\,km}{1\,mi}\right) = 112\,kph$

43. $8\,fl\,oz = \left(8\,fl\,oz\right)\left(\dfrac{30\,ml}{1\,fl\,oz}\right) = 240\,ml$

45. $(50\,ft)(30\,ft)(8\,ft) = 12{,}000\,ft^3$

$12{,}000\,ft^3 = (12{,}000\,ft^3)\left(\dfrac{0.03\,m^3}{1\,ft^3}\right) = 360\,m^3$

47. $1\,kg = (1\,kg)\left(\dfrac{1\,lb}{0.45\,kg}\right) = 2.\overline{2}\,lb$

$\dfrac{\$1.10}{2.\overline{2}} = \$0.495\,per\,pound$

49. $34.5\,kl = (34.5\,kl)\left(\dfrac{1000\,l}{1\,kl}\right)\left(\dfrac{1\,gal}{3.8\,l}\right) = 9078.947368 \approx 9078.95\,gal$

51. **a)** $8\,stones = (8\,stones)\left(\dfrac{70\,kg}{11\,stones}\right) = 50.\overline{90} \approx 50.91\,kg$

    b) $50.\overline{90}\,kg = (50.\overline{90}\,kg)\left(\dfrac{1\,lb}{0.45\,kg}\right) = 113.\overline{13} \approx 113.13\,lb$

53. **a)** $-282\,ft = (-282\,ft)\left(\dfrac{30\,cm}{1\,ft}\right) = -8460\,cm$

    b) $-8460\,cm = (-8460\,cm)\left(\dfrac{1\,m}{100\,cm}\right) = -84.6\,m$

55. **a)** $1\,m^2 = (1\,m^2)\left(\dfrac{(3.3)^2\,ft^2}{1\,m^2}\right) = 10.89\,ft^2$

    b) $1\,m^3 = (1\,m^3)\left(\dfrac{(3.3)^3\,ft^3}{1\,m^3}\right) = 35.937\,ft^3$

57. $56\,lb = (56\,lb)\left(\dfrac{0.45\,kg}{1\,lb}\right)\left(\dfrac{1\,mg}{1\,kg}\right) = 25.2\,mg$

59. $76\,lb = (76\,lb)\left(\dfrac{0.45\,kg}{1\,lb}\right)\left(\dfrac{200\,mg}{1\,kg}\right) = 6840\,mg$

$6840\,mg = (6840\,mg)\left(\dfrac{1\,g}{1000\,mg}\right) = 6.84\,g$

61. **a)** $2\,teaspoons = (2\,teaspoons)\left(\dfrac{12.5\,mg}{1\,teaspoon}\right) = 25\,mg$

    b) $12\,fl\,oz = (12\,fl\,oz)\left(\dfrac{30\,ml}{1\,fl\,oz}\right)\left(\dfrac{12.5\,mg}{5\,ml}\right) = 900\,mg$

63. $\left(0.5\,c\right)\left(\dfrac{0.24\,l}{1\,c}\right)=0.12\,l$ graham cracker crumbs

$\left(12\,oz\right)\left(\dfrac{28\,g}{1\,oz}\right)=336\,g$ nuts

$\left(8\,oz\right)\left(\dfrac{28\,g}{1\,oz}\right)=224\,g$ chocolate pieces

$\left(\dfrac{4}{3}\,c\right)\left(\dfrac{0.24\,l}{1\,c}\right)=0.32\,l$ flaked coconut

$\left(\dfrac{4}{3}\,c\right)\left(\dfrac{0.24\,l}{1\,c}\right)=0.32\,l$ condensed milk

$\left(9\,in\right)\left(\dfrac{2.54\,cm}{1\,in}\right)\times\left(13\,in\right)\left(\dfrac{2.54\,cm}{1\,in}\right)=22.86\,cm\times33.02\,cm$ baking pan

$350°F=\dfrac{5}{9}\left(350-32\right)=176.\overline{6}\approx176.7°C$

$\left(1.5\,in\right)\left(\dfrac{2.54\,cm}{1\,in}\right)\times\left(3\,in\right)\left(\dfrac{2.54\,cm}{1\,in}\right)=3.81\,cm\times7.62\,cm$ bars

65. $\left(0.2\,mg\right)\left(\dfrac{1\,grain}{60\,mg}\right)\left(\dfrac{1\,ml}{\frac{1}{300}\,grain}\right)=1.0\,cc$ or b)

67. a) $\left(3.6\,l\right)\left(\dfrac{1000\,ml}{1\,l}\right)\left(\dfrac{1\,cm^{3}}{1\,ml}\right)=3600\,cm^{3}$

b) $\left(3600\,cm^{3}\right)\left(\dfrac{1\,in^{3}}{\left(2.54\right)^{3}\,cm^{3}}\right)=219.6854787\approx219.7\,in^{3}$

Review Exercises

1. $\dfrac{1}{100}$ of base unit

2. $1000\times$ base unit

3. $\dfrac{1}{1000}$ of base unit

4. $100\times$ base unit

5. $10\times$ base unit

6. $\dfrac{1}{10}$ of base unit

7. 80 mg = 0.080 g

8. 3.2 l = 320 cl

9. 0.197 cm = 1.97 mm

10. 1 000 000 mg = 1 kg

11. 4.62 kl = 4620 l

12. 192.6 dag = 19 260 dg

13. 2.67 kl = 2 670 000 ml
     14 630 cl = 146 300 ml
     3000 ml, 14 630 cl, 2.67 kl

14. 0.047 km = 47 m
     47 000 cm = 470 m
     0.047 km, 47 000 cm,
     4700 m

15. Centimeters

16. Kilograms or grams

17. Degrees Celsius

18. Millimeters

19. Square meters

20. Milliliters or cubic
     centimeters

21. Millimeters

22. Kilograms or tonnes

23. Kilometers

24. Liters

25. Answers will vary.

26. Answers will vary.

27. c

28. b

29. c

30. a

31. a

32. b

33. $1640\,kg = (1640\,kg)\left(\dfrac{1\,lb}{0.45\,kg}\right)\left(\dfrac{1\,T}{2000\,lb}\right)\left(\dfrac{0.9\,t}{1\,T}\right) = 1.64\,t$

34. $6.3\,t = (6.3\,t)\left(\dfrac{1\,T}{0.9\,t}\right)\left(\dfrac{2000\,lb}{1\,T}\right)\left(\dfrac{0.45\,kg}{1\,lb}\right)\left(\dfrac{1000\,g}{1\,kg}\right) = 6\,300\,000\,g$

35. $28°C = \dfrac{9}{5}(28) + 32 = 82.4°F$

36. $68°F = \dfrac{5}{9}(68 - 32) = 20°C$

37. $-6°F = \dfrac{5}{9}(-6 - 32) = -21.\overline{1} \approx -21.1°C$

38. $39°C = \dfrac{9}{5}(39) + 32 = 102.2°F$

39. $l = 4\,cm, w = 1.6\,cm$, $P = 4 + 4 + 1.6 + 1.6 = 11.2\,cm$, $A = lw = 4(1.6) = 6.4\,cm^2$

40. base $= 3.2\,cm$, height $= 2.5\,cm$, hypotenuse $= 4.1\,cm$, $P = 3.2 + 2.5 + 4.1 = 9.8\,cm$,

    $A = \dfrac{1}{2}bh = \dfrac{1}{2}(3.2)(2.5) = 4\,cm^2$

41. a) $V = lwh = (10)(4)(2) = 80\,m^3$

    b) $(80\,m^3)\left(\dfrac{1\,kl}{1\,m^3}\right)\left(\dfrac{1000\,l}{1\,kl}\right)\left(\dfrac{1\,kg}{1\,l}\right) = 80\,000\,kg$

42. a) $A = lw = 30(22) = 660\,m^2$

    b) $660\,m^2 = (660\,m^2)\left(\dfrac{1\,km^2}{(1000)^2\,m^2}\right) = 0.000\,66\,km^2$

43. a) $V = lwh = (80)(40)(30) = 96\,000\,cm^3$

    b) $96\,000\,cm^3 = (96\,000\,cm^3)\left(\dfrac{1\,m^3}{(100)^3\,cm^3}\right) = 0.096\,m^3$

    c) $96\,000\,cm^3 = (96\,000\,cm^3)\left(\dfrac{1\,ml}{1\,cm^3}\right) = 96\,000\,ml$

    d) $0.096\,m^3 = (0.096\,m^3)\left(\dfrac{1\,kl}{1\,m^3}\right) = 0.096\,kl$

44. Since $1\,km = 100 \times 1\,dam, 1\,km^2 = 100^2 \times 1\,dam^2 = 10\,000\,dam^2$. Thus 1 square kilometer is 10,000 times larger than a square dekameter.

45. $(27\,in)\left(\dfrac{2.54\,cm}{1\,in}\right) = 68.58\,cm$

46. $(105\,kg)\left(\dfrac{1\,lb}{0.45\,kg}\right) = 233.\overline{3} \approx 233.3\,lb$

47. $(83\,yd)\left(\dfrac{0.9\,m}{1\,yd}\right) = 74.7\,m$

48. $(100\,m)\left(\dfrac{1\,yd}{0.9\,m}\right) = 111.\overline{1} \approx 111.1\,yd$

49. $(45\,mi)\left(\dfrac{1.6\,km}{1\,mi}\right) = 72\,kph$

50. $(200\,lb)\left(\dfrac{0.45\,kg}{1\,lb}\right) = 90\,kg$

51. $\left(15\,gal\right)\left(\dfrac{3.8\,l}{1\,gal}\right)=57\,l$

52. $\left(40\,m^3\right)\left(\dfrac{1\,yd^3}{0.76\,m^3}\right)=52.63157895\approx52.6\,yd^3$

53. $\left(72\,lb\right)\left(\dfrac{0.45\,kg}{1\,lb}\right)=32.4\,kg$

54. $\left(4\,qt\right)\left(\dfrac{0.95\,l}{1\,qt}\right)=3.8\,l$

55. $\left(15\,yd^3\right)\left(\dfrac{0.76\,m^3}{1\,yd^3}\right)=11.4\,m^3$

56. $\left(62\,mi\right)\left(\dfrac{1.6\,km}{1\,mi}\right)=99.2\,km$

57. $\left(27\,cm\right)\left(\dfrac{1\,ft}{30\,cm}\right)=0.9\,ft$

58. $\left(3.25\,in\right)\left(\dfrac{2.54\,cm}{1\,in}\right)\left(\dfrac{10\,mm}{1\,cm}\right)=82.55\,mm$

59. a) $700\left(1.5\,kg\right)=1050\,kg$

    b) $1050\,kg=\left(1050\,kg\right)\left(\dfrac{1\,lb}{0.45\,kg}\right)=2333.\overline{3}\approx2333.3\,lb$

60. $A=lw=\left(24\right)\left(15\right)=360\,ft^2$

    $360\,ft^2=\left(360\,ft^2\right)\left(\dfrac{0.09\,m^2}{1\,ft^2}\right)=32.4\,m^2$

61. a) $\left(2.5\,hr\right)\left(\dfrac{461.6\,km}{1\,hr}\right)=1154\,km$

    b) $1154\,km=\left(1154\,km\right)\left(\dfrac{1\,mi}{1.6\,km}\right)=721.25\,mi$

62. a) $35\,mi=\left(35\,mi\right)\left(\dfrac{1.6\,km}{1\,mi}\right)=56\,kph$

    b) $56\,km=\left(56\,km\right)\left(\dfrac{1000\,m}{1\,km}\right)=56\,000\,meters\ per\ hour$

63. a) $V=lwh=\left(90\right)\left(70\right)\left(40\right)=252\,000\,cm^3$

    $252\,000\,cm^3=\left(252\,000\,cm^3\right)\left(\dfrac{1\,ml}{1\,cm^3}\right)\left(\dfrac{1\,l}{1000\,ml}\right)=252\,l$

    b) $252\,l=\left(252\,l\right)\left(\dfrac{1\,kg}{1\,l}\right)=252\,kg$

64. $1\,kg=\left(1\,kg\right)\left(\dfrac{1\,lb}{0.45\,kg}\right)=2.\overline{2}\,lb$

    $\dfrac{\$2.75}{2.\overline{2}}=\$1.2375\approx\$1.24\,per\ pound$

Chapter Test

1. $67\,km=\left(67\,km\right)\left(\dfrac{1\,000\,000\,mm}{1\,km}\right)=67\,000\,000\,mm$

2. $96\,cg = (96\,cg)\left(\dfrac{1\,hg}{10\,000\,cg}\right) = 0.0096\,hg$

3. $1\,km = (1\,km)\left(\dfrac{100\,dam}{1\,km}\right) = 100\,dam$ or 100 times greater

4. $300(6) = 1800\,m$

$1800\,m\left(\dfrac{1\,km}{1000\,m}\right) = 1.8\,km$

5. b

6. a

7. c

8. b

9. b

10. $1\,m^2 = (1\,m^2)\left(\dfrac{100^2\,cm^2}{1\,m^2}\right) = 10\,000\,cm^2$ or 10,000 times greater

11. $1\,m^3 = (1\,m^3)\left(\dfrac{1000^3\,mm^3}{1\,m^3}\right) = 1\,000\,000\,000\,mm^3$ or 1,000,000,000 times greater

12. $452\,in = (452\,in)\left(\dfrac{2.54\,cm}{1\,in}\right) = 1148.08\,cm$

13. $8\,km = (8\,km)\left(\dfrac{1\,mi}{1.6\,km}\right) = 5\,mph$

14. $50°F = \dfrac{5}{9}(50 - 32) = 10°C$

15. $50°C = \dfrac{9}{5}(50) + 32 = 122°F$

16. $12\,ft = (12\,ft)\left(\dfrac{30\,cm}{1\,ft}\right) = 360\,cm$ or $12\,ft = (12\,ft)\left(\dfrac{12\,in}{1\,ft}\right)\left(\dfrac{2.54\,cm}{1\,in}\right) = 365.76\,cm$

17. a) $V = lwh = 20(20)(8) = 3200\,m^3$

 b) $3200\,m^3 = (3200\,m^3)\left(\dfrac{1000\,l}{1\,m^3}\right) = 3\,200\,000\,l$ or $3\,200\,000\,l = (3\,200\,000\,l)\left(\dfrac{1\,kl}{1000\,l}\right) = 3200\,kl$

 c) $3\,200\,000\,l = (3\,200\,000\,l)\left(\dfrac{1\,kg}{1\,l}\right) = 3\,200\,000\,kg$

18. Total surface area: $2lh + 2wh = 2(20)(6) + 2(15)(6) = 420\,m^2$

 Liters needed for first coat: $(420\,m^2)\left(\dfrac{1\,l}{10\,m^2}\right) = 42\,l$

 Liters needed for second coat: $(420\,m^2)\left(\dfrac{1\,l}{15\,m^2}\right) = 28\,l$

 Total liters needed: $42 + 28 = 70\,l$

 Total cost: $(70\,l)\left(\dfrac{\$3.50}{1\,l}\right) = \$245$

CHAPTER NINE

GEOMETRY

Exercise Set 9.1

1. An **axiom (postulate)** is a statement accepted as being true on the basis of its "obviousness" and its relation to the physical world. A **theorem** is a statement that has been proven using undefined terms, definitions, and axioms.

3. Two lines in the same plane that do not intersect are **parallel lines**.

5. Two angles in the same plane are **adjacent angles** when they have a common vertex and a common side but no common interior points.

7. Two angles the sum of whose measures is 180° are called **supplementary angles**.

9. An angle whose measure is less than 90° is an **acute angle**.

11. An angle whose measure is 180° is a **straight angle**.

---

13. Ray $\overrightarrow{BA}$

15. Line $\overleftrightarrow{AB}$

17. Ray $\overrightarrow{AB}$

19. Half open line segment $\overline{AB}$

21. $\overleftrightarrow{EG}$

23. $\overrightarrow{AD}$

25. $\varnothing$

27. {C}

29. $\overset{\circ}{BC}$

31. $\triangle BCF$

33. $\overrightarrow{ED}$

35. $\overleftrightarrow{DE}$

37. ⊰ FBE

39. {B}

41. $\varnothing$

43. {B}

45. Straight

47. Acute

49. None of these

51. Right

53. 90° - 51° = 39°

55. $90° - 25\frac{1}{2}° = 64\frac{1}{2}°$

57. 90° - 89° = 1°

59. 180° - 76° = 104°

61. 180° - 135° = 45°

63. $180° - 99\frac{1}{5}° = 80\frac{4}{5}°$

65. b

67. f

69. a

71. Let x = measure of angle 2
7x = measure of angle 1
$$x + 7x = 90$$
$$8x = 90$$
$$x = \frac{90}{8} = 11.25°, \text{ m} \angle 2$$
$$7x = 7(11.25) = 78.75°, \text{ m} \angle 1$$

73. Let x = measure of angle 1
180 - x = measure of angle 2
$$x - (180 - x) = 74$$
$$x - 180 + x = 74$$
$$2x - 180 = 74$$
$$2x = 254$$
$$x = \frac{254}{2} = 127°, \text{ m} \angle 1$$
$$180 - x = 180 - 127 = 53°, \text{ m} \angle 2$$

75. m $\angle$ 1 + 125° = 180°
m $\angle$ 1 = 55°
m $\angle$ 2 = m $\angle$ 1 (vertical angles)
m $\angle$ 3 = 125° (vertical angles)
m $\angle$ 5 = m $\angle$ 2 (alternate interior angles)
m $\angle$ 4 = m $\angle$ 3 (alternate interior angles)
m $\angle$ 7 = m $\angle$ 4 (vertical angles)
m $\angle$ 6 = m $\angle$ 5 (vertical angles)
Measures of angles 3, 4, and 7 are each 125°.
Measures of angles 1, 2, 5, and 6 are each 55°.

77. m $\angle$ 3 + 120° = 180°
m $\angle$ 3 = 60°
m $\angle$ 4 = 120° (vertical angles)
m $\angle$ 7 = m $\angle$ 3 (vertical angles)
m $\angle$ 6 = m $\angle$ 3 (alternate interior angles)
m $\angle$ 1 = m $\angle$ 6 (vertical angles)
m $\angle$ 5 = m $\angle$ 4 (alternate exterior angles)
m $\angle$ 2 = m $\angle$ 5 (vertical angles)
Measures of angles 2, 4, and 5 are each 120°.
Measures of angles 1, 3, 6, and 7 are each 60°.

79.
$$x + 5x + 6 = 90$$
$$6x + 6 = 90$$
$$6x = 84$$
$$x = \frac{84}{6} = 14°, \text{ m} \angle 2$$
$$5x + 6 = 5(14) + 6 = 76°, \text{ m} \angle 1$$

81.
$$x + 2x - 3 = 90$$
$$3x - 3 = 90$$
$$3x = 93$$
$$x = \frac{93}{3} = 31°, \text{ m} \angle 1$$
$$2x - 3 = 2(31) - 3 = 59°, \text{ m} \angle 2$$

83.
$$x + 3x - 12 = 180$$
$$4x - 12 = 180$$
$$4x = 192$$
$$x = \frac{192}{4} = 48°, \text{ m} \angle 2$$
$$3x - 12 = 3(48) - 12 = 132°, \text{ m} \angle 1$$

85.
$$x + 5x - 18 = 180$$
$$6x - 18 = 180$$
$$6x = 198$$
$$x = \frac{198}{6} = 33°, \text{ m} \angle 1$$
$$5x - 18 = 5(33) - 18 = 147°, \text{ m} \angle 2$$

87. a) An infinite number of lines can be drawn through a given point.
   b) An infinite number of planes can be drawn through a given point.
89. An infinite number of planes can be drawn through a given line.
In exercises 91-95, there may be more than one answer.

91. Plane AGB $\cap$ plane GBC = $\overleftrightarrow{BG}$

93. Plane HGD $\cap$ plane FGD $\cap$ plane BGD = $\overleftrightarrow{GD}$

95. $\overleftrightarrow{AB} \cap$ plane ABG = $\overleftrightarrow{AB}$

97. Always true. If any two lines are parallel to a third line, then they must be parallel to each other.

99. Sometimes true. Vertical angles are only complementary when each is equal to 45°.
101. Sometimes true. Alternate interior angles are only complementary when each is equal to 45°.

103.

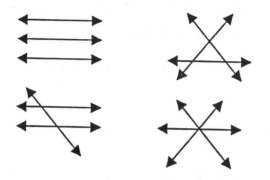

105.

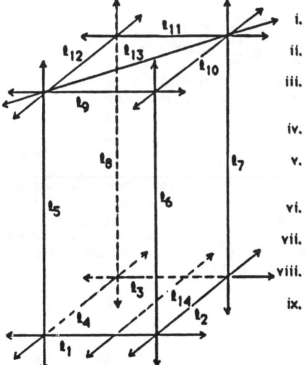

i.   Three parallel lines, two on the same plane ($\ell_1 \parallel \ell_3 \parallel \ell_9$)
ii.   Three lines on the same plane intersecting in three distinct points ($\ell_9, \ell_{10}, \ell_{13}$)
iii. Three lines in the same plane, two are $\parallel$ and the third intersects the other two ($\ell_2 \parallel \ell_4$ and ℓ_1 intersects ℓ_2 and ℓ_4)
iv.   Three lines intersect at a point, two lines on the same plane (ℓ_1, ℓ_2, ℓ_6)
v.   Two lines intersect. A 3rd line is $\parallel$ the 1st line and skewed to the 2nd. (ℓ_9 and ℓ_{10} intersect, $\ell_2 \parallel \ell_{10}$, ℓ_2 and ℓ_9 are skewed.)
vi.   Three lines that are skew to each other ($\ell_3, \ell_6, \ell_{13}$)
vii. Three $\parallel$ lines in the same plane. ($\ell_2 \parallel \ell_4 \parallel \ell_{14}$)
viii. Three lines in the same plane intersecting in a single point ($\ell_{10}, \ell_{11}, \ell_{13}$)
ix.   Two $\parallel$ lines and a third line skewed to the other two. ($\ell_6 \parallel \ell_8$ and ℓ_{13} is skewed to ℓ_6 and ℓ_8)

Exercise Set 9.2

1. A **polygon** is a closed figure in a plane determined by three or more straight line segments.
3. A **regular polygon** is one whose sides are all the same length and whose interior angles all have the same measure; other polygons may have sides of different length and interior angles with different meaures.
5. Figures that have the same shape but may be of different sizes are **similar figures**.

7. Octagon
9. Pentagon
11. Equilateral
13. Scalene
15. Isosceles
17. Right
19. Obtuse
21. Right

23. Rectangle   25. Trapezoid   27. Square

29. The measure of one angle of the triangle is 75° (by vertical angles). The measure of another angle of the triangle is 180° - 133° = 47°. The measure of the third angle of the triangle is 180° - 75° - 47° = 58°. Since angle x is a vertical angle with the 58° angle, the measure of angle x is 58°.

31. The given measure of one angle of the triangle is 35°. The measure of another angle of the triangle is 30° (by vertical angles). The measure of the third angle of the triangle is 180° - 35° - 30° = 115°. The measure of angle x is 180° - 115° = 65° (The 115° angle and angle x form a straight angle.).

33.

Angle	Measure	Reason
1	90°	∠ 1 and ∠ 7 are vertical angles
2	50°	∠ 2 and ∠ 4 are corresponding angles
3	130°	∠ 3 and ∠ 4 form a straight angle
4	50°	Vertical angle with the given 50° angle
5	50°	∠ 2 and ∠ 5 are vertical angles
6	40°	Vertical angle with the given 40° angle
7	90°	∠ 2, ∠ 6, and ∠ 7 form a straight angle
8	130°	∠ 3 and ∠ 8 are vertical angles
9	140°	∠ 9 and ∠ 10 form a straight angle
10	40°	∠ 10 and ∠ 12 are vertical angles
11	140°	∠ 9 and ∠ 11 are vertical angles
12	40°	∠ 6 and ∠ 12 are corresponding angles

35. n = 8
(8 - 2) × 180° = 6 × 180° = 1080°

37. n = 7
(7 - 2) × 180° = 5 × 180° = 900°

39. The sum of the measures of the interior angles of a quadrilateral is (4 - 2) × 180° = 2 × 180° = 360°. Dividing by 4, the number of angles, each interior angle measures 90°. Each exterior angle measures 180° - 90° = 90°.

41. The sum of the measures of the interior angles of a pentagon is (5 - 2) × 180° = 3 × 180° = 540°. Dividing by 5, the number of angles, each interior angle measures 108°. Each exterior angle measures 180° - 108° = 72°.

43. The sum of the measures of the interior angles of a heptagon is (7 - 2) × 180° = 5 × 180° = 900°. Dividing by 7, the number of angles, each interior angle measures $128\frac{4}{7}°$. Each exterior angle measures $180° - 128\frac{4}{7}° = 51\frac{3}{7}°$.

45. 180° - 125° = 55°

47. 180° - 90° - 55° = 35°

49. Let $x = A'C'$

$$\frac{A'C'}{AC} = \frac{A'B'}{AB}$$

$$\frac{x}{10} = \frac{2}{5}$$

$$5x = 20$$

$$x = 4$$

Let $y = B'C'$

$$\frac{B'C'}{BC} = \frac{A'B'}{AB}$$

$$\frac{y}{8} = \frac{2}{5}$$

$$5y = 16$$

$$y = \frac{16}{5}$$

51. Let $x = AB$

$$\frac{AB}{A'B'} = \frac{AD}{A'D'}$$

$$\frac{x}{5} = \frac{5}{12}$$

$$12x = 25$$

$$x = \frac{25}{12}$$

Let $y = C'D'$

$$\frac{C'D'}{CD} = \frac{A'D'}{AD}$$

$$\frac{y}{1} = \frac{12}{5}$$

$$5y = 12$$

$$y = \frac{12}{5}$$

53. Let $x = DC$

$$\frac{DC}{AC} = \frac{DE}{AB}$$

$$\frac{x}{10} = \frac{2}{6}$$

$$6x = 20$$

$$x = \frac{20}{6} = \frac{10}{3}$$

55. $BE = BC - EC = 6 - 2 = 4$

57. A' B' = AB = 14

59. AC = A'C' = 28

61. m ∠ ACB = m ∠ A'C'B' = 28°

63. A'B' = AB = 8

65. B'C' = BC = 16

67. m ∠ A'D'C' = m ∠ ADC = 70°

69. m ∠ x = 50°, m ∠ y = 130°

71. m ∠ w = 180° - 100° = 80°

73. m ∠ y = 180° - 80° = 100°

75. a) m ∠ CED = m ∠ ABC;
    m ∠ ACB = m ∠ DCE (vertical angles);
    m ∠ BAC = m ∠ CDE (alternate interior angles)
    b) Let $x = DE$

$$\frac{x}{AB} = \frac{CE}{BC}$$

$$\frac{x}{543} = \frac{1404}{356}$$

$$356x = 762{,}372$$

$$x \approx 2141.49 \text{ ft.}$$

77. Answers will vary.

Exercise Set 9.3

1. a) The **perimeter** of a two-dimensional figure is the sum of the lengths of the sides of the figure.
   b) The **area** of a two-dimensional figure is the region within the boundaries of the figure.
   c)

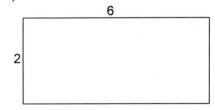

$A = lw = 6(2) = 12$ square units

$p = 2l + 2w = 2(6) + 2(2) = 12 + 4 = 16$ units

3. $A = \dfrac{1}{2}bh = \dfrac{1}{2}(10)(7) = 35\,in.^2$

5. $3\,yd. = 3(3) = 9\,ft.$

   $A = \dfrac{1}{2}bh = \dfrac{1}{2}(1)(9) = 4.5\,ft.^2 = \dfrac{4.5}{9} = 0.5\,yd.^2$

7. $A = lw = (15)(7) = 105\,ft.^2$

   $p = 2l + 2w = 2(15) + 2(7) = 44\,ft.$

9. $2\,ft. = 2(12) = 24\,in.$

   $A = \dfrac{1}{2}h(b_1 + b_2) = \dfrac{1}{2}(24)(5 + 19)$

   $\qquad = \dfrac{1}{2}(24)(24) = 288\,in.^2$

   $p = s_1 + s_2 + b_1 + b_2 = 25 + 25 + 5 + 19 = 74\,in.$

11. $A = \dfrac{1}{2}h(b_1 + b_2) = \dfrac{1}{2}(12)(6 + 16)$

    $\qquad = \dfrac{1}{2}(12)(22) = 132\,in.^2$

    $p = s_1 + s_2 + b_1 + b_2 = 13 + 13 + 6 + 16 = 48\,in.$

In exercises 13-15 and the other exercises involving π, the π key on a scientific calculator was used to determine the answers. If you use 3.14 for π, your answers may vary slightly.

13. $A = \pi r^2 = \pi(5)^2 = 25\pi \approx 78.54\,in.^2$

    $C = 2\pi r = 2\pi(5) = 10\pi \approx 31.42\,in.$

15. $r = \dfrac{7}{2} = 3.5\,ft.$

    $A = \pi r^2 = \pi(3.5)^2 = 12.25\pi \approx 38.48\,ft.^2$

    $C = 2\pi r = 2\pi(3.5) = 7\pi \approx 21.99\,ft.$

17. $c^2 = 5^2 + 12^2$

    $c^2 = 25 + 144$

    $c^2 = 169$

    $c = \sqrt{169} = 13\,ft.$

19. $b^2 + 15^2 = 39^2$

    $b^2 + 225 = 1521$

    $b^2 = 1296$

    $b = \sqrt{1296} = 36\,m.$

21. Area of square: $(10)^2 = 100\,m.^2$

    Area of circle: $\pi(5)^2 = 25\pi = 78.53981634\,m.^2$

    Shaded area:

    $100 - 78.53981634 = 21.46018366 \approx 21.46\,m^2$

23. Area of rectangle: $7(4) = 28\,ft.^2$

    Area of trapezoid: $\dfrac{1}{2}(4)(3 + 7) = \dfrac{1}{2}(4)(10) = 20\,ft.^2$

    Shaded area: $28 - 20 = 8\,ft.^2$

25. Area of circle: $\pi(5)^2 = 25\pi = 78.53981634 \, m.^2$

    Area of rectangle: $8(6) = 48 \, m.^2$

    Shaded area:

    $78.53981634 - 48 = 30.53981634 \approx 30.54 \, m.^2$

27. Area of small rectangle on the right side:

    $12(6) = 72 \, ft.^2$

    Area of semi-circle on the right side:

    $\frac{1}{2}\pi(6)^2 = 18\pi = 56.54866776 \, ft.^2$

    Area of shaded region on the right side:

    $72 - 56.54866776 = 15.45133224 \, ft.^2$

    Area of shaded region on the left side:

    $15.45133224 \, ft.^2$

    Area of triangle: $\frac{1}{2}(14)(12) = 84 \, ft.^2$

    Shaded area:

    $15.45133224 + 15.45133224 + 84 \approx 114.90 \, ft.^2$

29. $\dfrac{1}{x} = \dfrac{9}{15.2}$

    $9x = 15.2$

    $x = \dfrac{15.2}{9} \approx 1.69 \, yd.^2$

31. $\dfrac{1}{18.3} = \dfrac{9}{x}$

    $x = 18.3(9) = 164.7 \, ft.^2$

33. $\dfrac{1}{14.7} = \dfrac{10,000}{x}$

    $x = 14.7(10,000) = 147\,000 \, cm.^2$

35. $\dfrac{1}{x} = \dfrac{10,000}{608}$

    $10,000x = 608$

    $x = \dfrac{608}{10,000} = 0.0608 \, m.^2$

37. First floor: $A = 20(28) + 22(25) = 1110 \, ft.^2$

    Second floor: $A = 20(28) = 560 \, ft.^2$

    Total area: $1110 + 560 = 1670 \, ft.^2$

    Cost: $1670(\$65) = \$108,550$

39. Bedroom 1: $A = 10(20) = 200 \, ft.^2$

    Bedroom 2: $A = 10(14) = 140 \, ft.^2$

    Bedroom 3: $A = 10(14) = 140 \, ft.^2$

    Total area: $480 \, ft.^2 = \dfrac{480}{9} = 53\frac{1}{3} \approx 54 \, yd.^2$

    Cost: $\$14.95(54) = \$807.30$

41. Area of larger rectangle: $42(27) = 1134 \, ft.^2$

    Area of pool: $30(15) = 450 \, ft.^2$

    Area of deck: $1134 - 450 = 684 \, ft.^2$

43. Area of entire lawn if all grass:
    $200(100) = 20,000 \, ft.^2$

    Area of patio: $40(10) = 400 \, ft.^2$

    Area of shed: $10(8) = 80 \, ft.^2$

    Area of house: $50(25) = 1250 \, ft.^2$

    Area of drive: $30(10) = 300 \, ft.^2$

    Area of pool: $\pi(12)^2 = 144\pi = 452.3893421 \, ft.^2$

    Area of lawn:
    $20,000 - 400 - 80 - 1250 - 300 - 452.3893421$

    $= 17,517.61066 \, ft.^2 = \dfrac{17,517.61066}{9}$

    $= 1946.401184 \, yd.^2$

    Cost: $1946.401184(\$0.02) \approx \$38.93$

45. $A = 36(60) + 36(24) + \dfrac{1}{2}(24)(24)$

    $= 2160 + 864 + 288 = 3312 \, in.^2$

    $= \dfrac{3312}{36 \times 36} = \dfrac{3312}{1296} \approx 2.56 \, yd.^2$

47. $A = \dfrac{1}{2} s^2 = 72 \, cm.^2$

    $s^2 = 144 \, cm.^2$

    $s = \sqrt{144} = 12$

    The legs are each $12 \, cm.$

    The hypotenuse:

    $c^2 = 12^2 + 12^2$

    $c^2 = 144 + 144$

    $c^2 = 288$

    $c = \sqrt{288} \approx 16.97 \, cm.$

49. a) $A = s^2$

    b) $A = (2s)^2 = 4s^2$

    c) The area of the square in part b) is four times larger than the area of the square in part a).

51. a) $A = bh$

    b) $A = 2b(2h) = 4bh$

    c) The area of the parallelogram in part b) is four times larger than the area of the parallelogram in part a).

53. Area of top and bottom:

    $2\left(\pi(3)^2\right) = 18\pi = 56.54866776 \, in.^2$

    The side of the cylinder laid out flat would be a rectangle whose length is equal to the circumference of the circle and width is the height of the cylinder.

    $C = 2\pi(3) = 6\pi = 18.84955592 \, in.$

    Area of side: $7(18.84955592) \approx 131.9468915 \, in.^2$

    Total area:

    $56.54866776 + 131.9468915 \approx 188.50 \, in.^2$

55. $s = \dfrac{1}{2}(a + b + c) = \dfrac{1}{2}(8 + 6 + 10) = 12$

    $A = \sqrt{12(12-8)(12-6)(12-10)}$

    $= \sqrt{12(4)(6)(2)} = \sqrt{576} = 24 \, cm.^2$

Exercise Set 9.4

In this section we use the π key on the calculator to determine answers in calculations involving pi.
If you use 3.14 for π your answers may vary slightly.

1. **Volume** is a measure of the capacity of a figure.

3. A **polyhedron** is a closed surface formed by the union of polygonal regions. A **regular polyhedron** is one whose faces are all regular polygons of the same size and shape.

5. For any polyhedron, the number of vertices minus the number of edges plus the number of faces equals two.

7. $V = lwh = 2(2)(2) = 8\,ft.^3$

9. $2\,ft. = 2(12) = 24\,in.$

$$V = \pi r^2 h = \pi(6)^2(24) = 864\pi$$
$$= 2714.336053 \approx 2714.34\,in.^3$$

11. $V = \dfrac{1}{3}\pi r^2 h = \dfrac{1}{3}\pi(3)^2(14) = 42\pi$

$$= 131.9468915 \approx 131.95\,cm.^3$$

13. Area of the base: $B = \dfrac{1}{2}bh = \dfrac{1}{2}(8)(8) = 32\,in.^2$

$$V = Bh = 32(12) = 384\,in.^3$$

15. $r = \dfrac{13}{2} = 6.5\,cm.$

$$V = \dfrac{4}{3}\pi r^3 = \dfrac{4}{3}\pi(6.5)^3 = 366.1\overline{6}\pi$$
$$= 1150.34651 \approx 1150.35\,cm.^3$$

17. Area of the base: $B = s^2 = (11)^2 = 121\,cm.^2$

$$V = \dfrac{1}{3}Bh = \dfrac{1}{3}(121)(13) = 524.\overline{3} \approx 524.33\,cm.^3$$

19. Area of the base:

$$B = \dfrac{1}{2}h(b_1 + b_2) = \dfrac{1}{2}(5)(7+9) = 40\,in.^2$$
$$V = \dfrac{1}{3}Bh = \dfrac{1}{3}(40)(8) = 106.\overline{6} \approx 106.67\,in.^3$$

21. V = volume of rect. solid - volume of cylinder

$$= 4(4)(25) - \pi(2)^2(25) = 400 - 100\pi$$
$$= 400 - 314.1592654 = 85.84073464 \approx 85.84\,yd.^3$$

23. V = volume of rect. solid - volume of cylinder

$$= 6(4)(3) - \pi(1)^2(4) = 72 - 4\pi$$
$$= 72 - 12.56637061 = 59.43362939 \approx 59.43\,m.^3$$

25. V = vol. of large sphere - vol. of small sphere

$$= \dfrac{4}{3}\pi(6)^3 - \dfrac{4}{3}\pi(3)^3 = 288\pi - 36\pi = 252\pi$$
$$= 791.6813487 \approx 791.68\,cm.^3$$

27. V = volume of cylinder - volume of 3 spheres

$$= \pi(3.5)^2(20.8) - 3\left[\dfrac{4}{3}\pi(3.45)^3\right]$$
$$= 254.8\pi - 164.2545\pi = 90.5455\pi$$
$$= 284.4570776 \approx 284.46\,cm.^3$$

29. $5\,yd.^3 = 5(27) = 135\,ft.^3$

31. $212\,ft.^3 = \dfrac{212}{27} = 7.\overline{851} \approx 7.85\,yd.^3$

33. $2.7\,m.^3 = 2.7(1,000,000) = 2\,700\,000\,cm.^3$

35. $4\,000\,000\,cm.^3 = \dfrac{4,000,000}{1,000,000} = 4\,m.^3$

37. Tubs: $V = \pi r^2 h = \pi(3)^2(5) = 45\pi$

$$= 141.3716694 \approx 141.37\,in.^3$$

Boxes: $V = s^3 = (5)^3 = 125\,in.^3$

39. Wendy's Volume: $4(4)\left(\dfrac{3}{16}\right)=3\,in.^3$

    Magic Burger's Volume:

    $\pi\left(\dfrac{4.5}{2}\right)^2(0.25)=\pi(2.25)^2(0.25)$

    $=3.976078202\approx3.98\,in.^3$

    The Magic Burger has the greater volume by $0.98\,in.^3$

41. a) Cylinder 1:

    $V=\pi\left(\dfrac{10}{2}\right)^2(12)=300\pi=942.4777961\approx942.48\,in.^3$

    Cylinder 2:

    $V=\pi\left(\dfrac{12}{2}\right)^2(10)=360\pi=1130.973355\approx1130.97\,in.^3$

    The container with the larger diameter holds more.

    b) $1130.97-942.48=188.49\approx188.50\,in.^3$

43. a) $V=15(9)(2)=270\,m.^3$

    b) $270\,kl.$

45. $V=\pi r^2h=\pi\left(\dfrac{2.25}{2}\right)^2(3.5)=13.91627371\,in.^3$

    $2(13.91627371)=27.83254742\approx27.83\,in.^3$

47. a) $4\,in.=\dfrac{4}{12}=\dfrac{1}{3}\,ft.$

    $V=lwh=80(12.5)\left(\dfrac{1}{3}\right)=333.\overline{3}\approx333.33\,ft.^3$

    b) $333.\overline{3}\,ft.^3=\dfrac{333.\overline{3}}{27}=12.34567901\approx12.35\,yd.^3$

49. $V=\dfrac{1}{3}\pi r^2h=\dfrac{1}{3}\pi\left(\dfrac{3}{2}\right)^2(6)=4.5\pi$

    $=14.13716694\approx14.14\,in.^3$

51. a) $C=2\pi r=2\pi\left(\dfrac{19.6}{2}\right)=19.6\pi$

    $=61.57521601\approx61.58\,m.$

    b) $V=\pi r^2h=\pi\left(\dfrac{19.6}{2}\right)^2(60)=5762.4\pi$

    $=18,103.11351\approx18103.11\,m.^3$

53. $12-16+x=2$

    $-4+x=2$

    $x=6$ faces

55. $x-8+4=2$

    $x-4=2$

    $x=6$ vertices

57. $11-x+5=2$

    $16-x=2$

    $-x=-14$

    $x=14$ edges

59. Compare $V=x^3$ to $V=(2x)^3=8x^3$

    The new volume is eight times the original volume.

61. Compare $V=\dfrac{4}{3}\pi r^3$ to $V=\dfrac{4}{3}\pi(2r)^3=8\left(\dfrac{4}{3}\right)\pi r^3$

    The new volume is eight times the original volume.

63. Regular cone container: $V=\dfrac{1}{3}\pi r^2h$

    Right circular cylinder container: $V=\pi r^2h$

    Yes. The cylinder has three times the volume of the cone, but the customer is only charged twice as much.

65. Let $r =$ the radius of one of the cans of orange juice

The length of the box $= 6r$ and the width of the box $= 4r$

Volume of box - volume of cans:

$$lwh - 6(\pi r^2 h) = (6r)(4r)h - 6\pi r^2 h = 24r^2 h - 6\pi r^2 h = 6r^2 h(4 - \pi)$$

Percent of the volume of the interior of the box that is not occupied by the cans:

$$\frac{6r^2 h(4 - \pi)}{lwh} = \frac{6r^2(4 - \pi)}{(6r)(4r)} = \frac{4 - \pi}{4} = 0.2146018366 \approx 21.46\%$$

67. a) Find the volume of each numbered region. Since the length of each side is $a + b$, the sum of the volumes of each region will equal $(a + b)^3$.

   b) $V_1 = a(a)(a) = a^3$ $V_2 = a(a)(b) = a^2 b$ $V_3 = a(a)(b) = a^2 b$ $V_4 = a(b)(b) = ab^2$

   $V_5 = a(a)(b) = a^2 b$ $V_6 = a(b)(b) = ab^2$ $V_7 = b(b)(b) = b^3$

   c) The volume of the piece not shown is ab^2.

Exercise Set 9.5

1. A **Mobius strip** is a one-sided, one-edged surface.
3. A **Klein bottle** is a topological object that resembles a bottle but has only one side.
5. a) Six
   b) Seven
7. Two figures are **topologically equivalent** if one figure can be elastically twisted, stretched, bent, or shrunk into the other figure without puncturing or ripping the original figure.

9. One   11. One

13. a) No, it has an inside and an outside.
    b) Two
    c) Two
    d) Two strips, one inside the other
15. No, it does not.
17. - 21. 1 - Red; 2, 5 - Yellow; 3, 6 - Blue; 4, 7 - Green
23. Answers will vary.

25. Outside; a straight line from point A to a point clearly outside the curve crosses the curve an even number of times.

27. Outside; a straight line from point A to a point clearly outside the curve crosses the curve an even number of times.

29. Outside; a straight line from point C to a point clearly outside the curve crosses the curve an even number of times.

31. Inside; a straight line from point E to a point clearly outside the curve crosses the curve an odd number of times.

33. 1   35. 5   37. 0   39. 4
41. 3   43. - 45. Answers will vary.

Exercise Set 9.6

1. Janos Bolyai - discovered hyperbolic geometry
3. Nikolay Ivanovich Lobachevsky - discovered hyperbolic geometry

5. G.F. Bernhard Riemann - discovered elliptical geometry
7. a) Euclidean - The sum of the measures of the angles of a triangle is 180°.
   b) Hyperbolic - The sum of the measures of the angles of a triangle is less than 180°.
   c) Elliptical - The sum of the measures of the angles of a triangle is greater than 180°.
9. Sphere
11. Each type of geometry can be used in its own frame of reference.
13. Spherical - elliptical geometry; Flat - Euclidean geometry; Saddle shaped - hyperbolic geometry
15.

  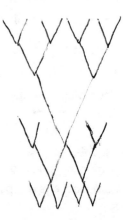

17.

 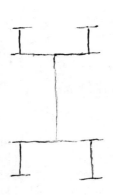 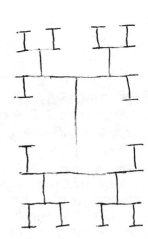

19. a)

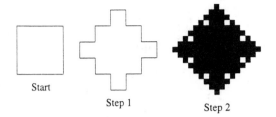

Start

Step 1

Step 2

b) Infinite since it is infinitely subdivided.

c) Finite since it covers a finite or closed area.

Review Exercises

1. {F}

2. $\triangle$ BFC

3. $\overline{BC}$

4. $\overleftrightarrow{BH}$

5. {F}

6. { }

7. $90° - 26.3° = 63.7°$

8. $180° - 105.2° = 74.8°$

9. Let $x = BC$

$$\frac{BC}{B'C} = \frac{AC}{A'C}$$

$$\frac{x}{3.4} = \frac{12}{4}$$

$$4x = 40.8$$

$$x = \frac{40.8}{4} = 10.2 \text{ in.}$$

10. Let $x = A'B'$

$$\frac{A'B'}{AB} = \frac{A'C}{AC}$$

$$\frac{x}{6} = \frac{4}{12}$$

$$12x = 24$$

$$x = \frac{24}{12} = 2 \text{ in.}$$

11. m $\angle$ ABC = m $\angle$ A'B'C

m $\angle$ A'B'C = 180° - 88° = 92°

Thus, m $\angle$ ABC = 92°

m $\angle$ BAC = 180° - 30° - 92° = 58°

12. m $\angle$ ABC = m $\angle$ A'B'C

m $\angle$ A'B'C = 180° - 88° = 92°

Thus, m $\angle$ ABC = 92°

13. The measure of the top angle of the triangle is 45°, by vertical angles. The measure of the angle on the bottom right of the triangle is 180° - 120° = 60°. Therefore, m $\angle$ 1 = 180° - 45° - 60° = 75°.

m $\angle$ 6 = 75° (angle 1 and angle 6 are vertical angles)

m $\angle$ 2 = 60° (angle 2 and the angle on the bottom right of the triangle are vertical angles)

The measure of the alternate interior angle of angle 2 is 60°. Thus, m $\angle$ 3 = 180° - 60° = 120°.

The measure of the alternate interior angle of angle 6 is 75°. Thus, m $\angle$ 5 = 180° - 75° = 105°.

m $\angle$ 4 = 180° - 105° = 75°.

14. n = 6

(n - 2)180° = (6 - 2)180° = 4(180°) = 720°

15. $A = lw = 7(4) = 28\, cm.^2$

16. $A = \frac{1}{2}bh = \frac{1}{2}(16)(7) = 56\, in.^2$

17. $A = \frac{1}{2}h(b_1 + b_2) = \frac{1}{2}(2)(4+9) = 13\, in.^2$

18. $A = bh = 12(7) = 84 \, in.^2$

19. $A = \pi r^2 = \pi(11)^2 = 121\pi$
$= 380.1327111 \approx 380.13 \, cm.^2$

20. $A = lw = 14(16) = 224 \, ft.^2$

$224 \, ft.^2 = \dfrac{224}{9} = 24.\overline{8} \, yd.^2 \approx 25 \, yd.^2$

$25(\$18.50) = \$462.50$

21. $V = \pi r^2 h = \pi(2)^2(6) = 24\pi$
$= 75.39822369 \approx 75.40 \, in.^3$

22. $V = lwh = 10(3)(4) = 120 \, cm.^3$

23. If h represents the height of the triangle which is the base of the pyramid, then

$$\begin{aligned} h^2 + 3^2 &= 5^2 \\ h^2 + 9 &= 25 \\ h^2 &= 16 \\ h &= \sqrt{16} = 4 \, ft. \end{aligned}$$

$B = \dfrac{1}{2}bh = \dfrac{1}{2}(6)(4) = 12 \, ft.^2$

$V = \dfrac{1}{3}Bh = \dfrac{1}{3}(12)(7) = 28 \, ft.^3$

24. If h represents the height of the triangle which is the base of the solid, then

$$\begin{aligned} h^2 + 5^2 &= 13^2 \\ h^2 + 25 &= 169 \\ h^2 &= 144 \\ h &= \sqrt{144} = 12 \, m. \end{aligned}$$

$B = \dfrac{1}{2}bh = \dfrac{1}{2}(10)(12) = 60 \, m.^2$

$V = Bh = 60(9) = 540 \, m.^3$

25. $V = \dfrac{1}{3}\pi r^2 h = \dfrac{1}{3}\pi(5)^2(15) = 125\pi$
$= 392.6990817 \approx 392.70 \, mm.^3$

26. $V = \dfrac{4}{3}\pi r^3 = \dfrac{4}{3}\pi(5)^3 = 166.\overline{6}\pi$
$= 523.5987756 \approx 523.60 \, ft.^3$

27.
$$\begin{aligned} h^2 + 1^2 &= 3^2 \\ h^2 + 1 &= 9 \\ h^2 &= 8 \\ h &= \sqrt{8} \end{aligned}$$

$A = \dfrac{1}{2}h(b_1 + b_2) = \dfrac{1}{2}(\sqrt{8})(2+4) = 8.485281374 \, ft.^2$

a) $V = Bh = 8.485281374(8)$
$= 67.88225099 \approx 67.88 \, ft.^3$

b) Weight:
$67.88(62.5) + 375 = 4617.5 \, lbs.$

Yes, it will support the trough filled with water.

c) $(4617.5 - 375) = 4242.5 \, lbs. \, of \, water$

$\dfrac{4242.5}{8.3} = 511.1445783 \approx 511.1 \, gal.$

28. 4

29. 1, 7 - Green; 2, 5 - Red; 3, 8 - Blue; 4, 6 - Yellow

30. Outside; a straight line from point A to a point clearly outside the curve crosses the curve an even number of times.

31. Euclidean: Given a line and a point not on the line, one and only one line can be drawn parallel to the given line through the given point.

   Elliptical: Given a line and a point not on the line, no line can be drawn through the given point parallel to the given line.

   Hyperbolic: Given a line and a point not on the line, two or more lines can be drawn through the given point parallel to the given line.

32.

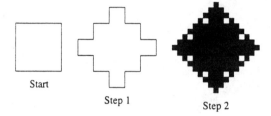

Start

Step 1

Step 2

Chapter Test

1. $\overleftrightarrow{EF}$

2. $\triangle BCD$

3. {D}

4. $\overleftrightarrow{AC}$

5. $90° - 17.4° = 72.6°$

6. $180° - 93.6° = 86.4°$

7. The other two angles of the triangle are 52° (by vertical angles) and $180° - 115° = 65°$. Thus, the measure of angle $x = 180° - 52° - 65° = 63°$.

8. $n = 8$

   $(n - 2)180° = (8 - 2)180° = 6(180°) = 1080°$

9. Let $x = B'C''$

$$\frac{B'C''}{BC} = \frac{A'C''}{AC}$$

$$\frac{x}{14} = \frac{10}{26}$$

$$26x = 140$$

$$x = \frac{140}{26} = 5.384615385 \approx 5.38 \, cm.$$

10. a)
$$x^2 + 5^2 = 13^2$$
$$x^2 + 25 = 169$$
$$x^2 = 144$$
$$x = \sqrt{144} = 12 \, in.$$

   b) $p = 5 + 13 + 12 = 30 \, in.$

   c) $A = \frac{1}{2}bh = \frac{1}{2}(5)(12) = 30 \, in.^2$

11. $r = \frac{16}{2} = 8 \, cm.$

$$V = \frac{4}{3}\pi r^3 = \frac{4}{3}\pi(8)^3 = 682.\overline{6}\pi$$

$$= 2144.660585 \approx 2144.66 \, cm.^3$$

12. $B = 18(28) + \pi(9)^2 = 504 + 81\pi = 758.4690049$

$$V = Bh = 758.4690049(6) = 4550.81403 \, ft.^3$$

$$4550.81403 \, ft.^3 = \frac{4550.81403}{27}$$

$$= 168.5486678 \approx 168.55 \, yd.^3$$

13. $B = lw = 3(9) = 27 \, ft.^2$

$$V = \frac{1}{3}Bh = \frac{1}{3}(27)(14) = 126 \, ft.^3$$

14. Answers will vary.

15. A **Mobius strip** is a one-sided, one-edged surface.

16. Answers will vary.

CHAPTER TEN

MATHEMATICAL SYSTEMS

Exercise Set 10.1

1. A binary operation is an operation that is performed on two elements, and the result is a single element.

3. Each of these operations can be performed on only two elements at a time and the result is always a single element.

    a) $2 + 3 = 5$ b) $5 - 3 = 2$ c) $2 \times 3 = 6$ d) $6 \div 3 = 2$

5. Closure, identity, each element must have a unique inverse, associative property, commutative property.

7. If a binary operation is performed on any two elements of a set and the result is an element of the set, then that set is closed under the given binary operation. For all integers a and b, $a + b$ is an integer. Therefore, the set of integers is closed under the operation of addition.

    Examples: $5 + 0 = 5$, $5 \times 1 = 5$

9. When a binary operation is performed on two elements in a set and the result is the identity element for the binary operation, then each element is said to be the inverse of the other. The additive inverse of 2 is (-2) since $2 + (-2) = 0$, and the multiplicative inverse of 2 is $(1/2)$ since $2 \times 1/2 = 1$.

11. The associative property of addition states that $(a + b) + c = a + (b + c)$, for any elements a, b, and c.

    Example: $(3 + 4) + 5 = 3 + (4 + 5)$

13. The commutative property of addition stated that $a + b = b + a$, for any elements a, b, and c.

    Example: $3 + 4 = 4 + 3$

15. $7 - 3 = 4$, but $3 - 7 = -4$

17. $(6 - 3) - 2 = 3 - 2 = 1$, but $6 - (3 - 2) = 6 - 1 = 5$

19. No; no identity element. $3 + \underline{?} = 3$, where ? must be a positive number.

21. Yes. Closure: The sum of any two rational numbers is a rational number.

    Identity element is zero.   Each element has a unique inverse.

        Example: $5 + 0 = 0 + 5 = 5$ Example: $6 + (-6) = 0$

    Associative property holds: Commutative property holds:

        Example: $(2 + 3) + 4 = 2 + (3 + 4)$ Example: $3 + 8 = 8 + 3$

23. No; subtraction is not associative, $(6 - 3) - 2 = 3 - 2 = 1$, but $6 - (3 - 2) = 6 - 1 = 5$.

25. No; the system is not closed, $\pi + (-\pi) = 0$ which is not an irrational number.

27. Yes. Closure: The sum of any two real numbers is a real number.

    The identity element is zero.

        Example: $5 + 0 = 0 + 5 = 5$

    Each element has a unique inverse.

        Example: $6 + (-6) = 0$

    Associative property holds:

        Example: $(2 + 3) + 4 = 2 + (3 + 4)$

29. Student activity problem.

Exercise Set 10.2

1. The clock addition table is formed by adding all pairs of integers between 1 and 12 using the 12 hour clock to determine the result. Example: If the clock is at 7 and we add 8, then the clock will read 3. Thus $7 + 8 = 3$ in clock arithmetic.

3. a) First add $(6 + 9)$ on the clock, then add that result to 5 on the clock to obtain the final answer.
   b) $(6 + 9) + 5 = (3) + 5 = 8$
   b) $5 - 9 = 8$

5. a) First add 12 to 3 to get 15, then subtract $15 - 10$.
   b) $3 - 10 = (12 + 3) - 10 = 15 - 10 = 5$.
   c) Since 12 is the identity element, you can add 12 to any number without changing the answer.

7. If a binary operation is performed on any two elements of a set and the result is an element of the set, then that set is closed under the given binary operation. For all integers a and b, $a + b$ is an integer. Therefore, the set of integers is closed under the operation of addition.

9. Yes. One and 11 are inverses, 2 and 10 are inverses, 3 and 9 are inverses, 4 and 8 are inverses, 5 and 7 are inverses, 6 is its own inverse, and 12 is its own inverse.

11. Yes. $6 + 9 = 3$ and $9 + 6 = 3$

13. $3 + 9 = 12$

15. $9 + 8 = 5$

17. $5 + 12 = 5$

19. $2 + (9 + 9) = 2 + 6 = 8$

21. $(6 + 4) + 8 = 10 + 8 = 6$

23. $(7 + 8) + (9 + 6) = 3 + 3 = 6$

25. $10 - 4 = 6$

27. $4 - 7 = 9$

29. $5 - 10 = 7$

31.

+	1	2	3	4	5	6
1	2	3	4	5	6	1
2	3	4	5	6	1	2
3	4	5	6	1	2	3
4	5	6	1	2	3	4
5	6	1	2	3	4	5
6	1	2	3	4	5	6

33. $3 + 4 = 1$

35. $5 - 2 = 3$

37. $2 - 6 = 2$

39. $(4 - 5) - 6 = 5 - 6 = 5$

41.

+	1	2	3	4	5	6	7
1	2	3	4	5	6	7	1
2	3	4	5	6	7	1	2
3	4	5	6	7	1	2	3
4	5	6	7	1	2	3	4
5	6	7	1	2	3	4	5
6	7	1	2	3	4	5	6
7	1	2	3	4	5	6	7

43. $4 + 5 = 2$

45. $7 + 6 = 6$

47. $3 - 6 = 4$

49. $(3 - 5) - 6 = 5 - 6 = 6$

51. Yes. The system is <u>closed</u> since all the elements in the table are from the set {1,2,3,4,5,6,7}.

The <u>identity</u> element is 7.

Each element has an <u>inverse</u>. 1 and 6 are inverses, 2 and 5 are inverses, 3 and 4 are inverses and 7 is its own inverse.

The <u>associative</u> property holds.

Example: (1 + 3) + 2 = 1 + (3 + 2)

$$4 + 2 = 1 + 5$$
$$6 = 6$$

The system is <u>commutative</u> since the table is symmetric about the main diagonal.

Since all 5 properties are satisfied, the system does form a commutative group.

53. a) {0, 1, 2, 3}   b) ✈
c) Yes. Whenever the binary operation is performed on any two elements of the set, the result is an element of the set.
d) Identity element is 0.
e) Yes; 0 − 0, 1 − 3, 2 − 2, 3 − 1
f) (1 ✈ 2) ✈ 3 = 3 ✈ 3 = 2
   and 1 ✈ (2 ✈ 3) = 1 ✈ 1 = 2
g) Yes; 3 ✈ 2 = 1 = 2 ✈ 3
h) Yes, the system satisfies all five properties.

55. a) {5, 8, 9, 11}   b) ⊙
c) Yes. Whenever the binary operation is performed on any two elements of the set, the result is an element of the set.
d) Yes, the identity element is 9.
e) Yes; 5 − 5, 8 − 11, 9 − 9, 11 − 8
f) (5 ⊙ 8) ⊙ 11 = 11 ⊙ 11 = 5
   and 5 ⊙ (8 ⊙ 11) = 5 ⊙ 9 = 5
g) Yes; 5 ⊙ 8 = 11 = 8 ⊙ 5
h) Yes, the system satisfies all five properties.

57. a) No, there is no identity element.
b) (1 w 3) w 4 ≠ 1 w (3 w 4)
$$4\ w\ 4 \neq 1\ w\ 3$$
$$2 \neq 3$$

59. Not associative: ⊡
(△ ⊡ □) ⊡ △ ≠ △ ⊡ (□ ⊡ △)
□ ⊡ △ ≠ △ ⊡ △
△ ≠ O
Not commutative:
□ ⊡ △ ≠ △ ⊡ □
△ ≠ □

61. No inverses for ~ and ∗.
Not associative:
(~ ∅ L) ∅ L ≠ ~ ∅ (L ∅ L)
∗ ∅ L ≠ ~ ∅ P
~ ≠ ∗

63. No identity element and therefore no inverses.
Not associative:
(d ⇔ e) ⇔ d ≠ d ⇔ (e ⇔ d)
d ⇔ d ≠ d ⇔ e
e ≠ d
Not commutative:
e ⇔ d ≠ d ⇔ e
e ≠ d

65. a)

+	E	O
E	E	O
O	O	E

b) The system is closed, the identity element is E, each element is its own inverse, and the system is commutative since the table is symmetric about the main diagonal. Since the system has fewer than 6 elements satisfying the above properties, it is a commutative group.

67. Student activity problem.

69. a) All elements in the table are in the set
    {1, 2, 3, 4, 5, 6} so the system is closed.
    The identity is 6. 5 and 1 are inverses of
    each other, and 2, 3, 4, and 6 are their own
    inverses. Thus, if the associative property
    is assumed, the system is a group.

    b) $4 \infty 5 = 2$, but $5 \infty 4 = 3$

71. $5^3 = 125$ ways

Examples of associativity:
$(2 \infty 3) \infty 4 = 5 \infty 4 = 3$ and
$2 \infty (3 \infty 4) = 2 \infty 5 = 3$
$(1 \infty 3) \infty 5 = 4 \infty 5 = 2$ and
$1 \infty (3 \infty 5) = 1 \infty 4 = 2$

Exercise Set 10.3

1. A modulo m system consists of m elements, 0 through m − 1, and a binary operation.
3. In a modulo 5 system there will be 5 modulo classes. When a number is divided by 5 the remainder will be a number from 0 − 4.

0	1	2	3	4
0	1	2	3	4
5	6	7	8	9
10	11	12	13	14
•	•	•	•	•

5. In a modulo 12 system there will be 12 modulo classes. When a number is divided by 12 the remainder will be a number 0 − 11.

7. 4 + 20 = 24 and
   24 ÷ 7 = 3, remainder 3
   day 3 = Wednesday

9. 4 + 366 = 370 and
   370 ÷ 7 = 52, remainder 6
   day 6 = Saturday

11. 3 years, 34 days = (3 × 365 + 34) days
    = 1129 days
    4 + 1129 = 1133 and
    1133 ÷ 7 = 161, remainder 6
    day 6 = Saturday

Answers to 13-17 will vary depending on the month used as the reference point.

13. 7 ÷ 12 = 0, remainder 7
    A remainder of 7 indicates 7 months from now.

15. 3 years, 5 months = (3 × 12 + 5) months
    = 41 months
    41 ÷ 12 = 3, remainder 5
    A remainder of 5 indicates 5 months from now.

17. Eight years from this month it will be this same month again.

19. 6 + 6 = 12 and 12 ÷ 5 = 2, remainder 2
    Thus 6 + 6 ≡ 2 (mod 5).

21. 4 + 7 + 12 = 23 and
    23 ÷ 5 = 4, remainder 3
    Thus 4 + 7 + 12 ≡ 3 (mod 5).

23. 3 − 9 = (3 + 10) − 9 = 13 − 9 = 4 and
    4 ÷ 5 = 0, remainder 4
    Thus 3 − 9 ≡ 4 (mod 5).

25. 7 × 9 = 63 and
    63 ÷ 5 = 12, remainder 3
    Thus 7 × 9 ≡ 3 (mod 5).

27. 4 − 8 ≡ (4 + 5) − 8 = 9 − 8 = 1
    Thus 4 − 8 ≡ 1 (mod 5).

29. (15 · 4) − 8 = 60 − 8 = 52 and
    52 ÷ 5 = 10, remainder 2
    Thus (15 · 4) − 8 ≡ 2 (mod 5).

31. 13 ÷ 4 = 3, remainder 1
    13 ≡ 1 (mod 4)

33. 84 ÷ 12 = 7, remainder 0
    84 ≡ 0 (mod 12)

35. 38 ÷ 9 = 4, remainder 2
    38 ≡ 2 (mod 9)

37. $34 \div 7 = 4$, remainder 6
    $34 \equiv 6 \pmod 7$

39. $-6 \equiv -6 + 7 = 1$
    $-6 \equiv 1 \pmod 7$

41. $-13 \equiv -13 + 2(11) = -13 + 22 = 9$
    $-13 \equiv 9 \pmod{11}$

43. $4 + 4 = 8$
    $8 \div 6 = 1$, remainder 2
    Thus, $4 + 4 \equiv 2 \pmod 6$

45. $3 + ? \equiv 4 \pmod 5$
    $3 + 0 \equiv 3 \pmod 5$
    $\boxed{3 + 1 \equiv 4 \pmod 5}$
    Thus, to make the statement true replace ?
    with 1.

47. $2 - ? \equiv 5 \pmod 6$
    $2 - 0 \equiv 2 \pmod 6$
    $2 - 1 \equiv 1 \pmod 6$
    $2 - 2 \equiv 0 \pmod 6$
    $\boxed{(2+6) - 3 \equiv 5 \pmod 6}$
    Thus, to make the statement true replace ?
    with 3.

49. $5 \cdot ? \equiv 7 \pmod 9$
    $5 \cdot 0 = 0 \equiv 0 \pmod 9$
    $5 \cdot 1 = 5 \equiv 5 \pmod 9$
    $5 \cdot 2 = 10 \equiv 1 \pmod 9$
    $5 \cdot 3 = 15 \equiv 6 \pmod 9$
    $5 \cdot 4 = 20 \equiv 2 \pmod 9$
    $\boxed{5 \cdot 5 = 25 \equiv 7 \pmod 9}$
    Thus $5 \cdot 5 \equiv 7 \pmod 9$ and the ?
    is replaced with 5.

51. $2 \cdot ? \equiv 3 \pmod 4$
    $2 \cdot 0 = 0 \equiv 0 \pmod 4$
    $2 \cdot 1 = 2 \equiv 2 \pmod 4$
    $2 \cdot 2 = 4 \equiv 0 \pmod 4$
    $2 \cdot 3 = 6 \equiv 2 \pmod 4$
    None of the numbers 0, 1, 2, or 3 make the
    statement true. Thus, there is no solution for ?.

53. $3 \cdot ? \equiv 2 \pmod 8$
    $3 \cdot 0 = 0 \equiv 0 \pmod 8$
    $3 \cdot 1 = 3 \equiv 3 \pmod 8$
    $3 \cdot 2 = 6 \equiv 6 \pmod 8$
    $3 \cdot 3 = 9 \equiv 9 \pmod 8$
    $3 \cdot 4 = 12 \equiv 4 \pmod 8$
    $3 \cdot 5 = 15 \equiv 7 \pmod 8$
    $\boxed{3 \cdot 6 = 18 \equiv 2 \pmod 8}$
    $3 \cdot 7 = 21 \equiv 5 \pmod 8$
    Thus, $3 \cdot 6 \equiv 2 \pmod 8$ and so ?
    is replaced with 6.

55. $5 - 7 \equiv ? \pmod{12}$
    $(12 + 5) - 7 \equiv ? \pmod{12}$
    $17 - 7 \equiv ? \pmod{12}$
    $10 \equiv 10 \pmod{12}$
    Thus, the ? is replaced with 10.

57. a) The next five presidential election years are 2012, 2016, 2020, 2024 and 2028.
    b) Election years are always evenly divisible by 4. Since 3000 is evenly divisible by 4, it is an election
        year, and the first one following it is 3004.
    c) $2550 \div 4 = 637$, remainder 2, so the next election year is 2 years after 2550. The election years
        between 2550 and 2575 are 2552, 2556, 2560, 2564, 2568, 2572.

59. The manager's schedule is repeated every seven weeks. If this is week two of her schedule then this is
    her second weekend that she works, or week 1 in a mod 7 system. In mod 7 her schedule on any given
    weekend is shown in the following table:

Weekend (mod 7):	0	**1**	2	3	4	5	6
work/off :	work	**work**	work	work	work	work	off

a) If this is weekend 1, then in 5 more weeks $(1 + 5 = 6)$ she will have the weekend off.
b) $25 \div 7 = 3$, remainder 4. Thus $25 \equiv 4 \pmod 7$ and 4 weeks from weekend 1 will be weekend 5. She will
    not have off.
c) $50 \div 7 = 7$, remainder 1. One week from weekend 1 will be weekend 2. It will be 4 more weeks before she
    has off. Thus, in 54 weeks she will have the weekend off.

61. The waiter's schedule in a mod 14 system is given in the following table:
    Day: 0 **1** 2 3 4 5 6 7 8 9 10 11 12 13
    shift: d d d d d e e e d d d   d   e   e
    Note: This is his second day shift which is day 1 in the mod 14 system.
    a) $20 \div 14 = 1$, remainder 6. Six days from day 1 is day 7 which is the evening shift.
    b) $52 \div 14 = 3$, remainder 10. Ten days from day 1 is day 11, which is the day shift.
    c) $365 \div 14 = 26$, remainder 1. One day from day 1 is day 2, which is the day shift.

63. a)

+	0	1	2	3
0	0	1	2	3
1	1	2	3	0
2	2	3	0	1
3	3	0	1	2

b) Yes. All the numbers in the table are from the set {0, 1, 2, 3}.

c) The identity element is 0.

d) Yes.

elem.	+	inverse	=	identity
0	+	0	=	0
1	+	3	=	0
2	+	2	=	0
3	+	1	=	0

e) $(1 + 3) + 2\ = 1 + (3 + 2)$
    $0\ \ +2\ = 1 + 1$
    $2\ = 2$

f) Yes, the table is symmetric about the main diagonal.
   $1 + 3 = 0 = 3 + 1$

g) Yes; all five properties are satisfied.

h) Yes; mod n under addition is a commutative group for all n. The system is closed since all elements in the system are from the set {0, 1, 2, ..., n}. The identity element is 0. The inverse for any number *a* is $n - a$. Addition is associative and commutative for any mod n system.

65. a)

×	0	1	2	3
0	0	0	0	0
1	0	1	2	3
2	0	2	0	2
3	0	3	2	1

b) Yes. All the elements in the table are from the set {0, 1, 2, 3}.

c) Yes. The identity element is 1.

d)

elem.	×	inverse	=	identity
0	×	none	=	1
1	×	1	=	1
2	×	none	=	1
3	×	3	=	1

Elements 0 and 2 do not have inverses.

e) $(1 \times 3) \times 0 = 1 \times (3 \times 0)$
   $3 \times 0 = 1 \times 0$
   $0 = 0$

f) Yes. $2 \times 3 = 3 \times 2$
   $2 = 2$

g) No. Not all elements have inverses.

For the operation of division in modular systems, we define $n \div d = n \cdot i$ where i is the multiplicative inverse of d.

67. $5 \div 7 \equiv ?$ (mod 9)
    Since $7 \cdot 4 = 28 \equiv 1$ (mod 9),
    4 is the inverse of 7. Thus
    $5 \div 7 \equiv 5 \cdot 4 \equiv 20 \equiv 2$ (mod 9)
    Replace ? with 2.

69. $? \div ? \equiv 1$ (mod 4)
    $0 \div 0$ is undefined.
    $1 \div 1 \equiv 1$ (mod 4)
    $2 \div 2 \equiv 1$ (mod 4)
    $3 \div 3 \equiv 1$ (mod 4)
    Replace ? with 1, 2, or 3.

71. $5k \equiv x \pmod 5$

$$\begin{array}{r} K \\ 5\overline{\smash{)}5K} \\ \underline{5K} \\ 0 \end{array}$$

$5k \equiv 0 \pmod 5$

$x = 0$

73. $4k - 2 \equiv x \pmod 4$

$$\begin{array}{r} K - 1 \\ 4\overline{\smash{)}4K - 2} \\ \underline{4K - 4} \\ 2 \end{array}$$

$4k - 2 \equiv 2 \pmod 4$

$x = 2$

75. If 10 is subtracted from each number on the wheel,

23 11 3 18 10 19 2 10 16 4 24   becomes

13 1 20 8   0 9 19 0   6 21 14   which is equivalent to

M A T H   I S   F U N

Review Exercises

1. A set of elements and at least one binary operation.

2. A binary operation is an operation that can be preformed on two and only two elements of a set. The result is a single element.

3. Yes. The sum of any two integers is always an integer.

4. No. Example: $2 - 3 = -1$, but -1 is not a natural number.

5. $5 + 10 = 3$

6. $5 + 12 = 5$

7. $6 - 10 = 8$

8. $(6 + 7) + 9 = 1 + 9 = 10$

9. $(7 - 4) + 6 = 3 + 6 = 9$

10. $(2 - 8) - 7 = 6 - 7 = 11$

11. a) The system is closed. If the binary operation is $*$, then for any elements a and b in the set, $a * b$ is a member of the set.

b) There exists an identity element in the set. For any element a in the set, if $a * i = i * a = a$, then i is called the identity element.

c) Every element in the set has a unique inverse. For any element a in the set, there exists an element b such that $a * b = b * a = i$. Then b is the inverse of a, and a is the inverse of b.

d) The set is associative under the operation $*$. For any elements a, b, and c in the set, $(a * b) * c = a * (b * c)$.

12. An Abelian group is a group in which the operation has the commutative property.

13. Yes. Closure: The sum of any two integers is an integer.
Identity element is zero.
Example: $5 + 0 = 0 + 5 = 5$

Associative property holds:
Example: $(2 + 3) + 4 = 2 + (3 + 4)$
Each element has a unique inverse.
Example: $6 + (-6) = 0$

14. The set of integers with the operation of multiplication does not form a group since not all elements have an inverse. $4 \times \underline{?} = 1$

15. Yes. Closure: The sum of any two rationals is a rational number.
Identity element is zero.
Example: $5 + 0 = 0 + 5 = 5$

Associative property holds:
Example: $(2 + 3) + 4 = 2 + (3 + 4)$
Each element has a unique inverse.
Example: $6 + (-6) = 0$

16. The set of rational numbers with the operation of multiplication does not form a group since zero does not have an inverse. $0 \times \underline{?} = 1$

17. There is no identity element. Therefore the system does not form a group.
18. The associative property does not hold.
    Example: (! ⌣ p) ⌣ ? ≠ ! ⌣ (p ⌣ ?)
    $$p ⌣ ? ≠ ! ⌣ !$$
    $$! ≠ ?$$

19. Not every element has an inverse.
    P does not have an inverse.
    Not associative:
    (4 ? 4) ? P ≠ 4 ? (4 ? P)
    $$P \ ? \ P ≠ 4 \ ? \ L$$
    $$L ≠ \#$$
    Therefore the system does not form a group.

20. a) { ⊢ , ⊙ , ? , Δ }
    c) Yes. All the elements in the table
       are from the set { ⊢ , ⊙ , ? , Δ }.
    e) Yes. | elem. | inverse | = | identity |
        | --- | --- | --- | --- |
        | ⊢ | ♪ ⊢ | = | ⊢ |
        | ⊙ | ♪ Δ | = | ⊢ |
        | ? | ♪ ? | = | ⊢ |
        | Δ | ♪ ⊙ | = | ⊢ |

    b) ♪
    d) The identity element is ⊢ .
    f) (⊢ ♪ ?) ♪ Δ = ⊢ ♪ (? ♪ Δ)
       ? ♪ Δ = ⊢ ♪ ⊙
       ⊙ = ⊙

    g) Yes. Δ ♪ ? = ? ♪ Δ
       ⊙ = ⊙
    h) Yes, all five properties are satisfied.

21. 15 ÷ 4 = 3, remainder 3
    15 ≡ 3 (mod 4)

22. 31 ÷ 8 = 3, remainder 7
    31 ≡ 7 (mod 8)

23. 27 ÷ 7 = 3, remainder 6
    27 ≡ 6 (mod 7)

24. 59 ÷ 8 = 7, remainder 3
    59 ≡ 3 (mod 8)

25. 82 ÷ 13 = 6, remainder 4
    82 ≡ 4 (mod 13)

26. 54 ÷ 4 = 13, remainder 2
    54 ≡ 2 (mod 4)

27. 37 ÷ 6 = 6, remainder 1
    37 ≡ 1 (mod 6)

28. 54 ÷ 14 = 3, remainder 12
    54 ≡ 12 (mod 14)

29. 97 ÷ 11 = 8, remainder 9
    97 ≡ 9 (mod 11)

30. 42 ÷ 11 = 3, remainder 9
    42 ≡ 9 (mod 11)

31. 8 + 8 = 16 ≡ 7 (mod 9)
    Thus, replace ? with 7.

32. ? − 3 ≡ 0 (mod 5)
    0 − 3 ≡ 2 (mod 5)
    1 − 3 ≡ 3 (mod 5)
    2 − 3 ≡ 4 (mod 5)
    3 − 3 ≡ 0 (mod 5)
    Replace ? with 3.

33. $4 \cdot ? \equiv 3 \pmod 6$

$4 \cdot 0 \equiv 0 \pmod 6$

$4 \cdot 1 \equiv 4 \pmod 6$

$4 \cdot 2 = 8 \equiv 2 \pmod 6$

$4 \cdot 3 = 12 \equiv 0 \pmod 6$

$4 \cdot 4 = 16 \equiv 4 \pmod 6$

$4 \cdot 5 = 20 \equiv 2 \pmod 6$

There is no solution. $? = \{ \}$

34. $3 - ? \equiv 5 \pmod 7$

$3 - 0 \equiv 3 \pmod 7$

$3 - 1 \equiv 2 \pmod 7$

$3 - 2 \equiv 1 \pmod 7$

$3 - 3 \equiv 0 \pmod 7$

$3 - 4 \equiv (3+7) - 4 = 6 \equiv 6 \pmod 7$

$\boxed{3 - 5 \equiv (3+7) - 5 = 5 \equiv 5 \pmod 7}$

Replace ? with 5.

35. $? \cdot 4 \equiv 0 \pmod 8$

$\boxed{0 \cdot 4 \equiv 0 \pmod 8}$

$1 \cdot 4 \equiv 4 \pmod 8$

$\boxed{2 \cdot 4 \equiv 8 \equiv 0 \pmod 8}$

$3 \cdot 4 \equiv 12 \equiv 4 \pmod 8$

$\boxed{4 \cdot 4 \equiv 16 \equiv 0 \pmod 8}$

$5 \cdot 4 \equiv 20 \equiv 4 \pmod 8$

$\boxed{6 \cdot 4 \equiv 24 \equiv 0 \pmod 8}$

$7 \cdot 4 \equiv 28 \equiv 4 \pmod 8$

Replace ? with 0, 2, 4, or 6.

36. $9 \cdot 7 \equiv ? \pmod{12}$

$9 \cdot 7 = 63; \quad 63 \div 12 = 5$, remainder 3

Thus, $9 \cdot 7 \equiv 3 \pmod{12}$

Replace ? with 3.

37. $3 - 5 \equiv ? \pmod 7$

$3 - 5 = (3+7) - 5 = 5 \equiv 5 \pmod 7$

Replace ? with 5.

38. $? \cdot 7 \equiv 3 \pmod 6$

$0 \cdot 7 \equiv 0 \pmod 6$

$1 \cdot 7 \equiv 1 \pmod 6$

$2 \cdot 7 \equiv 14 \equiv 2 \pmod 6$

$\boxed{3 \cdot 7 \equiv 21 \equiv 3 \pmod 6}$

Replace ? with 3.

39. $5 \cdot ? \equiv 3 \pmod 8$

$5 \cdot 0 \equiv 0 \pmod 8$

$5 \cdot 1 \equiv 5 \pmod 8$

$5 \cdot 2 \equiv 10 \equiv 2 \pmod 8$

$5 \cdot 3 \equiv 15 \equiv 7 \pmod 8$

$5 \cdot 4 \equiv 20 \equiv 4 \pmod 8$

$5 \cdot 5 \equiv 25 \equiv 1 \pmod 8$

$5 \cdot 6 \equiv 30 \equiv 6 \pmod 8$

$\boxed{5 \cdot 7 \equiv 35 \equiv 3 \pmod 8}$

Replace ? with 7.

40. $7 \cdot ? \equiv 2 \pmod 9$

$7 \cdot 0 \equiv 0 \pmod 9$

$7 \cdot 1 \equiv 7 \pmod 9$

$7 \cdot 2 \equiv 14 \equiv 5 \pmod 9$

$7 \cdot 3 \equiv 21 \equiv 3 \pmod 9$

$7 \cdot 4 \equiv 28 \equiv 1 \pmod 9$

$7 \cdot 5 \equiv 35 \equiv 7 \pmod 9$

$7 \cdot 6 \equiv 42 \equiv 6 \pmod 9$

$7 \cdot 7 \equiv 49 \equiv 4 \pmod 9$

$\boxed{7 \cdot 8 \equiv 56 \equiv 2 \pmod 9}$

Replace ? with 8.

41.

+	0	1	2	3	4	5
0	0	1	2	3	4	5
1	1	2	3	4	5	0
2	2	3	4	5	0	1
3	3	4	5	0	1	2
4	4	5	0	1	2	3
5	5	0	1	2	3	4

Since all the numbers in the table are elements of {0, 1, 2, 3, 4, 5}, the system has the closure property. The commutative property holds since the elements are symmetric about the main diagonal. The identity element is 0 and the inverses of each element are

$$0 - 0,\ 1 - 5,\ 2 - 4,\ 3 - 3,\ 4 - 2,\ 5 - 1$$

If it is assumed the associative property holds as illustrated by the example: (2 + 3) + 5 = 4 = 2 +(3 + 5), then the system is a commutative group.

42.

×	0	1	2	3
0	0	0	0	0
1	0	1	2	3
2	0	2	0	2
3	0	3	2	1

The identity element for the system is 1, but since 0 and 2 do not have inverses, the system does not form a group.

43. Day (mod 10):

Day (mod 10):	0	1	2	3	4	5	6	7	8	9
Work/off :	w	w	w	o	o	w	w	o	o	o

a) If today is the first day of her work pattern, day 0, then $18 \equiv 8$ (mod 10) indicates Toni will not be working in 18 days.

b) $38 \equiv 8$ (mod 10) indicates that Toni will have the evening off in 38 days.

Chapter Test

1. A mathematical system consists of a set of elements and at least one binary operation.

2. Closure, identity element, inverses, associative property, and commutative property.

3. No, the numbers greater than 0 do not have inverses.

4.

+	1	2	3	4	5
1	2	3	4	5	1
2	3	4	5	1	2
3	4	5	1	2	3
4	5	1	2	3	4
5	1	2	3	4	5

5. Yes. It is closed since the only elements in the table are from the set {1, 2, 3, 4, 5}. The identity element is 5. The inverses are 1 – 4, 2 – 3, 3 – 2, 4 – 1, and 5 – 5. The system is associative. The system is commutative since the table is symmetric about the main diagonal. Thus, all five properties are satisfied.

6. $4 + 3 + 2 = 2 + 2 = 4$

7. $6 - 18 = (15 + 6) - 18 = 21 - 18 = 3$

8. a) The binary operation is □
   b) Yes. All elements in the table are from the set {W, S, T, R}.
   c) The identity element is T, since T □ x = x = x □ T, where x is any member of the set {W, S, T, R}.
   d) The inverse of R is S, since R □ S = T
   e) (T □ R) □ W = R □ W = S

9. The system is not a group. It does not have the closure property since c * c = d, and d is not a member of {a, b, c}.

10. Since all the numbers in the table are elements of {1, 2, 3}, the system is closed. The commutative property holds since the elements are symmetric about the main diagonal. The identity element is 2 and the inverses are 1 – 3, 2 – 2, 3 – 1. If it is assumed the associative property holds as illustrated by the example:

    (1 ? 2) ? 1 = 2 = 1 ? (2 ? 3), then the system is a commutative group.

11. Since all the numbers in the table are elements of {@, $, &, %}, the system is closed. The commutative property holds since the elements are symmetric about the main diagonal. The identity element is $ and the inverses are @ – &, $ – $, & – @, % – %. It is assumed the associative property holds as illustrated by the example: (@ O $) O % = & = @ O ($ O %), then the system is a commutative group.

12. 73 ÷ 9 = 8, remainder 1
    73 ≡ 1 (mod 9)

13. 58 ÷ 11 = 5, remainder 3
    58 ≡ 3 (mod 11)

14. 6 + 9 = 15 and 15 ÷ 7 = 2, remainder 1
    6 + 9 ≡ 1 (mod 7)

15. ? – 9 ≡ 4 (mod 5)
    ? – 9 ≡ ? – 9 + 10 ≡ ? + 1 ≡ 4 (mod 5)
    3 + 1 ≡ 4 (mod 5)
    Replace ? with 3.

16. 3 – ? ≡ 7 (mod 9)
    3 – ? ≡ 3 + 9 – ? ≡ 12 – ? ≡ 7 (mod 9)
    12 – 5 ≡ 7 (mod 9)
    Replace ? with 5.

17. 4 · 2 = 8 and 8 ÷ 6 = 1, remainder 2
    4 · 2 ≡ 2 (mod 6)
    Replace ? with 2.

18. 3 · ? ≡ 2 (mod 6)
    3 · 0 ≡ 0 (mod 6)
    3 · 1 ≡ 3 (mod 6)
    3 · 2 ≡ 0 (mod 6)
    3 · 3 ≡ 3 (mod 6)
    3 · 4 ≡ 0 (mod 6)
    3 · 5 ≡ 3 (mod 6)
    There is no solution for ?
    The answer is { }.

19. 96 ÷ 7 = 13, remainder 5
    96 ≡ 5 (mod 7)
    Replace ? with 5.

20. a)

×	0	1	2	3	4
0	0	0	0	0	0
1	0	1	2	3	4
2	0	2	4	1	3
3	0	3	1	4	2
4	0	4	3	2	1

   b) The system is closed. The identity is 1. However, 0 does not have an inverse, so the system is <u>not</u> a group.

CHAPTER ELEVEN

CONSUMER MATHEMATICS

Exercise Set 11.1

1. A percent is a ratio of some number to 100.

3. Multiply the decimal number by 100 and add a percent sign.

5. Percent change = $\dfrac{(\text{Amount in latest period}) - (\text{Amount in previous period})}{\text{Amount in previous period}} \times 100$

7. $\dfrac{3}{8} = 0.375 = (0.375 \times 100)\% = 37.5\%$

9. $\dfrac{5}{8} = 0.625 = (0.625 \times 100)\% = 62.5\%$

11. $0.007654 = (0.007654 \times 100)\% = 0.8\%$

13. $3.78 = (3.78 \times 100)\% = 378\%$

15. $12\% = \dfrac{12}{100} = 0.12$

17. $3.75\% = \dfrac{3.75}{100} = 0.0375$

19. $\dfrac{1}{4}\% = 0.25\% = \dfrac{0.25}{100} = 0.0025$

21. $\dfrac{1}{5}\% = 0.2\% = \dfrac{0.2}{100} = 0.002$

23. $1\% = \dfrac{1}{100} = 0.01$

25. $\dfrac{830}{5820} \approx 0.1426 = (0.1426 \times 100)\%$
$= 14.3\%$ for food

27. 36% of 693,905 is what number?
$0.36(693905) = 249,805.8 \approx 249,806$ miles

29. 41.4% of \$43,281.7 million is what amount?
$0.414(43281.7) \approx \$17,918.6$ million loss

31. 10.7% of 148,847,000 is what number?
$0.107(148847000) = 15,926,629$ A-A workers

33. x% of 7534 = 2227
$0.01x(7534) = 2227$
$75.34x = 2227$
$x = \dfrac{2227}{75.34} \approx 29.6\%$

35. x% of 13815 = 2491
$0.01x(13815) = 2491$
$138.15x = 2491$
$x = \dfrac{2491}{138.15} \approx 18.0\%$

37.a) Percent increase from 1990 to 1998
$= \dfrac{1998\,pop. - 1990\,pop.}{1990\,pop.} \times 100$

$= \dfrac{270.3 - 248.7}{248.7} \times 100$

$= \dfrac{21.6}{248.7} \times 100 = 0.087 \times 100 = 8.7\%$

b) $270.3 + 0.087(270.3) = 270.3 + 23.5$
$= 293.8$ million people

39. a)   percent change $= \dfrac{34467 - 31583}{31583} \times 100$

        $= 0.091 \times 100 = 9.1\%$ increase

   b)   percent change $= \dfrac{36820 - 34467}{34467} \times 100$

        $= 0.068 \times 100 = 6.8\%$ increase

   c)   percent change $= \dfrac{37005 - 36820}{36820} \times 100$

        $= 0.005 \times 100 = 0.5\%$ increase

   d)   percent change $= \dfrac{37005 - 31583}{31583} \times 100$

        $= 0.172 \times 100 = 17.2\%$ increase

41. a)   increase from 1966 to 1976 is

$\dfrac{23.8 - 22.8}{22.8} \times 100 = 4.4\%$

increase from 1976 to 1986 is

$\dfrac{25.7 - 23.8}{23.8} \times 100 = 8.0\%$

increase from 1986 to 1996 is

$\dfrac{27.1 - 25.7}{25.7} \times 100 = 5.4\%$

Thus, the largest percent increase took place from 1976 to 1986.

   b)   increase from 1966 to 1976 is

$\dfrac{21.3 - 20.5}{20.5} \times 100 = 3.9\%$

increase from 1976 to 1986 is

$\dfrac{23.1 - 21.3}{21.3} \times 100 = 8.5\%$

increase from 1986 to 1996 is

$\dfrac{24.8 - 23.1}{23.1} \times 100 = 7.4\%$

The largest percent increase took place from 1976 to 1986.

43. $0.18(x) = 54$

$x = \dfrac{54}{0.18}$

$x = 300$

Fifty-four is 18% of 300.

45. $0.07(9) = x$

$0.63 = x$

0.63 is 7% of 9.

47. $(0.01x)(346) = 86.5$

$3.46x = 86.5$

$x = \dfrac{86.5}{3.46}$

$x = 25$

Twenty-five percent of 346 is 86.5.

49. a)   tax = 6% of $43.50 = 0.06(43.50) = \$2.61$
   b)   total bill before tip= $43.50 + \$2.61 = \$46.11$
   c)   tip = 15% of $46.11 = 0.15(46.11) = \$6.92$
   d)   total cost = $46.11 + 6.92 = \$53.03$

51. $1.50(x) = 18$

$x = \dfrac{18}{1.50}$

$x = 12$

12 students got an A on the 2nd test.

53. Mr. Browns' increase was
$0.07(36{,}500) = \$2{,}555$
His new salary = $\$36{,}500 + \$2{,}555 = \$39{,}055$

55. Percent change = $\dfrac{407430}{430} \times 100$

    $= \dfrac{23}{430} \times 100 = -5.3\%$

    There was a 5.3% decrease in the number of units sold.

57. percent change = $\dfrac{35.6 - 39.3}{39.3} \times 100 = -9.4\%$, or a 9.4% decrease

59. Percent decrease from regular price

    $= \dfrac{\$439539.62}{539.62} \times 100$

    $= -0.1864 \times 100 = -18.6\%$

    The sale price is 18.6% lower than the regular price.

61. 0.18(sale price) = \$675

    sale price $= \dfrac{\$675}{0.18} = \$3,750$

63. \$1000 increased by 10% is \$1000 + 0.10(\$1000) = \$1000 + \$100 = \$1,100.
    \$1,100 decreased by 10% is \$1,100 − 0.10(\$1,100) = \$1,100 − \$110 = \$990.
    Therefore if he sells the car at the reduced price he will lose \$10.

65. Total profit must = 0.40(\$5901.79) = \$2,360.72
    Total revenue must = \$5901.79 + \$2360.72 = \$8,262.51
    Revenue from first sale = 100 × \$9.00 = \$900
    Revenue from second sale = 150 × \$12.50 = \$1,875.00
    Total Revenue = Rev. from 1st sale + Rev. from 2nd sale + Rev. from final sale
        \$8262.51 = \$900 + \$1875 + 250 × (final price)
        \$5487.51 = 250 × (final price)
        $\dfrac{\$5487.51}{250}$ = final price;   final price = \$21.95

Exercise Set 11.2

1. Interest is the money the borrower pays for the use of the lender's money.
3. Security is anything of value pledged by the borrower that the lender may sell or keep if the borrower does not repay the loan.
5. A personal note is an agreement that states the conditions of the loan.
7. The United States Rule states that if a partial payment is made on a loan, interest is computed on the principal from the first day of the loan (or previous partial payment) up to the date of the partial payment. For each partial payment, the partial payment is used to pay the interest first, then the remainder of the payment is applied to the principle. On the due date of the loan the interest is calculated from the date of the last partial payment.

9. i = prt = \$420 × 0.09 × 3 = \$113.40

11. i = prt = $\$875 \times 0.12 \times \dfrac{30}{360} = \$8.75$

13. i = prt = \$587 × 0.00045 × 60 = \$15.85

15. i = $\$2,756.78 \times 0.1015 \times \dfrac{103}{360} = \$80.06$

17. i = \$12,752 × 0.015 × 9 = \$1,721.52

19.
    $22.75 = 1300 \times r \times \dfrac{157}{360}$

    $22.75 = 566.94 \times r$

    $\dfrac{22.75}{566.94} = r$

    $r = 0.04$ or 4%

21. $12.00 = p \times 0.08 \times \dfrac{3}{12}$

       $12.00 = p \times 0.02$

       $\dfrac{12.00}{0.02} = r$

       $p = \$600$

25. rate: $r = 5.08\% + 1\% = 6.08\%$

     $i = prt = 2000 \times 0.0608 \times \dfrac{9}{12} = \$91.20$

     amt. due: $A = p + i = 2000 + 91.20 = \$2091.20$

29. a) $i = prt$

       $i = \$3650 \times 0.075 \times \dfrac{8}{12} = \$182.50$

   b) $\$3650 - 182.50 = \$3467.50$ is the amount Julie received.

   c) $i = prt$

       $182.50 = 3467.50 \times r \times \dfrac{8}{12}$

       $182.50 = 2311.67r$

       $\dfrac{182.50}{2311.67} = r$

       $r = 0.0789$ or 7.9%

33. April 4 is day 94.
     Oct. 11 is day 284.
     $284 - 94 = 190$ days

37. August 24 is day 236
     May 15 is day 135
     $(365 - 236) + 135 = 129 + 135 = 264$ days

41. November 25 is day 329
     $329 + 120 = 449$; $449 - 365 = 84$
     $84 - 1$ leap year day = day 83
     day 83 = March 24

23. $124.49 = 957.62 \times 0.065 \times t$
       $124.49 = 62.2453t$

     $\dfrac{124.49}{62.2453} = t$

       $t = 2$ years

27. a) $i = prt$

       $i = 3500 \times 0.075 \times \dfrac{6}{12}$

       $= \$131.25$

   b) $A = p + i$
       $A = 3500 + 131.25$
       $= \$3,631.25$

31. Amt. collected $= 470 \times \dfrac{4500}{2} = \$1,057,500.$

   $i = prt = 1057500 \times 0.054 \times \dfrac{5}{12} = \$23,793.75$

35. June 19 is day 170.
     Nov. 5 is day 309.
     $309 - 170 = 139$ days

39. April 18 is day 108
     $108 + 90 =$ day 198
     Day 198 = July 17

43. Partial payment on August 1 (31 days)

   $i = 2500 \times .08 \times (31/360) = \$17.22$

   $\$300.00$ partial payment
   $\underline{-\ 17.22}$ interest
   $\$282.78$ amount applied to principal

   $\$2500.00$ original principal
   $\underline{-\ 282.78}$ amount applied to principal
   $\$2217.22$ principal after Aug.1 payment

   Maturity date is Oct. 15 (75 days)
   $i = 2217.22 \times .08 \times (75/360) = \$36.95$
   Balance due at maturity is
   $\$2217.22 + 36.95 = \$2254.17$

45. Partial payment on June 15 (45 days)

    $i = 8000 \times .09 \times (45/360) = \$90.00$

    $2000.00 partial payment
    – 90.00 interest
    $1,910.00 amount applied to principal

    $8000.00 original principal
    – 1910.00 amount applied to principal
    $6090.00 principal after June 15 pmt.

    Maturity date is Nov. 1 (139 days)

    $i = 6090.00 \times .09 \times (139/360)$
    $= \$211.63$

    Balance due at maturity is
    $6090.00 + 211.63 = \$6,301.63$

47. Partial payment on Dec. 27 (165 days)

    $i = 9000 \times 0.06 \times (165/360) = \$247.50$

    $4000.00 partial payment
    – 247.50 interest
    $3752.50 amount applied to principal

    $9000.00 original principal
    – 3752.50 amount applied to principal
    $5247.50 principal after Dec. 27 payment

    Maturity date is Feb. 1 (36 days)

    $i = 5247.50 \times 0.06 \times (36/360) = \$31.49$

    Balance due at maturity is
    $5247.50 + 31.49 = \$5278.99$

49. Partial payment on Sept. 1 (31 days)

    $i = 1800 \times .15 \times (31/360) = \$23.25$

    $500.00 partial payment
    – 23.25 interest
    $476.75 amount applied to principal

    $1800.00 original principal
    – 476.75 amount applied to principal
    $1323.25 principal after Sept.1 payment

    Partial payment on Oct. 1 (30 days)

    $i = 1323.25 \times 0.15 \times (30/360) = \$16.54$

    $500.00 partial payment
    – 16.54 interest
    $483.46 amount applied to principal

    $1323.25 principal after Sept.1 payment
    – 483.46 amount applied to principal
    $839.79 principal after Oct. 1 payment

    Maturity date is Nov. 1 (31 days)

    $i = 839.79 \times 0.15 \times (31/360) = \$10.85$

    Balance due at maturity is
    $839.79 + 10.85 = \$850.64$

51. Partial payment on May 1 (61 days)

    $i = 6500 \times 0.105 \times (61/360) = \$115.65$

    $1750.00 partial payment
    – 115.65 interest
    $1634.35 amount applied to principal

    $6500.00 original principal
    – 1634.35 amount applied to principal
    $4865.65 principal after May 1 payment

    Partial payment on July 1 (61 days)

    $i = 4865.65 \times 0.105 \times (61/360) = \$86.57$

    $2350.00 partial payment
    – 86.57 interest
    $2263.43 amount applied to principal

    $4865.65 new principal
    – 2263.43 amount applied to principal
    $2602.22 principal after July 1 payment

    On the maturity date (58 days)
    $i = 2602.22 \times 0.105 \times (58/360) = \$44.02$
    Balance due at maturity is
    $2602.22 + 44.02 = \$2,646.24$

53. a) May 5 is day 125
125 + 182 = 307
day 307 is Nov. 3, 1999

   b) i = 1000 × 0.0434 × (182/360) = $21.94
   Amt. paid = 1000 − 21.94 = $978.06

   c) interest = $21.94

   d) $r = \dfrac{i}{pt} = \dfrac{21.94}{978.06\left(\frac{182}{360}\right)} = 0.0444$ or 4.44%

55. a) Amt. received = 743.21 − 39.95 = $703.26
   i = p × r × t
   39.95 = 703.26 × r × (5/360)
   39.95 = 9.7675 × r
   r = 39.95/9.7675 = 4.09 or 409%

   b) 39.95 = 703.26 × r × (10/360)
   39.95 = 19.535 × r
   r = 39.95/19.535 = 2.045 or 204.5%

   c) 39.95 = 703.26 × r × (20/360)
   39.95 = 39.07 × r
   r = 39.95/39.07 = 1.023 or 102.3%

57. a) interest per $100 = 100 − 93.337 = $6.663
   rate = 6.663/100 = 0.0663 or 6.663%

   b) 0.0663 × 100,000 = $6,663.

   c) 6663 = 93337 × r × 1
   $\dfrac{6663}{93337}$ = r; r = 0.07139 or 7.139%

   d) i = 6663 × 0.05 × 1 = 333.15
   total interest = 6663 + 333.15 = $6,996.15

Exercise Set 11.3

1. An investment is the use of money or capital for income or profit.
3. For a variable investment neither the principal nor the interest is guaranteed.
5. The effective annual yield on an investment is the simple interest rate that gives the same amount of interest as a compound rate over the same period of time.

7. a) n = 1, r = 4.0%, t = 2, p = $4000

   $A = 4000\left(1+\dfrac{0.04}{1}\right)^{1\bullet 2} = \$4{,}326.40$

   b) i = $4326.40 − $4000 = $326.40

9. a) n = 2, r = 5.0%, t = 5, p = $3000

   $A = 3000\left(1+\dfrac{0.05}{2}\right)^{2\bullet 5} = \$3840.25$

   b) i = $3840.25 − $3000 = $840.25

11. a) n = 4, r = 4.75%, t = 3, p = $1500

   $A = 1500\left(1+\dfrac{0.0475}{4}\right)^{4\bullet 3} = \$1728.28$

   b) i = $1728.28 − $1500 = $228.28

13. a) n = 12, r = 6.25%, t = 2, p = $2500

   $A = 2500\left(1+\dfrac{0.0625}{12}\right)^{12\bullet 2} = \$2831.95$

   b) i = $2831.95 − $2500 = $331.95

15. n = 360, r = 6.75%, t = 5 yr., p = $5000

   a) $A = 5000\left(1+\dfrac{0.0675}{360}\right)^{360\bullet 5} = \$7006.98$

   b) i = $7006.98 − $5000 = $2006.98

17. p = 250,000 − 10,000 = 240,000

   $A = 240{,}000\left(1+\dfrac{0.056}{12}\right)^{12\bullet 10} = \$419{,}614.45$

19. $A = 5000\left(1+\dfrac{0.06}{4}\right)^{4\cdot 5} = \$6,734.28$

21. a) $\dfrac{A}{\left(1+\frac{i}{n}\right)^{n\cdot t}} = \dfrac{290000}{\left(1+\frac{0.0825}{2}\right)^{20}} = \$129,210.47$

   b) surcharge $= \dfrac{129210.47}{958} = \$134.88$

23. The amount Troy owes the bank after two years is, $A = 1500\left(1+\frac{0.10}{4}\right)^{4\times 2} = \$1,827.60$

   Bank's interest charge: $i = 1827.60 - 1500 = \$327.60$
   Grandfather's interest charge: $i = prt = 1500 \times 0.07 \times 2 = \$210.00$
   Troy will save $327.60 - 210.00 = \$117.60$

25. $A = 2000\left(1+\dfrac{0.06}{2}\right)^{2\cdot 10}$

   $= \$3612.22$ for first 10 years

   $A = 3612.22\left(1+\dfrac{0.06}{4}\right)^{4\cdot 8}$

   $= \$5,816.85$ after 18 years

27. $A = 6000\left(1+\dfrac{0.0525}{12}\right)^{24} = \$6,662.74$

   $i = \$6662.74 - \$6000 = \$662.74$

29. Let $p = 1.00$. Then

   $A = 1\left(1+\dfrac{0.056}{360}\right)^{360} = \$1.0576$

   $i = 1.0576 - 1.00 = 0.0576$
   The effective annual yield is 5.76%

31. a) $A = 100\left(1+\dfrac{0.12}{12}\right)^{24} = \$126.97$
       $i = \$126.97 - \$100 = \$26.97$

   b) $A = 200\left(1+\dfrac{0.12}{12}\right)^{24} = \$253.95$
       $i = \$253.95 - \$200 = \$53.95$

   c) $A = 400\left(1+\dfrac{0.12}{12}\right)^{24} = \$507.89$
       $i = \$507.89 - \$400 = \$107.89$

   d) The interest doubles also.

33. Let $p = 1.00$. Then

   $A = 1\left(1+\dfrac{0.075}{4}\right)^{4} = \$1.0771$

   $i = 1.0771 - 1.00 = 0.0771$
   The effective annual yield is 7.71%

35. Let $p = 1.00$. Then

   $A = 1\left(1+\dfrac{0.0677}{360}\right)^{360} = \$1.0700$

   $i = 1.0700 - 1.00 = 0.0700$ or 7.00%
   The accounts have the same effective rate.

37.   Present value $= \dfrac{200000}{\left(1+\frac{0.075}{4}\right)^{80}} = \$45,250.17$

39.   Present value $= \dfrac{20000}{\left(1+\frac{0.07}{12}\right)^{180}} = \$7,020.14$

41. $p = 1.35$, $r = 0.035$, $t = 10$, $n = 1$
   $A = 1.35(1 + 0.035)^{10} = \$1.90$

43. a) 72/3 = 24 years
   b) 72/6 = 12 years
   c) 72/8 = 9 years
   d) 72/12 = 6 years
   e) 72/r = 22
       72 = 22r
       r = 72/22 = 0.0327
       r = 3.27%

45. R = $500, r = 5.5%, n = 2, t = 17

$$S = 500 \frac{\left[\left(1+\frac{0.055}{2}\right)^{34} - 1\right]}{\frac{0.055}{2}}$$

$$= 500\, [1.51526] \left(\frac{2}{0.055}\right) = \$27{,}550.11$$

47. Use the formula given in exercise 45.
  a) R = 150, r = 0.056, n = 12, t = 18
      ans. S = $55,726.01
  b) R = 900, r = 0.058, n = 2, t = 18
      ans. S = $55,821.15

Exercise Set 11.4

1. With an installment plan, the borrower repays the principal plus the interest with weekly or monthly payments that usually begin shortly after the loan is made. With a personal note, the borrower repays the principal plus the interest as a single payment at the end of the specified time period.

3. The APR is the true rate of interest charged on a loan.

5. The total installment price is the sum of all the monthly payments and the down payment, if any.

7. The unpaid balance method and the average daily balance method.

9. a) Amount financed = 36000 − 0.20(36000) = $28,800
    From table 11.2 the finance charge per $100 at 11% for 60 payments is 30.45.

    Total finance charge = $30.45 \times \dfrac{28{,}800}{100} = \$8769.60$

  b) Total amount due after down payment = 28800 + 8769.60 = $37,569.60

    monthly payment = $\dfrac{37569.60}{60}$ = $626.16

11. a) From table 11.2, the finance charge per $100 financed at 7.5% for 60 months is $20.23.

    Total finance charge is $20.23 \times \dfrac{4000}{100} = \$809.20$

  b) Total amount due = 4000 + 809.20 = $4,809.20

    monthly payment = $\dfrac{4809.20}{60}$ = $80.15

13. a) down payment = 0.20(3200) = $640.
    Total installment price = 640 + (60 × 53.14) = $3828.40
    Finance charge = 3828.40 − 3200 = $628.40

  b) $\dfrac{finance\ charge}{amt.\ financed} \times 100 = \dfrac{628.40}{2560} \times 100 = 24.55$

    From Table 11.2, for 60 payments, the closest value to 24.55 is 24.55 which corresponds to an APR of 9.0%.

15. a) Total installment price = 175 + (12 × 44.66) = $710.92
    Finance charge = 710.92 − 675 = $35.92

  b) $\dfrac{finance\ charge}{amt.\ financed} \times 100 = \dfrac{35.92}{500} \times 100 = 7.18$

    From Table 11.2, for 12 payments, the closest value to 7.18 is 7.18 which corresponds to an APR of 13.0%.

17. a) Finance charge = $(60 \times 260.90) - 12000$

$$= \$3654.00$$

$$\frac{finance\ charge}{amt.\ financed} \times 100$$

$$= \frac{3654}{12000} \times 100 = 30.45$$

From Table 11.2, for 60 payments, the APR is 11.0%.

b) $n = 60 - 24 = 36$, $p = 260.90$, $v = 17.86$

$$u = \frac{(36)(260.90)(17.86)}{100 + 17.86} = \$1,423.28$$

c) 9392.40   Total of remaining payments

$-$ 1423.28   Interest saved

$\$7969.12$ Balance due

$+$ 260.90   24th monthly payment

$\$8,230.02$ Total amount due

21. a) From table 11.2, at 12.5% for 48 payments the finance charge per 100 is 27.58.

Finance charge $= 27.58 \times \dfrac{7345}{100} = \$2025.75$

b) Total installment price = 7345 + 2025.75

$$= \$9370.75$$

Monthly payment $= \dfrac{9370.75}{48} = \$195.22$

c) $K = 36$, $n = 48$, $f = 2025.75$

$$u = \frac{(2025.75)(36)(37)}{(48)(49)} = \$1,147.24$$

d) $\$7027.92$ Total of remaining payments

$-$ 1147.24   Interest saved

$\$5880.68$ Balance due

$+$ 195.22   12th monthly payment

$\$6,075.90$ Total amount due

19. a) Amount financed = $32000 - 10000 = \$22000$

From table 11.2, the finance charge per 100 financed at 12% for 36 payments is 19.57.

Total finance charge $= 19.57 \times \dfrac{22000}{100} = 4305.40$

b) Total amt. due = 22000 + 4305.40

$$= \$26,305.40$$

Monthly payment $= \dfrac{26305.40}{36} = \$730.71$

c) $n = 36 - 24 = 12$, $p = 730.71$, $v = 6.62$

$$u = \frac{(12)(730.71)(6.62)}{100 + 6.62} = \$544.43$$

d) $\$8768.52$ Total of remaining payments

$-$ 544.43   Interest saved

$\$8224.09$ Balance due

$+$ 730.71   12th monthly payment

$\$8954.80$ Total amount due

23. a) Interest = $500 + (151.39 \times 18) - 3000$

$$= \$225.02$$

$k = 6$, $n = 18$, and $f = 225.02$

$$u = \frac{(225.02)(6)(6+1)}{18(18+1)} = \frac{9450.84}{342} = \$27.63$$

b) $\$908.34$ Total of remaining payments

$-$ 27.63   Interest saved

$\$880.71$ Balance due

$+$ 151.39   12th monthly payment

$\$1032.10$ Total amount due

25. a) Balance due = 365 + 180 + 195 + 84 = $824

min. payment = $\dfrac{bal.\ due}{48} = \dfrac{824}{48} \approx 17.17 \approx \$18$

b) Bal. due after Dec. 1 payment = 824 – 200
= $624
interest for Dec. = 0.011 × 624 = $6.86
Bal. due Jan. 1 = 624 + 6.86 = $630.86

27. a) Bal. due = 423 + 36 + 145 + 491 = $1095

min. payment = $\dfrac{bal.\ due}{36} = \dfrac{1095}{36} \approx 30.42 \approx \$31$

b) Bal. due after Mar. 1 payment = 1095 – 548
= $547
interest for March = 0.011 × 547 = $6.02
Bal. due Apr. 1 = 547 + 6.02 = $553.02

29. a) Finance charge = 1097.86 × 0.018 × 1
= $19.76

b) Bal. due May 5
= 1097.86 + 19.76 + 425.79 – 800 = $743.41

31. a) Finance charge
= 124.78 × 0.0125 × 1 = $1.56

b)
```
   124.78  old balance
+    1.56  finance charge
–  100.00  payment
+   25.64  art sup.
+   67.23  flowers
+   13.90  music CD
   133.11  new balance, March 3
```

33. a)

Date	Balance Due	Number of Days	(Balance)(Days)
May 12	$378.50	1	(378.50)(1) = $378.50
May 13	$508.29	2	(508.29)(2) = $1,016.58
May 15	$458.29	17	(458.29)(17) = $7,790.93
June 1	$594.14	7	(594.14)(7) = $4,158.98
June 8	$631.77	4	(631.77)(4) = $2,527.08
		31	sum = $15,872.07

Average daily balance = $\dfrac{15872.07}{31}$ = $512.00

b) Finance charge = prt = 512.00 × 0.013 × 1 = $6.66
c) Balance due = 631.77 + 6.66 = $638.43

35. a)

Date	Balance Due	Number of Days	(Balance)(Days)
Feb. 3	$124.78	5	(124.78)(5) = $623.90
Feb. 8	$150.42	4	(150.42)(4) = $601.68
Feb. 12	$50.42	2	(50.42)(2) = $100.84
Feb. 14	$117.65	11	(117.65)(11) = $1294.15
Feb. 25	$131.55	6	(131.55)(6) = $789.30
		28	sum = $3,409.87

Average daily balance = $\dfrac{3409.87}{28}$ = $121.78

b) Finance charge = prt = 121.78 × 0.0125 × 1 = $1.52
c) Balance due = 131.55 + 1.52 = $133.07
d) The interest charged using the ave. daily balance method is $0.04 less than the interest charged using the unpaid balance method.

37. a) Interest charge = prt = $1500 \times 0.0005751 \times 24 = \$20.70$
    b) Amount due = 1500 + 20.70 = $1,520.70

39. a) ABC interest = $250 \times 0.074 \times \dfrac{6}{12} = \$9.25$

    b) Installment price = $22.19 \times 12 = \$266.28$
        XYZ Interest = 266.28 − 250 = $16.28

    c) $\dfrac{finance\ charge}{amt.\ financed} \times 100 = \dfrac{9.25}{250} \times 100 = 3.7$

    From Table 11.2, for 6 payments, the APR is
    12.5% for ABC.

    d) $\dfrac{finance\ charge}{amt.\ financed} \times 100 = \dfrac{16.28}{250} \times 100 = 6.51$

    From Table 11.2, for 12 payments, the APR is
    12.0% for XYZ.

41. a) Amount financed = 3450 − 1150 = $2300

Month	Finance charge	Payment	Balance
1	None	$384.00	$1,916.00
2	1916 × 0.013 = $24.91	$408.91	$1,532.00
3	1532 × 0.013 = $19.92	$403.92	$1,148.00
4	1148 × 0.013 = $14.92	$398.92	$764.00
5	764 × 0.013 = $9.93	$393.93	$380.00
6	380 × 0.013 = $4.94	$384.94	$0.00
	Total = $74.62		

It will take 6 months to repay the loan.

    b) The total amount of interest paid is $74.62
    c) The finance charge is $13.38 less using the credit card.

43. With her billing date on the 25th of the month she can buy the camera during the period of June 26 - June 29 and the purchase will be on the July 25th bill. Purchasing during these dates she can pay the bill on August 5th or later without paying interest.

Exercise Set 11.5
1. A mortgage is a long term loan in which the property is pledged as security for payment of the difference between the down payment and the sale price.

3. The major difference between these two types of loans is that the interest rate for a conventional loan is fixed for the duration of the loan, whereas the interest rate for a variable-rate loan may change every period, as specified in the loan agreement.

5. A buyer's adjusted monthly income is found by subtracting any fixed monthly payment with more than 10 months remaining from the gross monthly income.

7. An add on rate, or margin, is the percent added to the interest rate on which the adjustable rate mortgage is based.

9. Equity is the difference between the appraised value of your home and the loan balance.

11. a) down payment = 20% of $90,000

    = 0.20 × 90000 = $18,000.

    b) amt. of mortgage = 90000 − 18000= $72,000

    Table 11.4 yields 7.75 per 1000 of mortgage

    monthly payment = $\dfrac{72000}{1000}$ × 7.75 = $558.00

13. a) down payment = 0.20 × $74,000 = $14,800

    b) amount of mortgage

    $74,000 − $14,800 = $59,200

    Table 11.4 yields 8.05 per $1000

    of mortgage.

    Monthly mortgage payment

    = $\dfrac{59200}{1000}$ × 8.05 = $476.56

15. a) down payment = 0.15 × $93,500 = $14,025

    b) amount of mortgage

    $93,500 − $14,025 = $79,475

    c) cost of points = 0.03 × $79,475 = $2,384.25

17. a) $7200   gross monthly income

    −$290   car payment

    $6910   adjusted monthly income

    28% of the adjusted monthly income

    0.28×$6910 = $1,934.80, the amount the

    bank feels they can afford.

    b) At a rate of 6.5% for 30 years,

    Table 11.4 yields 6.32.

    monthly mortgage payment

    $\dfrac{140000}{1000}$ × 6.32 = $884.80

    $884.80   monthly mortgage payment

    +$400   taxes and insurance

    $1284.80   total monthly payment

    Since $1,284.80 is less than $1,934.80,

    they qualify for the loan

19. a) down payment:
    $160,000 − $110,000 = $50,000
    Total cost of house:
    $50,000 + (1038.40 × 12 × 25) = $361,520

b) interest = $361,520 − $160,000 = $201,520

c) interest on first payment

$$i = prt = 110,000 \times 0.105 \times \frac{1}{12} = \$962.50$$

amount applied to principal
$1,038.40 − $962.50 = $75.90

21. a) down payment = 0.28 × $113,500 = $31,780

b) amount of mortgage
    $113,500 − $31,780 = $81,720
    cost of three points
    = 0.03 × $81,720 = $2,451.60

c) $4750 gross monthly income
    −$420 monthly payments
    $4330 adjusted monthly income

d) maximum monthly payment
    0.28 × 4330 = $1,212.40

e) At a rate of 10% for 20 years,
    Table 11.4 yields 9.66.
    monthly mortgage payment

$$\frac{81720}{1000} \times 9.66 = \$789.42$$

f) $789.42   mortgage payment
    +$126.67 taxes and insurance
    $916.09   total monthly payment

g) Since $1,212.40 is greater than
    $916.09, the Yakomo's qualify.

h) interest on first payment

$$i = prt = 81,720 \times 0.10 \times \frac{1}{12} = \$681.00$$

amount applied to principal
$789.42 − $681.00 = $108.42

23.   <u>Bank A</u>

down payment = 0.10 × $105,000 = $10,500

amount of mortgage

$105000 − $10500 = $94,500

At a rate of 10% for 30 years,

Table 11.4 yields 8.70.

monthly mortgage payment

$\dfrac{94500}{1000} \times 8.70 = \$822.15$

cost of three points

0.03 × 94500 = $2835

Total cost of the house

10500 + 2835 + (822.15 × 12 × 30)

  = $309,309

<u>Bank B</u>

down payment = 0.20 × $105,000 = $21,000

amount of mortgage

$105000 − $21000 = $84,000

At a rate of 11.5% for 25 years,

Table 11.4 yields 10.16.

monthly mortgage payment

$\dfrac{84000}{1000} \times 10.16 = \$853.44$

Total cost of the house

21000 + (853.44 × 12 × 25) = $277,032

The Nagrockis should select Bank B.

25. a) $\dfrac{\textit{amount of mortgage}}{1000} \times 8.4 = 950$

amount of mortgage = $113,095.24

b)   0.75(total price) = 113,095.24

total price = $150,793.65

27. a)   Amount of mortgage = $105000 − $5000 = $100,000

Initial monthly payment = $\dfrac{100000}{1000} \times 8.05 = \$805.00$

b)

Payment Number	Interest	Principal	Balance of Loan
1	$750.00	$55.00	$99,945.00
2	$749.59	$55.41	$99,889.59
3	$749.17	$55.83	$99,833.76

c)   effective interest rate = 6.13% + 3.25% = 9.38%.
The new rate is 9.38%.

d)

Payment Number	Interest	Principal	Balance of Loan
4	$780.37	$24.63	$99,809.13
5	$780.17	$24.83	$99,784.30
6	$779.98	$25.02	$99,759.28

e)   New rate = 6.21% + 3.25% = 9.46%

Review Exercises

1. $1/4 = 0.25 = (0.25 \times 100)\% = 25\%$
2. $2/3 \approx 0.667 = (0.667 \times 100)\% = 66.7\%$
3. $5/8 = 0.625 = (0.625 \times 100)\% = 62.5\%$
4. $0.039 = (0.039 \times 100)\% = 3.9\%$
5. $0.0098 = (0.0098 \times 100)\% = 0.98\%$
6. $3.141 = (3.141 \times 100)\% = 314.1\%$

7. $26\% = \dfrac{26}{100} = 0.26$
8. $12.1\% = \dfrac{12.1}{100} = 0.121$

9. $123\% = \dfrac{123}{100} = 1.23$
10. $\dfrac{2}{5}\% = 0.4\% = \dfrac{0.4}{100} = 0.004$

11. $\dfrac{5}{6}\% = \dfrac{0.8\overline{3}}{100} = 0.008\overline{3}$
12. $0.00045\% = \dfrac{0.00045}{100} = 0.0000045$

13. percent increase
    $$\frac{13065 - 11916}{11916} \times 100 \approx 9.6\%$$

14. percent increase
    $$\frac{51300 - 46200}{46200} \times 100 \approx 11.0\%$$
    Her salary went up by 11%.

15. $(0.01x)80 = 25$
    $0.8x = 25$
    $x = \dfrac{25}{0.8} = 31.25$
    Twenty-five is 31.25% of 80.

16. $0.16x = 44$
    $x = \dfrac{44}{0.16} = 275$
    Forty-four is 16% of 275.

17. $0.17(540) = x$
    $91.8 = x$
    Seventeen percent of 540 is 91.8.

18. Tip = 15% of $42.79
    Tip = $0.15 \times 42.79 = \$6.42$

19. $0.20(x) = 8$
    $x = \dfrac{8}{0.20} = 40$
    The original number was 40 people.

20. $\dfrac{95 - 75}{75} \times 100 = 26.7$
    The increase was 26.7%.

21. $i = 2400 \times 0.07 \times (30/360)$
    $= \$14.00$

22. $41.56 = 1575 \times r \times (100/360)$
    $41.56 = \dfrac{157500}{360} \times r$
    $r = 0.095$ or 9.5%

23. $114.75 = p \times 0.085 \times 3$
    $114.75 = p \times 0.255$
    $\$450 = p$

24. $316.25 = 5500 \times 0.115 \times t$
    $316.25 = 632.50 \times t$
    $t = 0.5$ years or 6 months

25. $i = 3600 \times 0.1125 \times 2$
    $= \$810.00$

    Total amount due at maturity
    $3600 + 810 = \$4,410$

27. a) $i = 6000 \times 0.115 \times \dfrac{24}{12} = \$1380.00$

    b) amount received:
    $\$6000.00 - \$1380.00 = \$4,620.00$

    c) $i = prt$

    $1380 = 4620 \times r \times \dfrac{24}{12}$

    $1380 = 9240r$
    $r = 0.1494$ or 14.94%

29. a) $A = 1500\left(1 + \dfrac{0.06}{1}\right)^{5} = \$2,007.34$

    b) $A = 1500\left(1 + \dfrac{0.06}{4}\right)^{4 \cdot 5} = \$2,020.28$

    c) $A = 1500\left(1 + \dfrac{0.06}{12}\right)^{12 \cdot 5} = \$2,023.28$

30. $A = p\left(1 + \dfrac{r}{n}\right)^{nt}$

    $A = 2500\left(1 + \dfrac{0.0475}{4}\right)^{4 \cdot 15}$

    $A = \$5,076.35$

32. $p\left(1 + \dfrac{0.055}{4}\right)^{80} = 40000$

    $p = \dfrac{40000}{(1.01375)^{80}} = 13415.00$

    You need to invest $\$13,415.00$

26. a) $i = 3000 \times 0.081 \times \dfrac{240}{360} = \$162$

    b) She paid $3000 + 162 = \$3,162$

28. a) $5\dfrac{1}{2}\% + 2\% = 7\dfrac{1}{2}\%$

    b) $i = 800 \times 0.75 \times \dfrac{6}{12}$

    $= \$30$
    $A = \$800 + \$30$
    $A = \$830.00$

    c) $x =$ amount of money in the account
    85% of $x = 800$
    $0.85x = 800$
    $x = \$941.18$

$i = \$2007.34 - \$1500.00 = \$507.34$

$i = \$2020.28 - \$1500.00 = \$520.28$

$i = \$2023.28 - \$1500.00 = \$523.28$

31. Let $p = 1.00$. Then

    $A = 1\left(1 + \dfrac{0.56}{360}\right)^{360} = 1.05759$

    $i = 1.05759 - 1.00 = 0.05759$
    The effective annual yield is 5.76%

33. a) Installment price
    $193.75 \times 48 = \$9,300$
    Finance charge $= 9300 - 7500 = \$1,800$

    $\dfrac{finance\ charge}{amt.\ financed} \times 100 = \dfrac{1800}{7500} \times 100 = 24$

    From Table 11.2, for 48 payments, the closest value to 24 is 24.06 which corresponds to an APR of 11%.

  b) $n = 24,\ p = 193.75,\ v = 11.86$

    $u = \dfrac{(24)(193.75)(11.86)}{100 + 11.86} = \$493.02$

  c)
$4650.00	total of remaining payments
− 493.02	interest saved
$4156.98	balance due
+ 193.75	24th payment
$4350.73	total amount due

34. a) Amount financed = $3,500
    Finance charge
    $= (163.33 \times 24) - 3500 = \$419.92$

    $f = 419.92,\ k = 12,\ n = 24$

    $u = \dfrac{(419.92)(12)(13)}{(24)(25)} = \$109.18$

  b)
$1959.96	total of remaining payments
− 109.18	interest saved
$1850.78	balance due
+ 163.33	12th payment
$2014.11	total amount due

35. a) Amount financed $= \$3420 - \$860 = \$2,560$
    Interest $= (119.47 \times 24) - 2560 = \$307.28$

    $\dfrac{finance\ charge}{amt.\ financed} \times 100 = \dfrac{307.28}{2560} \times 100 = 12.0$

    From Table 11.2, for 24 payments, the closest value to 12.0 is 11.86 which corresponds to an APR of 11.0%.

  b) $n = 12,\ p = 119.47,\ v = 6.06$

    $u = \dfrac{(12)(119.47)(6.06)}{100 + 6.06} = \$81.91$

  c)
$1433.64	total of remaining payments
− 81.91	interest saved
$1351.73	balance due
+ 119.47	24th payment
$1471.20	total amount due

36. a) finance charge on Dec. 1
    $i = 485.75 \times 0.013 \times 1 = \$6.31$

  b)
485.75	old balance
+ 6.31	interest
− 375.00	payment
+ 370.00	airline ticket
+ 175.80	hotel bill
+ 184.75	clothing
$847.61	balance on Dec. 1

37. a)

Date	Balance Due	Number of Days	(Balance)(Days)
Mar. 5	185.72	3	$(185.72)(3) = 557.16$
Mar. 8	271.47	2	$(271.47)(2) = 542.94$
Mar. 10	196.47	5	$(196.47)(5) = 982.35$
Mar. 15	269.32	6	$(269.32)(6) = 1615.92$
Mar. 21	544.32	15	$(544.32)(15) = 8164.80$
		31	sum = 11,863.17

Average daily balance $= \dfrac{11863.17}{31} = \$382.68$

Finance charge $= 382.68 \times 0.014 \times 1 = \$5.36$

  b) Balance due on April 5 = $544.32 + $5.36 = \$549.68$

38. a) down payment = 0.25 × 14900 = $3,725

    b) amount financed = 14900 − 3725 = $11,175

    c) total interest paid
       i = 0.065 × 11175 × 4 = $2,905.50

    d) $\frac{2905.50}{11175} \times 100 = 26$
       Using Table 11.2, with 48 payments the APR is 12%

40. a) down payment = 0.25 × 135700 = $33,925
    b) gross monthly income = 64000/12
                            = $5,333.33
       $5333.33 gross monthly income
       − 528.00 total of monthly payments
       $4,805.33 adjusted monthly income

    c) maximum monthly payment:
       0.28 × 4805.33 = $1,345.49

    e) $825.40 mortgage payment
       + 316.67 taxes & insurance
       $1,142.07 total monthly payment

    f) Yes, $1345.49 is greater than $1142.07.

42. a) amount of mortgage:
       $105,000 − $26,250 = $78,750

       First payment = $\frac{78750}{1000} \times 6.99 = \$550.46$

39. a) Amt. finance = 135 − 35 = $100
       interest = 8.79 × 12 − 100 = $5.48

    b) $\frac{5.48}{100} \times 100 = 5.48$

    Using Table 11.2 for 12 payments, the closest value to 5.48 is 5.50 which corresponds to an APR of 10%.

41. a) down payment = 0.15 × 89900 = $13,485

    b) amount of mortgage
       $89,900 − $13,485 = $76,415
       At 11.5% for 30 years, Table 11.4 yields 9.90.
       monthly mortgage payment:
       $\frac{76415}{1000} \times 9.90 = \$756.51$

    c) i = prt = $76415 \times 0.115 \times \frac{1}{12} = \$732.31$
       amount applied to principal:
       756.51 − 732.51 = $24.20

    d) total cost of house:
       13485 + (756.51 × 12 × 30) = $285,828.60

    e) total interest paid:
       285,828.60 − 89900 = $195,928.60

    b) 5.00% + 3.00% = 8.00%

    c) 4.75% + 3.00% = 7.75%

Chapter Test

1. i = 1500 × 0.08 × (8/12)
     = $80.00

2. 288 = 1200 × 0.08 × t
   288 = 96t
     t = 3 years

3. i = prt = 5000 × 0.085 × (18/12)
         = $637.50

4. Total amount paid to the bank
   $5000 + $637.50 = $5,637.50

5. down payment = 0.15(2350) = $352.50
   loan amount = $2350 − $352.50
               = $1,997.50

6. finance charge
   = 352.50 + (94.50 × 24) − 2350
   = $270.50

7. $\dfrac{\textit{finance charge}}{\textit{amt. financed}} \times 100$

$\dfrac{270.50}{1997.50} \times 100 = 13.54$

From Table 11.2 for 24 payments, the closest value to 13.54 is 13.54 which corresponds to an APR of 12.50%.

8. a)   original finance charge
   $= 1550 + (465.85 \times 12) - 6750 = \$390.20$

   $k = 6,\ n = 12,\ f = 390.20$
   $u = \dfrac{(390.20)(6)(7)}{(12)(13)} = \$105.05$

   b)
2795.10	total of remaining payments
− 105.05	interest saved
2690.05	balance due
+465.85	6th monthly payment
\$3,155.90	total amount due

9. a)

Date	Balance Due	Number of Days	(Balance)(Days)
May 8	378.50	5	(378.50)(5) = 1892.50
May 13	655.29	2	(655.29)(2) = 1310.58
May 15	405.29	3	(405.29)(3) = 1215.87
May 18	550.14	11	(550.14)(11) = 6051.54
May 29	605.77	10	(605.77)(10) = 6057.70
		31	sum = \$16,528.19

Average daily balance = $\dfrac{16528.19}{31} = \$533.17$

Finance charge = $533.17 \times 0.013 \times 1 = \$6.93$

b) Remaining balance on June 8 is (605.77 + 6.93) = \$612.70

10. a)   Finance charge
   $= 878.25 \times 0.014 \times 1 = \$12.30$

   b)
878.25	old balance
+ 706.02	total of charges
− 450.00	payment
1134.27	
+ 12.30	interest
\$1146.57	new balance

11. Partial payment on Sept. 15 (45 days)
   $i = 5400 \times 0.125 \times (45/360) = \$84.38$
\$3000.00	partial payment
− 84.38	interest
\$2,915.62	amount applied to principal

\$5400.00	original principal
− 2915.62	amount applied to principal
\$2,484.38	principal after Sept. payment

   Maturity date is Oct. 29 (45 days)
   $i = 2484.38 \times 0.125 \times (45/360) = \$38.82$
   Amount owed at maturity
   $\$2484.38 + 38.82 = \$2,523.20$

12. Total interest = 84.38 + 38.82 = \$123.20

3. $A = 7500\left(1 + \dfrac{0.08}{4}\right)^{20} = \$11,144.61$

   interest = 11144.61 − 7500 = \$3,644.61

14. $A = 2500\left(1 + \dfrac{0.065}{12}\right)^{36} = \$3,036.68$

   interest = 3036.68 − 2500 = \$536.68

15. down payment = 0.15 × 144500
   $= \$21,675.00$

16. gross monthly income = 86500 ÷ 12
    = $7208.33

7,208.33	gross monthly income
− 605.00	total of monthly bills
$ 6,603.33	adjusted monthly income

17. maximum monthly payment is
    0.28 × 6603.33 = $1,848.93

18. At 10.5% interest for 30 years,
    Table 11.4 yields 9.15.
    amount of loan = 144500 − 21675 = $122,825

    The monthly payments are:
    $$\frac{122825}{1000} \times 9.15 = \$1,123.85$$

19.
1123.85	monthly mortgage payment
+ 304.17	taxes and ins. per month
$1,428.02	total monthly payment

20. Yes, the bank feels he can afford $1,848.93 per month and his payments would be $1,428.02.

21. a) Total cost of the house:
    21675 + (1123.85 × 12 × 30) = $426,261

    b) interest = $426,261 − $144,500
    = $281,761

CHAPTER TWELVE

PROBABILITY

Exercise Set 12.1

1. An experiment is a controlled operation that yields a set of results.
   b) An event is a subcollection of the outcomes of an experiment.

3. Empirical probability is the relative frequency of occurrence of an event. It is determined by actual observation of an experiment.

$$P(E) = \frac{\text{number of times the event occurred}}{\text{number of times the experiment was performed}}$$

5. Relative frequency over the long run can accurately be predicted, not individual events or totals.

7. The official definition by the Weather Service is (d). The specific location is the place where the rain gauge is. The Weather Service uses sophisticated mathematical equations to calculate these probabilities.

9. The "average" man in Mr. Reebe's category will live another 42.94 years. Some will die sooner, others will live longer.

11. Student activity exercise.

15. a) $P(\text{red hair}) = \dfrac{5}{60} = \dfrac{1}{12}$

    b) $P(\text{brown hair}) = \dfrac{28}{60} = \dfrac{7}{15}$

    c) $P(\text{blond hair}) = \dfrac{12}{60} = \dfrac{1}{5}$

19. a) $P(\text{AT\&T}) = 0.372$
    b) $P(\text{MCI}) = 0.294$
    c) 22.4% of $500 = 0.224 \times 500 = 112$ people

23. a) $P(\text{age 15-24 in 1950}) = 0.147$
    b) $P(\text{age 15-24 in 1996}) = 0.130$
    c) $P(\text{age 65+ in 1950}) = 0.085$
    d) $P(\text{age 65+ in 1996}) = 0.147$

13. Student activity exercise.

17. a) $P(\text{grouper}) = \dfrac{18}{62} = \dfrac{9}{31}$

    b) $P(\text{shark}) = \dfrac{6}{62} = \dfrac{3}{31}$

    c) $P(\text{flounder}) = \dfrac{30}{62} = \dfrac{15}{31}$

21. a) $P(\text{increase}) = \dfrac{\text{freq. of increases}}{\text{no. of observations}} = \dfrac{12}{12} = 1$

    b) Yes, the answer in part (a) is only an estimate based on observation.

25. a) $P(\text{bulls-eye}) = \dfrac{6}{20} = \dfrac{3}{10}$

    b) $P(\text{not bulls-eye}) = \dfrac{14}{20} = \dfrac{7}{10}$

    c) $P(\text{at least 20 pts.}) = \dfrac{14}{20} = \dfrac{7}{10}$

    d) $P(\text{does not score}) = \dfrac{2}{20} = \dfrac{1}{10}$

27. a)   P(affecting circular) = $\dfrac{0}{150}$ = 0

    b)   P(affecting elliptical) = $\dfrac{50}{250}$ = 0.2

    c)   P(affecting irregular) = $\dfrac{100}{100}$ = 1

29. a)   P(white flowers) = $\dfrac{224}{929}$ = 0.24

    b)   P(purple flowers) = $\dfrac{705}{929}$ = 0.76

Exercise Set 12.2

1. If each outcome of an experiment has the same chance of occurring as any other outcome, they are said to be equally likely outcomes.
3. P(A) + P(not A) = 1
5. None of the possible outcomes is the event in question.
7. All probabilities are between 0 and 1.
9. a) P(correct) = 1/5   b) P(correct) = 1/4

11. P(you win) = $\dfrac{one \text{ choice}}{48 \text{ } possible \text{ choices}}$ = $\dfrac{1}{48}$

13. P(4) = $\dfrac{4}{52}$ = $\dfrac{1}{13}$

15. P (not a 4) = 1 – P(4) = 1 – $\dfrac{1}{13}$ = $\dfrac{12}{13}$

17. P(heart) = $\dfrac{13}{52}$ = $\dfrac{1}{4}$

19. P(red or black card) = $\dfrac{52}{52}$ = 1

21. P(greater than 6 and less than 10) = $\dfrac{12}{52}$ = $\dfrac{3}{13}$

23. a)   P(red) = $\dfrac{2}{4}$ = $\dfrac{1}{2}$

    b)   P(blue) = $\dfrac{1}{4}$

    c)   P(yellow) = $\dfrac{1}{4}$

25. a)   P(red) = $\dfrac{2}{6}$ = $\dfrac{1}{3}$

    b)   P(blue) = $\dfrac{2}{6}$ = $\dfrac{1}{3}$

    c)   P(yellow) = $\dfrac{1}{3}$

27. P(Duracell) = $\dfrac{25}{100}$ = $\dfrac{1}{4}$ = 0.25

29. P(Duracell or Eveready or Kodak)

    = $\dfrac{25+40+20}{100}$ = $\dfrac{85}{100}$ = $\dfrac{17}{20}$ = 0.85

31. P($400) = $\dfrac{1}{12}$

33. P(more than $500) = $\dfrac{4}{12}$ = $\dfrac{1}{3}$

35. P(Penn) = $\dfrac{12}{40}$ = $\dfrac{3}{10}$ = 0.3

37. P(not Penn) = 1 – P(Penn)

    = 1 – $\dfrac{3}{10}$ = $\dfrac{7}{10}$ = 0.7

39. P(light is red) = $\dfrac{30}{75}$ = $\dfrac{2}{5}$

41. P(light is not red) = 1 – $\dfrac{2}{5}$ = $\dfrac{3}{5}$

43. P(a) = $\dfrac{3}{10}$ = 0.3

45. P(vowel) = $\dfrac{6}{10}$ = $\dfrac{3}{5}$ = 0.6

47. P(not t) = $\dfrac{9}{10}$ = 0.9

49. P(exactly 80 sites) = $\dfrac{1}{8}$

51. P(Florida site) = $\dfrac{55}{603}$ ≈ 0.09

53. P(25) = $\dfrac{1}{26}$

55. P(greater than or equal to 24) = $\dfrac{3}{26}$

57. P(female) = $\dfrac{310}{575} \approx 0.54$

59. P(public college) = $\dfrac{396}{575} \approx 0.69$

61. P(male and private college) = $\dfrac{73}{575} \approx 0.13$

63. 159

65. P(Skippy) = $\dfrac{39}{159} = \dfrac{13}{53} \approx 0.25$

67. P(smooth) = $\dfrac{93}{159} = \dfrac{31}{53} \approx 0.58$

69. P(red) = $\dfrac{2}{18} + \dfrac{1}{12} + \dfrac{1}{6} = \dfrac{4}{36} + \dfrac{3}{36} + \dfrac{6}{36} = \dfrac{13}{36}$

71. P(yellow) = $\dfrac{1}{6} + \dfrac{1}{12} + \dfrac{1}{12} = \dfrac{2}{12} + \dfrac{2}{12} = \dfrac{4}{12} = \dfrac{1}{3}$

73. P(yellow or green) = $\dfrac{1}{3} + \dfrac{11}{36} = \dfrac{23}{36}$

75.

	S_1	S_2
S_1	$S_1 S_1$	$S_1 S_2$
S_2	$S_1 S_2$	$S_2 S_2$

a) $P\left(S_2 S_2\right) = \dfrac{1}{4}$

b) $P\left(S_1 S_2\right) = \dfrac{2}{4} = \dfrac{1}{2}$

c) $P\left(S_1 S_1\right) = \dfrac{1}{4}$

77. a) P(red and red) = P(red) · P(red) = $\dfrac{2}{4} \cdot \dfrac{2}{4} = \dfrac{1}{2} \cdot \dfrac{1}{2} = \dfrac{1}{4}$

b) P(green and green) = P(green) · P(green) = $\dfrac{2}{4} \cdot \dfrac{2}{4} = \dfrac{1}{2} \cdot \dfrac{1}{2} = \dfrac{1}{4}$

c) P(1st red and 2nd green) = P(red) · P(green) = $\dfrac{2}{4} \cdot \dfrac{2}{4} = \dfrac{1}{2} \cdot \dfrac{1}{2} = \dfrac{1}{4}$

Exercise Set 12.3

1. The odds against an event are found by dividing the probability that the event does not occur by the probability that the event does occur. The probabilities used should be expressed in fractional form.

3. Odds against are more commonly used.

5. 15 to 2

7. a) P(event occurs) = $\dfrac{1}{1+1} = \dfrac{1}{2}$

9. a) P(tie goes well) = $\dfrac{11}{24}$

b) P(tie does not go well) = $\dfrac{13}{24}$

c) odds against tie going well =

$\dfrac{P(\text{tie does not go well})}{P(\text{tie goes well})} = \dfrac{13/24}{11/24} = \dfrac{13}{24} \cdot \dfrac{24}{11} = \dfrac{13}{11}$

  or 13:11

d) odds in favor of it going well are 11:13.

11. odds against rolling a 5 = $\dfrac{\text{P(failure to roll a 5)}}{\text{P(roll a 5)}} = \dfrac{5/6}{1/6} = \dfrac{5}{6} \cdot \dfrac{6}{1} = \dfrac{5}{1}$ or 5:1

13. odds against rolling greater than 4 = $\dfrac{\text{P(failure to roll greater than 4)}}{\text{P(roll greater than 4)}} = \dfrac{4/6}{2/6} = \dfrac{4}{6} \cdot \dfrac{6}{2} = \dfrac{4}{2} = \dfrac{2}{1}$ or 2:1

15. odds against a 6 = $\dfrac{\text{P(failure to pick a 6)}}{\text{P(pick a 6)}} = \dfrac{48/52}{4/52} = \dfrac{48}{52} \cdot \dfrac{52}{4} = \dfrac{12}{1}$ or 12:1

    Therefore, odds in favor of picking a 6 are 1:12.

17. odds against a picture card = $\dfrac{\text{P(failure to pick a picture)}}{\text{P(pick a picture)}} = \dfrac{40/52}{12/52} = \dfrac{40}{52} \cdot \dfrac{52}{12} = \dfrac{40}{12} = \dfrac{10}{3}$ or 10:3

    Therefore, odds in favor of picking a picture card are 3:10.

19. odds against red = $\dfrac{\text{P(not red)}}{\text{P(red)}} = \dfrac{1/2}{1/2} = \dfrac{1}{2} \cdot \dfrac{2}{1} = \dfrac{1}{1}$ or 1:1

21. odds against red = $\dfrac{\text{P(not red)}}{\text{P(red)}} = \dfrac{5/8}{3/8} = \dfrac{5}{8} \cdot \dfrac{8}{3} = \dfrac{5}{3}$ or 5:3

23. a) odds against selecting female = $\dfrac{\text{P(failure to select female)}}{\text{P(select female)}} = \dfrac{15/27}{12/27} = \dfrac{15}{12} = \dfrac{5}{4}$ or 5:4.

    b) odds against selecting male = $\dfrac{\text{P(failure to select male)}}{\text{P(select male)}} = \dfrac{12/27}{15/27} = \dfrac{12}{15} = \dfrac{4}{5}$ or 4:5.

25. odds against a stripe = $\dfrac{\text{P(not a stripe)}}{\text{P(stripe)}} = \dfrac{8/15}{7/15} = \dfrac{8}{15} \cdot \dfrac{15}{7} = \dfrac{8}{7}$ or 8:7

27. odds in favor of not the 8 ball are $\dfrac{\text{P(not the 8 ball)}}{\text{P(the 8 ball)}} = \dfrac{14/15}{1/15} = \dfrac{14}{15} \cdot \dfrac{15}{1} = \dfrac{14}{1}$ or 14:1

29. odds against a ball with 9 or greater are $\dfrac{\text{P(less than 9)}}{\text{P(9 or greater)}} = \dfrac{8/15}{7/15} = \dfrac{8}{15} \cdot \dfrac{15}{7} = \dfrac{8}{7}$ or 8:7

31. The odds against testing negative = $\dfrac{\text{P(test positive)}}{\text{P(test negative)}} = \dfrac{2/72}{70/72} = \dfrac{2}{70} = \dfrac{1}{35}$ or 1:35

33. a) P(Carrie wins) = $\dfrac{7}{7+5} = \dfrac{7}{12}$ b) P(Carrie loses) = $\dfrac{5}{7+5} = \dfrac{5}{12}$

35. P(promoted) = $\dfrac{9}{5+9} = \dfrac{9}{14}$

37. P(N) = $\dfrac{15}{75} = \dfrac{1}{5}$

39. Odds in favor of N = $\dfrac{P(N)}{P(\text{not } N)} = \dfrac{1/5}{4/5} = \dfrac{1}{4}$ or 1:4

41. Odds against I-27 = $\dfrac{P(\text{not I-27})}{P(\text{I-27})} = \dfrac{74/75}{1/75} = \dfrac{74}{75} \cdot \dfrac{75}{1} = \dfrac{74}{1}$ or 74:1

43. P(absence for stress in 1995) = 0.06

45. Odds against absence for stress in 1995 = $\dfrac{P(\text{not stress})}{P(\text{stress})} = \dfrac{94/100}{6/100} = \dfrac{94}{6} = \dfrac{47}{3}$ or 47:3

47. Odds in favor of absence for entitlement in 1998 = $\dfrac{P(\text{for entitlement})}{P(\text{not for entitlement})} = \dfrac{16/100}{84/100} = \dfrac{16}{84} = \dfrac{4}{21}$ or 4:21

49. If P(sell your car this week) = $0.4 = \dfrac{4}{10} = \dfrac{2}{5}$, then P(do not sell your car this week) = $1 - \dfrac{2}{5} = \dfrac{3}{5}$.

The odds against selling your car this week = $\dfrac{3/5}{2/5} = \dfrac{3}{2}$ or 3:2.

51. If P(fixes car right the first time) = $0.8 = \dfrac{8}{10} = \dfrac{4}{5}$, then P(does not fix the car right the first time) = $\dfrac{1}{5}$

The odds against the car being fixed right the first time = $\dfrac{1/5}{4/5} = \dfrac{1}{4}$ or 1:4.

53. a) The male to female ratio of gout is 20 to 1. The 20 to 1 indicates that this is actually an odds statement. Thus, the odds against J. Douglas being male are 1:20, and the odds against J. Douglas being female are 20:1.

b) odds against female = $\dfrac{P(\text{not female})}{P(\text{female})} = \dfrac{20/21}{1/21}$. The probability of being a male is 20/21.

55. P(# 1 wins) = $\dfrac{2}{7+2} = \dfrac{2}{9}$, P(# 2 wins) = $\dfrac{1}{2+1} = \dfrac{1}{3}$, P(# 3 wins) = $\dfrac{1}{15+1} = \dfrac{1}{16}$,

P(# 4 wins) = $\dfrac{5}{7+5} = \dfrac{5}{12}$, P(# 5 wins) = $\dfrac{1}{1+1} = \dfrac{1}{2}$

Exercise Set 12.4

1. Expected value is used to determine the average gain or loss of an experiment over the long run.
3. The fair price is the amount charged for the game to be fair and result in an expected value of 0.
5. No, fair price is the price to pay to make the expected value 0. The expected value is the expected outcome of an experiment when the experiment is performed many times.
7. $0.50. Since you would lose $1.00 on average for each game you played, the fair price of the game should be $1.00 less. Then the expected value would be 0, and the game would be fair.
9. a) A $10 bet is the same as five $2 bets, thus Marty's expected value is $5(-0.40) = -\$2.00$
   b) On average he can expect to lose $2.00
11. $E = P_1A_1 + P_2A_2 = 0.65(70000) + 0.35(-30000) = 45500 - 10500 = \$35,000$
13. $E = P_1A_1 + P_2A_2 = 0.50(78) + 0.50(62) = 39 + 31 = 70$ points

15. a) $E = P(\text{sunny})(1/2) + P(\text{cloudy})(1/4)$
    $E = 0.75(1/2) + 0.25(1/4) = 0.375 + 0.0625 = 0.4375$ inches per day
    b) (0.4375 inches per day)(31 days) = 13.5625 inches of growth during July is expected

17. a) $E = P_1A_1 + P_2A_2 = \dfrac{7}{10}(20\%) + \dfrac{3}{10}(30\%) = 14\% + 9\% = 23\%$

    b) Expected amount $= 100 - 0.23(100) = 100 - 23 = \$77$.

19. a) $E_{\text{guess}} = P(\text{guess correct})(\text{points gained}) + P(\text{guess incorrect})(\text{points lost})$
    $$= \frac{1}{4}(5) + \frac{3}{4}(-2) = \frac{5}{4} - \frac{6}{4} = -\frac{1}{4}$$
    Since $E_{\text{guess}} = -\dfrac{1}{4}$ point, it is to your advantage to leave a question blank.
    b) $E_{\text{guess}} = P(\text{guess correct})(\text{points gained}) + P(\text{guess incorrect})(\text{points lost})$
    $$= \frac{1}{3}(5) + \frac{2}{3}(-2) = \frac{5}{3} - \frac{4}{3} = \frac{1}{3} \text{ point}$$
    Therefore if you can eliminate one possible choice, it is to your advantage to guess.

21. a) $E = P(\text{wins})(\text{amount won}) + P(\text{loses})(\text{amount lost})$
    $$= \frac{1}{1000}(\$499) + \frac{999}{1000}(-\$1) = \frac{499}{1000} - \frac{999}{1000} = \frac{500}{1000} = -\$0.50$$
    b) A fair price for the ticket = cost to play + expectation = $\$1.00 + (-\$0.50) = \$0.50$
    c) Profit $= 1000(\$0.50) = \$500$

23. a) fair price $= P(\$1)(\$1) + P(\$5)(\$5) = \dfrac{1}{2}(1) + \dfrac{1}{2}(5) = 0.50 + 2.50 = \$3.00$

    b) expectation = fair price − cost to play $= \$3.00 - \$2.00 = \$1.00$

25. a) fair price $= P(\$1) \cdot (\$1) + P(\$5) \cdot (\$5) + P(\$10) \cdot (\$10)$
    $$= \frac{1}{2} \cdot (1) + \frac{1}{4} \cdot (5) + \frac{1}{4} \cdot (10) = 0.50 + 1.25 + 2.50 = \$4.25$$

    b) expectation = fair price − cost to play $= \$4.25 - \$2.00 = \$2.25$

27. $E_{\text{company}} = P(\text{insured lives}) \cdot (\text{amount gained}) + P(\text{insured dies}) \cdot (\text{amount lost})$
    $$= 0.994 \cdot (\$100) + 0.006 \cdot (-\$9,900) = 99.4 - 59.4 = \$40$$
    Thus, the company gains $40 on this type of policy.

29. a) $E = P_1A_1 + P_2A_2 + P_3A_3 = \dfrac{3}{10}(4) + \dfrac{5}{10}(3) + \dfrac{2}{10}(1) = 1.2 + 1.5 + 0.2 = 2.9$ points

    b) Fair price = 2.9 points
    c) $3 \times E = 3(2.9) = 8.7$ points

31. $E = P_1A_1 + P_2A_2 + P_3A_3$
    $= P(\text{hit oil}) \cdot (\text{oil profits}) + P(\text{hit gas}) \cdot (\text{gas profits}) + P(\text{hit nothing}) \cdot (\text{loss})$
    $= 0.08 \cdot (\$500,000) + 0.20 \cdot (\$100,000) + 0.72 \cdot (-\$30,000)$
    $= \$40,000 + \$20,000 - \$21,600 = \$38,400$
    Yes, if the company drills many of these wells, they can expect to make an average of $38,400 per well drilled.

33. $E = P_1A_1 + P_2A_2$

   = P(granted new routes)(# of new employees) + P(not granted)(# of new employees)

   = $0.36 \cdot (920) + 0.64 \cdot (170) = 331.2 + 108.8 = 440$

35. $E = P_1A_1 + P_2A_2 + P_3A_3$

   = $0.70(40,000) + 0.10(0) + 0.20(-30,000) = 28,000 + 0 - 6,000 = \$22,000$

37. Profit if Jorge sells the house = $0.06(100,000) = \$6,000$

   Profit if another Realtor sells the house = $0.03(100,000) = \$3,00$

   $E = P_1A_1 + P_2A_2 + P_3A_3$

   = $0.2 \cdot (\$5,000) + 0.5 \cdot (\$2,000) + 0.3 \cdot (-\$1,000)$

   = $\$1,000 + \$1,000 - \$300 = \$1,700$ gain

   Yes, in the long run if Jorge lists many of these $100,000 homes, he can expect to make, on average, $1,700 per listing.

39. a) $P(\$1) = \frac{1}{2} + \frac{1}{16} = \frac{8}{16} + \frac{1}{16} = \frac{9}{16}$, $P(\$10) = \frac{1}{4} = \frac{4}{16}$, $P(\$20) = \frac{1}{8} = \frac{2}{16}$, $P(\$100) = \frac{1}{16}$

   b) $E = P_1A_1 + P_2A_2 + P_3A_3 + P_4A_4$

   $= \frac{9}{16}(\$1) + \frac{4}{16}(\$10) + \frac{2}{16}(\$20) + \frac{1}{16}(\$100) = \frac{9}{16} + \frac{40}{16} + \frac{40}{16} + \frac{100}{16} = \frac{189}{16} = \$11.81$

   c) fair price = expected value − cost to play = $\$11.81 - 0 = \$11.81$

41. $E = $ P(insured lives) · (cost) + P(insured dies) · (cost − \$40,000)

   = $0.97(\text{cost}) + 0.03(\text{cost} - 40,000) = 0.97(\text{cost}) + 0.03(\text{cost}) - 1200$

   = $1.00(\text{cost}) - 1200$

   Thus, in order for the company to make a profit, the cost must exceed $1,200.

43. $E = $ P(red) · (amount won) + P(not red) · (amount lost)

   $= \frac{18}{38} \cdot (1) + \frac{20}{38} \cdot (-1) = \frac{18}{38} - \frac{20}{38} = -\frac{2}{38} = -5.3¢$

45. a) $E = \frac{1}{12}(100) + \frac{1}{12}(200) + \frac{1}{12}(300) + \frac{1}{12}(400) + \frac{1}{12}(500) + \frac{1}{12}(600) + \frac{1}{12}(700)$

   $+ \frac{1}{12}(800) + \frac{1}{12}(900) + \frac{1}{12}(1000) + \frac{1}{12}(0) = \frac{550}{12} = \$458.33$

   b) $E = \frac{1}{12}(5500) + \frac{1}{12}(-1800) = \frac{3700}{12} = \$308.33$

Exercise Set 12.5

1. If a first experiment can be performed in M distinct way and a second experiment can be performed in N distinct ways, then the two experiments in that specific order can be performed in M · N distinct ways.

3. $3 \times 5 = 15$ ways. Using the counting principle.

5. The first selection is made. Then the second selection is made before the first selection is returned to the group of items being selected.

7. a) $50 \times 50 = 2500$ possibilities   b) $50 \times 49 = 2450$ possibilities

9. a) 5 × 5 = 25 sample points   b) 5 × 4 = 20 sample points

11. a) 2 × 2 = 4 points
    b)

		Sample
Coin 1	Coin 2	Space
H	H	H, H
H	T	H, T
T	H	T, H
T	T	T, T

c) P(no heads) = $\frac{1}{4}$

d) P(exactly one head) = $\frac{2}{4}$ = $\frac{1}{2}$

e) P(two heads) = $\frac{1}{4}$

13. a) 3 × 2 = 6 points
    b)

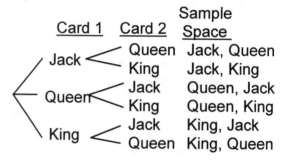

		Sample
Card 1	Card 2	Space
Jack	Queen	Jack, Queen
Jack	King	Jack, King
Queen	Jack	Queen, Jack
Queen	King	Queen, King
King	Jack	King, Jack
King	Queen	King, Queen

c) P(two Jacks) = $\frac{0}{6}$ = 0

d) P(Jack and then Queen) = $\frac{1}{6}$

e) P(at least one King) = $\frac{4}{6}$ = $\frac{2}{3}$

15. a) 4 × 3 = 12 points
    b)

		Sample
marble 1	marble 2	Space
yellow	red	yellow, red
yellow	blue	yellow, blue
yellow	green	yellow, green
red	yellow	red, yellow
red	blue	red, blue
red	green	red, green
blue	yellow	blue, yellow
blue	red	blue, red
blue	green	blue, green
green	yellow	green, yellow
green	red	green, red
green	blue	green, blue

c) P(exactly one red) = $\frac{6}{12}$ = $\frac{1}{2}$

d) P(at least one is not red) = $\frac{12}{12}$ = 1

e) P(no green) = $\frac{6}{12}$ = $\frac{1}{2}$

17. a) $6 \times 6 = 36$ points

b)

	1st die	2nd die	Sample Space
	1	1	1, 1
		2	1, 2
		3	1, 3
		4	1, 4
		5	1, 5
		6	1, 6
	2	1	2, 1
		2	2, 2
		3	2, 3
		4	2, 4
		5	2, 5
		6	2, 6
	3	1	3, 1
		2	3, 2
		3	3, 3
		4	3, 4
		5	3, 5
		6	3, 6
	4	1	4, 1
		2	4, 2
		3	4, 3
		4	4, 4
		5	4, 5
		6	4, 6
	5	1	5, 1
		2	5, 2
		3	5, 3
		4	5, 4
		5	5, 5
		6	5, 6
	6	1	6, 1
		2	6, 2
		3	6, 3
		4	6, 4
		5	6, 5
		6	6, 6

17. c)   P(double is rolled) $= \dfrac{6}{36} = \dfrac{1}{6}$

d)   P(sum of 7) $= \dfrac{6}{36} = \dfrac{1}{6}$

e)   P(sum of 2) $= \dfrac{1}{36}$

f)   No, there are 6 combinations, out of 36 possibilities, that result in a sum of 7 and only 1 way, out of 36 possibilities, of getting a sum of 2.

19. a) $3 \times 3 \times 3 = 27$ points

b)

motion 1	motion 2	motion 3	Sample Space
		Yes	yes, yes, yes
	Yes	No	yes, yes, no
		Abs.	yes, yes, abs.
		Yes	yes, no, yes
	No	No	yes, no, no
		Abs.	yes, no abs.
Yes		Yes	yes, abs. yes
	Abs.	No	yes, abs., no
		Abs.	yes, abs., abs.
		Yes	no, yes, yes
	Yes	No	no, yes, no
		Abs.	no, yes, abs.
		Yes	no, no, yes
No	No	No	no, no, no
		Abs.	no, no, abs.
		Yes	no, abs., yes
	Abs.	No	no, abs., no
		Abs.	no, abs., abs.
		Yes	abs., yes, yes
	Yes	No	abs., yes, no
		Abs.	abs., yes, abs.
		Yes	abs., no, yes
Abs.	No	No	abs., no, no
		Abs.	abs., no, abs.
		Yes	abs., abs., yes
	Abs.	No	abs., abs., no
		Abs.	abs., abs., abs.

c)   P(No vote on all three motions) = $\dfrac{1}{27}$

d)   P(Yes vote on exactly two motions) = $\dfrac{6}{27} = \dfrac{2}{9}$

e)   P(at least one yes vote) = $\dfrac{19}{27}$

21. a) $3 \times 3 \times 2 = 18$ points

b)

Bachelors	Masters	Ph.D.	Sample Space
T	H	E	T, H, E
		C	T, H, C
	M	E	T, M, E
		C	T, M, C
	W	E	T, W, E
		C	T, W, C
B	H	E	B, H, E
		C	B, H, C
	M	E	B, M, E
		C	B, M, C
	W	E	B, W, E
		C	B, W, C
J	H	E	J, H, E
		C	J, H, C
	M	E	J, M, E
		C	J, M, C
	W	E	J, W, E
		C	J, W, C

c)   P(SUNY-B) = $\frac{1}{3}$

d)   P(U. Mass. or U. Hawaii for masters) = $\frac{2}{3}$

e)   P(U. Texas for B.A. and UCLA for Ph.D.) = $\frac{3}{18} = \frac{1}{6}$

23. a) $4 \times 2 \times 2 = 16$ points

b)

computer	printer	monitor	Sample Space
		O	C, H, O
	H	T	C, H, T
C		O	C, E, O
	E	T	C, E, T
		O	I, H, O
	H	T	I, H, T
I		O	I, E, O
	E	T	I, E, T
		O	A, H, O
	H	T	A, H, T
A		O	A, E, O
	E	T	A, E, T
		O	D, H, O
	H	T	D, H, T
D		O	D, E, O
	E	T	D, E, T

c) $P(\text{Apple}) = \dfrac{1}{4}$

d) $P(\text{H-P}) = \dfrac{1}{2}$

e) $P(\text{Apple and H-P}) = \dfrac{2}{16} = \dfrac{1}{8}$

25. a) $2 \times 4 \times 3 = 24$ sample points

b)

sex	hair	eyes	Sample Space
		brown	M, red, brown
	red	blue	M, red, blue
		green	M, red, green
		brown	M, brown, brown
	brown	blue	M, brown, blue
		green	M, brown, green
M		brown	M, black, brown
	black	blue	M, black, blue
		green	M, black, green
		brown	M, blonde, brown
	blonde	blue	M, blonde, blue
		green	M, blonde, green
		brown	F, red, brown
	red	blue	F, red, blue
		green	F, red, green
		brown	F, brown, brown
	brown	blue	F, brown, blue
		green	F, brown, green
F		brown	F, black, brown
	black	blue	F, black, blue
		green	F, black, green
		brown	F, blonde, brown
	blonde	blue	F, blonde, blue
		green	F, blonde, green

c) $P(M, \text{black, blue}) = \dfrac{1}{24}$

d) $P(F, \text{blonde}) = \dfrac{3}{24} = \dfrac{1}{8}$

27. a) m or n
    c) m, 3
        m, 4
        n, 3
        n, 4
    f) Yes, each sample point would have the same probability.

b) 3 or 4
d) No, not unless we know that all outcomes are equally likely.
e) No, not unless we know that all outcomes are equally likely.

Exercise Set 12.6

1. a) "or" means at least one event A or B must occur.
    b) "and" means both events, A and B, must occur.

3. a) Two events are mutually exclusive if it is impossible for both events to occur simultaneously.
    b) P(A or B) = P(A) + P(B)

5. We assume that event A has already occurred.

7. Two events are dependent if the occurrence of either event affects the probability of occurrence of the other event. Ex. Select two cards from a deck (without replacement); find P (King and King).

9. a) No, it is possible for an individual to be both happy and healthy at the same time.
    b) No, if you are healthy, you are more likely to be happy.

11. Student activity problem.

13. P(A or B) = P(A) + P(B) − P(A and B)
    $$= 0.4 + 0.5 - 0.2 = 0.7$$

15. P(B) = P(A or B) + P(A and B) − P(A)
    $$= 0.8 + 0.1 - 0.4 = 0.5$$

17. P(3 or 5) $= \dfrac{2}{6} = \dfrac{1}{3}$

19. P(greater than 5 or less than 3) $= \dfrac{3}{6} = \dfrac{1}{2}$

21. Since these events are mutually exclusive,
    P(queen or king) = P(queen) + P(king)
    $$= \frac{4}{52} + \frac{4}{52} = \frac{8}{52} = \frac{2}{13}$$

23. Since it is possible to obtain a card that is a picture card and a red card, these events are not mutually exclusive.
    P(picture or red)
    = P(pict.) + P(red) − P(pict. and red)
    $$= \frac{12}{52} + \frac{26}{52} - \frac{6}{52} = \frac{32}{52} = \frac{8}{13}$$

25. Since it is possible to obtain a card less than 9 that is a club, these events are not mutually exclusive.
    P(less than 9 or club)
    $$= \frac{32}{52} + \frac{13}{52} - \frac{8}{52} = \frac{37}{52}$$

27. a) P(3 and 3) $= \dfrac{4}{20} \cdot \dfrac{4}{20} = \dfrac{1}{5} \cdot \dfrac{1}{5} = \dfrac{1}{25}$

    b) P(3 and 3) $= \dfrac{4}{20} \cdot \dfrac{3}{19} = \dfrac{1}{5} \cdot \dfrac{3}{19} = \dfrac{3}{95}$

29. a) P(monkey first and bird second) $= \dfrac{5}{20} \cdot \dfrac{5}{20} = \dfrac{1}{4} \cdot \dfrac{1}{4} = \dfrac{1}{16}$

    b) P(monkey first and bird second) $= \dfrac{5}{20} \cdot \dfrac{5}{19} = \dfrac{1}{4} \cdot \dfrac{5}{19} = \dfrac{5}{76}$

31. a) P(frog first and yellow bird second) $= \dfrac{5}{20} \cdot \dfrac{2}{20} = \dfrac{1}{4} \cdot \dfrac{1}{10} = \dfrac{1}{40}$

    b) P(frog first and yellow bird second) $= \dfrac{5}{20} \cdot \dfrac{2}{19} = \dfrac{1}{2} \cdot \dfrac{1}{19} = \dfrac{1}{38}$

33. a) P(not odd and not odd) = $\dfrac{8}{20} \cdot \dfrac{8}{20} = \dfrac{2}{5} \cdot \dfrac{2}{5} = \dfrac{4}{25}$

    b) P(not odd and not odd) = $\dfrac{8}{20} \cdot \dfrac{7}{19} = \dfrac{2}{5} \cdot \dfrac{7}{19} = \dfrac{14}{95}$

35. P(frog or odd) = P(frog) + P(odd) − P(frog and odd) = $\dfrac{5}{20} + \dfrac{12}{20} - \dfrac{3}{20} = \dfrac{14}{20} = \dfrac{7}{10}$

37. P(monkey or a 5) = P(monkey) + P(5) − P(monkey and a 5) = $\dfrac{5}{20} + \dfrac{4}{20} - \dfrac{1}{20} = \dfrac{8}{20} = \dfrac{2}{5}$

39. P(2 yellows) = P(yellow and yellow) = P(yellow) × P(yellow) = $\dfrac{1}{2} \times \dfrac{1}{2} = \dfrac{1}{4}$

41. P(red and then green) = P(red) × P(green) = $\dfrac{1}{4} \times \dfrac{1}{2} = \dfrac{1}{8}$

43. P(2 yellows) = P(yellow and yellow) = P(yellow) × P(yellow) = $\dfrac{3}{8} \times \dfrac{3}{8} = \dfrac{9}{64}$

45. P(2 yellows) = P(yellow on 1st wheel) × P(yellow on 2nd wheel) = $\dfrac{1}{2} \times \dfrac{1}{4} = \dfrac{1}{8}$

47. P(both not yellow) = P(not yellow on 1st wheel)×P(not yellow on 2nd wheel) = $\dfrac{1}{2} \times \dfrac{3}{4} = \dfrac{3}{8}$

49. P(3 girls) = P(1st girl) × P(2nd girl) × P(3rd girl) = $\dfrac{1}{2} \times \dfrac{1}{2} \times \dfrac{1}{2} = \dfrac{1}{8}$

51. P(1st girl, 2nd girl, 3rd boy) = P(1st girl) × P(2nd girl) × P(3rd boy) = $\dfrac{1}{2} \times \dfrac{1}{2} \times \dfrac{1}{2} = \dfrac{1}{8}$

53. a) P(Haefners have 5 boys)

    = P(1st boy) × P(2nd boy) × P(3rd boy) × P(4th boy) × P(5th boy) = $\dfrac{1}{2} \times \dfrac{1}{2} \times \dfrac{1}{2} \times \dfrac{1}{2} \times \dfrac{1}{2} = \dfrac{1}{32}$

    b) P(next child is a boy) = $\dfrac{1}{2}$

55. a) P(cola 1st and orange 2nd) = $\dfrac{3}{6} \cdot \dfrac{2}{6} = \dfrac{1}{2} \cdot \dfrac{1}{3} = \dfrac{1}{6}$ 　　　　b) P(cola 1st and orange 2nd) = $\dfrac{3}{6} \cdot \dfrac{2}{5} = \dfrac{1}{2} \cdot \dfrac{2}{5} = \dfrac{1}{5}$

57. a) P(at least on cola) = P(cola and not cola) + P(not cola and cola) + P(cola and cola)

    $= \dfrac{3}{6} \cdot \dfrac{3}{6} + \dfrac{3}{6} \cdot \dfrac{3}{6} + \dfrac{3}{6} \cdot \dfrac{3}{6} = \dfrac{1}{4} + \dfrac{1}{4} + \dfrac{1}{4} = \dfrac{3}{4}$

    b) P(at least on cola) = P(cola and not cola) + P(not cola and cola) + P(cola and cola)

    $= \dfrac{3}{6} \cdot \dfrac{3}{5} + \dfrac{3}{6} \cdot \dfrac{3}{5} + \dfrac{3}{6} \cdot \dfrac{2}{5} = \dfrac{9}{30} + \dfrac{9}{30} + \dfrac{6}{30} = \dfrac{24}{30} = \dfrac{4}{5}$

59. P(both are 40-59) = (0.23)(0.23) = 0.0529

61. P(first is 0-19 and second is 20-39) = (0.27)(0.25) = 0.0675

63. P(all three exercise daily) = (0.20)(0.20)(0.20) = 0.008

65. P(at least 3 times per week and daily and never) = (0.31)(0.20)(0.11) = 0.00682

67. The probability that any individual reacts favorably is 70/100 or 0.7.
     P(Mrs. Rivera reacts favorably) = 0.7

69. P(all 3 react favorably) = 0.7 × 0.7 × 0.7 = 0.343

71. Since each question has four possible answers of which only one is correct, the probability of guessing correctly on any given question is 1/4.
    P(correct answer on any one question) = 1/4

73. P(only the 3rd and 4th questions correct)= $\frac{3}{4} \times \frac{3}{4} \times \frac{1}{4} \times \frac{1}{4} \times \frac{3}{4} = \frac{27}{1024}$

75. P(none of the 5 questions correct) = $\frac{3}{4} \times \frac{3}{4} \times \frac{3}{4} \times \frac{3}{4} \times \frac{3}{4} = \frac{243}{1024}$

77. P(orange on 1st reel) = $\frac{5}{22}$

79. P(no 7s) = P(not 7 on 1st reel) × P(not 7 on 2nd reel) × P(not 7 on 3rd reel) = $\frac{21}{22} \times \frac{21}{22} \times \frac{21}{22} = \frac{9261}{10648}$

81. P(red on outer and red on inner) = $\frac{4}{12} \cdot \frac{3}{8} = \frac{1}{3} \cdot \frac{3}{8} = \frac{1}{8}$

83. P(not red on outer and not red on inner) = $\frac{8}{12} \cdot \frac{5}{8} = \frac{5}{12}$

85. P(both miss) = 0.6 × 0.6 = 0.36

87. P(both hit) = 0.4 × 0.9 = 0.36

89. a) No, they are dependent. Occurrence of the syndrome in the first child increases the probability of the syndrome occurring in the second child.
    b) P(born with affliction) = 0.001
    c) (i) P(both born with affliction) = P(1st afflicted) × P(2nd afflicted) = 0.001 × 0.001 = 0.00004
       (ii) P(1st afflicted and 2nd not afflicted) = P(1st afflicted) × P(2nd not afflicted) = 0.001 × 0.96 = 0.00096
       (iii) P(1st not afflicted and 2nd is afflicted) = 0.999 × 0.001 = 0.000999
       (iv) P(neither has affliction) = P(1st not afflicted) × P(2nd not afflicted) = 0.999 × 0.999 = 0.998001

91. P(audited next 2 years) = P(audited this year) × P(audited next year) = 0.028 × 0.028 = 0.000784

93. P(not audited either of next 2 years)
    = P(not audited this year) × P(not audited next year) = 0.972 × 0.972 = 0.944784

95. P(2) = $\frac{2}{6} = \frac{1}{3}$

97. P(even or less than 3) = P(even) + P(less than 3) − P(even and less than 3) = $\frac{2}{6} + \frac{3}{6} - \frac{2}{6} = \frac{3}{6} = \frac{1}{2}$

99. P(2 the same color) = P(2 red) + P(2 blue) + P(2 yellow)
    = P(1st red) × P(2nd red) + P(1st blue) × P(2nd blue) + P(1st yellow) × P(2nd yellow)
    = $\frac{5}{10} \times \frac{4}{9} + \frac{3}{10} \times \frac{2}{9} + \frac{2}{10} \times \frac{1}{9} = \frac{20}{90} + \frac{6}{90} + \frac{2}{90} = \frac{28}{90} = \frac{14}{45}$

101. P(2 C and 1 D) = P(C, C, D) + P(C, D, C) + P(D, C, C)
     = $\frac{10}{15} \times \frac{9}{14} \times \frac{5}{13} + \frac{10}{15} \times \frac{5}{14} \times \frac{9}{13} + \frac{5}{15} \times \frac{10}{14} \times \frac{9}{13} = \frac{450}{2730} + \frac{450}{2730} + \frac{450}{2730} = \frac{1350}{2730} = \frac{45}{91}$

103. The other card could be the ace or the queen and it is equally likely that it is either one. Thus, the probability the card is the queen is 1/2.

Exercise Set 12.7

1. The probability of E_2 given that E_1 has occurred.

3. $P(E_2 \mid E_1) = \dfrac{n(E_1 \cap E_2)}{n(E_1)} = \dfrac{4}{12} = \dfrac{1}{3}$

5. $P(3 \mid \text{orange}) = \dfrac{n(\text{orange and } 3)}{n(\text{orange})} = \dfrac{1}{3}$

7. $P(\text{even} \mid \text{greater than } 2) = \dfrac{n(\text{greater than 2 and even})}{n(\text{greater than } 2)} = \dfrac{2}{4} = \dfrac{1}{2}$

9. $P(\text{green number} \mid \text{circle is orange}) = \dfrac{n(\text{orange circle and green number})}{n(\text{orange circle})} = \dfrac{2}{3}$

11. $P(4 \mid \text{its purple}) = \dfrac{n(\text{purple and } 4)}{n(\text{purple})} = \dfrac{1}{5}$

13. $P(\text{purple} \mid \text{its odd}) = \dfrac{n(\text{odd and purple})}{n(\text{odd})} = \dfrac{2}{6} = \dfrac{1}{3}$

15. $P(\text{greater than 4} \mid \text{its purple}) = \dfrac{n(\text{purple and greater than } 4)}{n(\text{purple})} = \dfrac{3}{5}$

17. $P(\text{purple} \mid \text{its greater than 5}) = \dfrac{n(\text{greater than 5 and purple})}{n(\text{greater than } 5)} = \dfrac{3}{7}$

19. $P(\text{both \$5s}) = \dfrac{1}{16}$

21. $P(\text{both \$5s} \mid \text{at least one is a \$5}) = \dfrac{1}{7}$

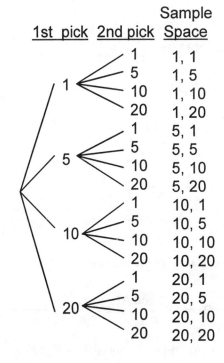

23. $P(\text{sum is 7}) = \dfrac{6}{36} = \dfrac{1}{6}$

25. $P(\text{sum is 7} \mid \text{first die is a 3}) = \dfrac{1}{6}$

27. $P(\text{sum is greater than 7} \mid 2^{nd} \text{ die is a 5})$

$= \dfrac{4}{6} = \dfrac{2}{3}$

Sample space

1 1	3 1	5 1
1 2	3 2	5 2
1 3	3 3	5 3
1 4	3 4	5 4
1 5	3 5	5 5
1 6	3 6	5 6
2 1	4 1	6 1
2 2	4 2	6 2
2 3	4 3	6 3
2 4	4 4	6 4
2 5	4 5	6 5
2 6	4 6	6 6

29. $P(\text{more than \$1 million}) = \dfrac{18}{25}$

31. $P(\text{more than \$2 million} \mid \text{begins with C}) = \dfrac{2}{3}$

33. $P(\text{dh} \mid \text{earns less than \$1 million}) = \dfrac{0}{7} = 0$

35. $P(\text{good}) = \dfrac{95}{135} = \dfrac{19}{27}$

37. $P(\text{poor} \mid \text{dinner}) = \dfrac{25}{70} = \dfrac{5}{14}$

39. $P(\text{back}) = \dfrac{214}{400} = \dfrac{107}{200}$

41. $P(\text{back} \mid \text{male}) = \dfrac{180}{200} = \dfrac{9}{10}$

43. $P(\text{good}) = \dfrac{300}{330} = \dfrac{10}{11}$

45. $P(\text{defective} \mid \text{20 watts}) = \dfrac{15}{95} = \dfrac{3}{19}$

47. $P(\text{good} \mid \text{50 or 100 watts}) = \dfrac{220}{235} = \dfrac{44}{47}$

49. $P(\text{ABC or NBC}) = \dfrac{110}{210} = \dfrac{11}{21}$

51. $P(\text{ABC or NBC} \mid \text{man}) = \dfrac{50}{115} = \dfrac{10}{23}$

53. $P(\text{ABC,NBC,or CBS} \mid \text{man}) = \dfrac{90}{115} = \dfrac{18}{23}$

55. $P(\text{green circle} \mid +) = \dfrac{1}{3}$

59. $P(\text{green or orange circle} \mid \text{green} +) = 1$

57. $P(\text{yellow circle} \mid -) = \dfrac{1}{3}$

61. a) $n(A) = 60 + 80 = 140$

c) $P(A) = \dfrac{140}{200} = \dfrac{7}{10}$

e) $P(A \mid B) = \dfrac{n(B \text{ and } A)}{n(B)} = \dfrac{80}{120} = \dfrac{2}{3}$

g) A and B are not independent events.

63. a) $P(A \mid B) = \dfrac{n(B \text{ and } A)}{n(B)} = \dfrac{0.12}{0.4} = 0.3$

b) $P(B \mid A) = \dfrac{n(A \text{ and } B)}{n(A)} = \dfrac{0.12}{0.3} = 0.4$

c) Yes, $P(A) = P(A \mid B)$ and $P(B) = P(B \mid A)$.

Exercise Set 12.8

1. The counting principle is a method for determining the number of ways that multiple experiments can be performed.

3. Multiply the counting numbers from n down to 1.

5. The number of permutations of n items taken r at a time.

7. $\dfrac{n!}{n_1!\, n_2!\cdots n_r!}$

9. $5! = 5 \cdot 4 \cdot 3 \cdot 2 \cdot 1 = 120$

11. $9! = 9 \cdot 8 \cdot 7 \cdot 6 \cdot 5 \cdot 4 \cdot 3 \cdot 2 \cdot 1 = 362,880$

13. $0! = 1$

15. $_8P_0 = \dfrac{8!}{(8-0)!} = \dfrac{8!}{8!} = 1$

17. $_8P_7 = \dfrac{8!}{(8-7)!} = \dfrac{8!}{1!} = \dfrac{8 \cdot 7 \cdot 6 \cdot 5 \cdot 4 \cdot 3 \cdot 2 \cdot 1}{1} = 40,320$

19. $_8P_8 = \dfrac{8!}{(8-8)!} = \dfrac{8!}{0!} = \dfrac{8 \cdot 7 \cdot 6 \cdot 5 \cdot 4 \cdot 3 \cdot 2 \cdot 1}{1} = 40,320$

21. number of 4 digit codes
    $= 10 \cdot 10 \cdot 10 \cdot 10 = 10^4$
    $= 10,000$ codes

23. a) number of 5 button possibilities
       $= 5^5 = 3,125$

    b) P(correct sequence) $= \dfrac{1}{3125} = 0.00032$

25. a) $7 \times 12 \times 10 = 840$
    b) $12 \times 11 \times 7 = 924$

27. number of possible sound systems
    $= 8 \cdot 10 \cdot 9 = 720$ systems

29. a) $5! = 5 \cdot 4 \cdot 3 \cdot 2 \cdot 1 = 120$
    b) $5! = 5 \cdot 4 \cdot 3 \cdot 2 \cdot 1 = 120$
    c) $4 \cdot 3 \cdot 2 \cdot 1 \cdot 1 = 24$
    d) $1 \cdot 3 \cdot 2 \cdot 1 \cdot 1 = 6$

31. $_8P_3 = \dfrac{8!}{(8-3)!} = \dfrac{8!}{5!} = \dfrac{8 \cdot 7 \cdot 6 \cdot 5!}{5!} = 336$

33. $10^{10} = 10,000,000,000$ possible ISBN numbers

35. $26 \cdot 26 \cdot 10 \cdot 10 \cdot 10 \cdot 10 = 6,760,000$

37. $4 \cdot 25 \cdot 10 \cdot 9 \cdot 8 \cdot 7 = 504,000$

39. $10 \cdot 10 \cdot 10 \cdot 26 \cdot 26 = 676,000$

41. $5 \cdot 4 \cdot 8 \cdot 26 \cdot 25 = 104,000$

43. a) $8 \cdot 10 \cdot 10 \cdot 10 \cdot 10 \cdot 10 \cdot 10$
       $= 8,000,000$

    b) $8 \cdot 10 \cdot 10 \cdot 8,000,000$
       $= 6,400,000,000$

    c) $8 \cdot 10 \cdot 10 \cdot 8 \cdot 10^{10} = 64 \cdot 10^{12}$
       $= 64,000,000,000,000$

45. $_{12}P_3 = \dfrac{12!}{9!} = \dfrac{12 \cdot 11 \cdot 10 \cdot 9!}{9!} = 1,320$

47. $_7P_7 = \dfrac{7!}{0!} = \dfrac{7!}{1} = 7! = 5,040$

49. $5 \cdot 3 \cdot 12 \cdot 4 = 720$

51. $7! = 7 \cdot 6 \cdot 5 \cdot 4 \cdot 3 \cdot 2 \cdot 1 = 5,040$

53. $\dfrac{9!}{4!3!} = \dfrac{9 \cdot 8 \cdot 7 \cdot 6 \cdot 5 \cdot 4 \cdot 3 \cdot 2 \cdot 1}{4 \cdot 3 \cdot 2 \cdot 1 \cdot 3 \cdot 2 \cdot 1} = 2,520$

55. $\dfrac{7!}{2!2!2!} = \dfrac{7 \cdot 6 \cdot 5 \cdot 4 \cdot 3 \cdot 2 \cdot 1}{2 \cdot 1 \cdot 2 \cdot 1 \cdot 2 \cdot 1} = 630$

57. The order of the flags is important. Thus, it is a permutation problem.

$_8P_5 = \dfrac{8!}{(8-5)!} = \dfrac{8!}{3!} = 8 \cdot 7 \cdot 6 \cdot 5 \cdot 4 = 6,720$

59. a) Since the pitcher must bat last, there is only one possibility for the last position.

$$\underline{\ }\ \underline{\ }\ \underline{\ }\ \underline{\ }\ \underline{\ }\ \underline{\ }\ \underline{\ }\ \underline{\ }\ \underline{1}$$

There are 8 possible batters left for the first position. Once the first batter has been selected, there are 7 batters left for the second position, 6 for the third, etc.

$$\underline{8} \cdot \underline{7} \cdot \underline{6} \cdot \underline{5} \cdot \underline{4} \cdot \underline{3} \cdot \underline{2} \cdot \underline{1} \cdot \underline{1} = 40,320$$

   b) $9! = 9 \cdot 8 \cdot 7 \cdot 6 \cdot 5 \cdot 4 \cdot 3 \cdot 2 \cdot 1 = 362,880$

61. a) $5^5 = 3125$ different ways   b) $400,000 \div 3,125 = 128$ cars

   c) $\dfrac{128}{400000} = \dfrac{1}{3125} = 0.00032$

63. $_7P_5 = \dfrac{7!}{2!} = \dfrac{7 \cdot 6 \cdot 5 \cdot 4 \cdot 3 \cdot 2!}{2!} = 2,520$ different letter permutations

   Time $= 2520 \times 5$ sec. $= 12,600$ sec. or 210 min. or 3.5 hours

65. No, Ex. $_3P_2 \neq {_3P_{(3-2)}}$

$$\frac{3!}{1!} \neq \frac{3!}{2!}$$

$$6 \neq 3$$

Exercise Set 12.9

1. The selection of a certain number of items without regard to their order.

3. $_nC_r = \dfrac{n!}{(n-r)! \cdot r!}$

5. If the order of the items is important then it is a permutation problem. If order is not important then it is a combination problem.

7. $_6C_3 = \dfrac{6!}{(6-3)!3!} = \dfrac{6 \cdot 5 \cdot 4 \cdot 3 \cdot 2 \cdot 1}{3 \cdot 2 \cdot 1 \cdot 3 \cdot 2 \cdot 1} = 20$

9. a) $_7C_3 = \dfrac{7!}{4!3!} = \dfrac{7 \cdot 6 \cdot 5 \cdot 4 \cdot 3 \cdot 2 \cdot 1}{4 \cdot 3 \cdot 2 \cdot 1 \cdot 3 \cdot 2 \cdot 1} = 35$

   b) $_7P_3 = \dfrac{7!}{(7-3)!} = \dfrac{7 \cdot 6 \cdot 5 \cdot 4!}{4!} = 7 \cdot 6 \cdot 5 = 210$

11. a) $_8C_2 = \dfrac{8!}{(8-2)!2!} = \dfrac{8 \cdot 7 \cdot 6!}{6! \cdot 2!} = \dfrac{8 \cdot 7}{2 \cdot 1} = 28$

   b) $_8P_2 = \dfrac{8!}{(8-2)!} = \dfrac{8 \cdot 7 \cdot 6!}{6!} = 8 \cdot 7 = 56$

13. a) $_{10}C_3 = \dfrac{10!}{7!3!} = \dfrac{10 \cdot 9 \cdot 8 \cdot 7!}{7! \cdot 3 \cdot 2 \cdot 1} = 120$

   b) $_{10}P_3 = \dfrac{10!}{(10-3)!} = \dfrac{10 \cdot 9 \cdot 8 \cdot 7!}{7!} = 10 \cdot 9 \cdot 8 = 720$

15. $\dfrac{_5C_3}{_5P_3} = \dfrac{\frac{5!}{2!3!}}{\frac{5!}{2!}} = \dfrac{5!}{2!3!} \cdot \dfrac{2!}{5!} = \dfrac{1}{3!} = \dfrac{1}{6}$

17. $\dfrac{_8C_5}{_8P_5} = \dfrac{\frac{8!}{3!5!}}{\frac{8!}{6!2!}} = \dfrac{8!}{3!5!} \cdot \dfrac{6!2!}{8!}$

   $= \dfrac{6 \cdot 5 \cdot 4 \cdot 3 \cdot 2 \cdot 1 \cdot 2 \cdot 1}{3 \cdot 2 \cdot 1 \cdot 5 \cdot 4 \cdot 3 \cdot 2 \cdot 1} = 2$

19. $_{20}C_3 = \dfrac{20!}{17!3!} = \dfrac{20 \cdot 19 \cdot 18 \cdot 17!}{17! \cdot 3 \cdot 2 \cdot 1} = 1140$

21. $_5C_4 = \dfrac{5!}{1!4!} = 5$

23. $_{12}C_8 = \dfrac{12!}{4!8!} = \dfrac{12 \cdot 11 \cdot 10 \cdot 9 \cdot 8!}{4 \cdot 3 \cdot 2 \cdot 1 \cdot 8!} = 495$

25. $_8C_4 = \dfrac{8!}{4!4!} = \dfrac{8 \cdot 7 \cdot 6 \cdot 5 \cdot 4!}{4! \cdot 4 \cdot 3 \cdot 2 \cdot 1} = 70$

29. $3 \cdot 2 = 6$

27. $3 \cdot 2 = 6$

31. $_8C_2 = \dfrac{8!}{6!2!} = \dfrac{8 \cdot 7}{2 \cdot 1} = 28$ tickets

33. Fast songs:

$_{10}C_6 = \dfrac{10!}{4!6!} = \dfrac{10 \cdot 9 \cdot 8 \cdot 7}{4 \cdot 3 \cdot 2 \cdot 1} = 210$

210 · 35 = 7,350 possible combinations

Slow songs:

$_7C_4 = \dfrac{7!}{3!4!} = \dfrac{7 \cdot 6 \cdot 5}{3 \cdot 2 \cdot 1} = 35$

35. Mathematics:

$_8C_5 = \dfrac{8!}{3!5!} = \dfrac{8 \cdot 7 \cdot 6}{3 \cdot 2 \cdot 1} = 56$

56 · 10 = 560 different choices

Computer Science:

$_5C_3 = \dfrac{5!}{2!3!} = \dfrac{5 \cdot 4}{2 \cdot 1} = 10$

37. Teachers:

$_6C_2 = \dfrac{6!}{4!2!} = \dfrac{6 \cdot 5}{2 \cdot 1} = 15$

15 • 19,600 = 294,000 ways to select the committee

Students:

$_{50}C_3 = \dfrac{50!}{47!3!} = \dfrac{50 \cdot 49 \cdot 48}{3 \cdot 2 \cdot 1} = 19,600$

39. Total combinations $= _{12}C_5 \bullet {}_9C_7 = \dfrac{12!}{4! \cdot 5!} \cdot \dfrac{9!}{2! \cdot 7!} = (792)(36) = 28,512$

41. Oat:

$_6C_3 = \dfrac{6!}{3!3!} = \dfrac{6 \cdot 5 \cdot 4}{3 \cdot 2 \cdot 1} = 20$

Rice:

$_4C_2 = \dfrac{4!}{2!2!} = \dfrac{4 \cdot 3}{2 \cdot 1} = 6$

Wheat:

$_5C_2 = \dfrac{5!}{3!2!} = \dfrac{5 \cdot 4}{2 \cdot 1} = 10$

Total number of combinations = 20 · 10 · 6 = 1,200

43. a) $_{10}C_8 = \dfrac{10!}{2!8!} = \dfrac{10 \cdot 9}{2 \cdot 1} = 45$

b) $_{10}C_8 + {}_{10}C_9 + {}_{10}C_{10} = 45 + 10 + 1 = 56$

45. a) The order of the numbers is important. For example: if the combination is 12 - 4 - 23, the lock will not open if 4 - 12 - 23 is used. Since repetition is permitted, it is not a true permutation problem.

b) 40 · 40 · 40 = 64,000

c) 40 · 39 · 38 = 59,280

47. a) $_{46}C_6 = \dfrac{46!}{40!6!} = 9,366,819$

    b) $_{47}C_6 = \dfrac{47!}{41!6!} = 10,737,573$

    c) $_{48}C_6 = \dfrac{48!}{42!6!} = 12,271,512$

    d) $_{49}C_6 = \dfrac{49!}{43!6!} = 13,983,816$

    e) No

49. a) $4! = 24$ b) $4! = 24$

Exercise Set 12.10

1. $P(\text{4 red balls}) = \dfrac{\text{no. of 4 red ball comb.}}{\text{no. of 4 ball comb.}} = \dfrac{_6C_4}{_{10}C_4}$

3. $P(\text{12 girls}) = \dfrac{\text{no. of 12 girl comb.}}{\text{no. of 12 children comb.}} = \dfrac{_{19}C_{12}}{_{34}C_{12}}$

5. $P(\text{all 8 are wilson}) = \dfrac{\text{no. of 8 wilson comb.}}{\text{no. of 8 ball comb.}} = \dfrac{_{22}C_8}{_{70}C_8}$

7. $P(\text{none of the 9 are oak}) = \dfrac{\text{no. of 9 non-oak comb.}}{\text{no. of 9 tree comb.}} = \dfrac{_{14}C_9}{_{30}C_9}$

9. $_5C_3 = \dfrac{5!}{2!3!} = \dfrac{5 \cdot 4}{2 \cdot 1} = 10$

    $_9C_3 = \dfrac{9!}{6!3!} = \dfrac{9 \cdot 8 \cdot 7}{3 \cdot 2 \cdot 1} = 84$

    $P(\text{3 reds}) = \dfrac{10}{84} = \dfrac{5}{42}$

11. $_4C_3 = \dfrac{4!}{1!3!} = \dfrac{4}{1} = 4$

    $_8C_3 = \dfrac{8!}{5!3!} = \dfrac{8 \cdot 7 \cdot 6}{3 \cdot 2 \cdot 1} = 56$

    $P(\text{3 good batteries}) = \dfrac{4}{56} = \dfrac{1}{14}$

13. $_5C_3 = \dfrac{5!}{2!3!} = \dfrac{5 \cdot 4}{2 \cdot 1} = 10$

    $_{10}C_3 = \dfrac{10!}{7!3!} = \dfrac{10 \cdot 9 \cdot 8}{3 \cdot 2 \cdot 1} = 120$

    $P(\text{3 greater than 4}) = \dfrac{10}{120} = \dfrac{1}{12}$

15. $_6C_4 = \dfrac{6!}{2!4!} = \dfrac{6 \cdot 5}{2 \cdot 1} = 15$

    $_{10}C_4 = \dfrac{10!}{6!4!} = \dfrac{10 \cdot 9 \cdot 8 \cdot 7}{4 \cdot 3 \cdot 2 \cdot 1} = 210$

    $P(\text{all 4 ride Huffy}) = \dfrac{15}{210} = \dfrac{1}{14}$

17. $_{46}C_6 = \dfrac{46!}{40!6!} = 9,366,819$ $_6C_6 = 1$, $P(\text{win grand prize}) = \dfrac{1}{9,366,819}$

19. $_2C_2 = \dfrac{2!}{0!2!} = 1$

    $_5C_2 = \dfrac{5!}{3!2!} = \dfrac{5 \cdot 4}{2 \cdot 1} = 10$

    $P(\text{both cars}) = \dfrac{1}{10}$

21. $P(\text{at least 1 car}) = 1 - P(\text{no cars}) = 1 - \dfrac{3}{10} = \dfrac{7}{10}$

For problems 23 – 25 we will use the fact that, $_{25}C_3 = \dfrac{25!}{22!\cdot 3!} = 2300$

23. $_{10}C_3 = \dfrac{10!}{7!3!} = 120$

P(all 3 are pitchers) $= \dfrac{120}{2300} = \dfrac{6}{115}$

25. $_{10}C_2 = \dfrac{10!}{8!\cdot 2!} = 45$; $\quad _6C_1 = \dfrac{6!}{5!\cdot 1!} = 6$

P(2 pitchers and 1 infielder) $= \dfrac{45\cdot 6}{2300} = \dfrac{27}{230}$

For problems 27 – 29 use the fact that, $_{39}C_{12} = \dfrac{39!}{27!12!} = 3{,}910{,}797{,}436$

27. $_{22}C_{12} = \dfrac{22!}{10!12!} = 646{,}646$

P(all women) $= \dfrac{646646}{3910797436} = 0.0001653$

29. $_{17}C_6 = \dfrac{17!}{11!6!} = 12{,}376$

$_{22}C_6 = \dfrac{22!}{16!6!} = 74{,}613$

P(6 men and 6 women)

$= \dfrac{(12376)(74613)}{3910797436} = 0.236$

For problems 31 – 33 use the fact that, $_{15}C_4 = \dfrac{15!}{11!4!} = \dfrac{15\cdot 14\cdot 13\cdot 12}{4\cdot 3\cdot 2\cdot 1} = 1365$

31. $_5C_2 = \dfrac{5!}{3!2!} = \dfrac{5\cdot 4}{2\cdot 1} = 10$

$_6C_2 = \dfrac{6!}{4!2!} = \dfrac{6\cdot 5}{2\cdot 1} = 15$

P(2 A, 2 B) $= \dfrac{10\cdot 15}{1365} = \dfrac{10}{91}$

33. $_9C_4 = \dfrac{9!}{5!4!} = \dfrac{9\cdot 8\cdot 7\cdot 6}{4\cdot 3\cdot 2\cdot 1} = 126$

P(no C) $= \dfrac{126}{1365} = \dfrac{6}{65}$

P(at least 1 C) $= 1 - P(\text{no C}) = 1 - \dfrac{6}{65} = \dfrac{59}{65}$

For problems 35 – 37 use the fact that, $_{11}C_5 = \dfrac{11!}{6!5!} = \dfrac{11\cdot 10\cdot 9\cdot 8\cdot 7}{5\cdot 4\cdot 3\cdot 2\cdot 1} = 462$

35. $_6C_5 = \dfrac{6!}{1!5!} = \dfrac{6}{1} = 6$

P(5 women first) $= \dfrac{6}{462} = \dfrac{1}{77}$

37. Any one of the 6 women can sit in any one of the five seats - 30 possibilities.

P(exactly 1 woman) $= \dfrac{30}{462} = \dfrac{5}{77}$

39. $_{24}C_6 = \dfrac{24!}{18!6!} = 134{,}596$; $\quad _3C_3 = 1$; $\quad _{21}C_3 = \dfrac{21!}{18!3!} = 1{,}330$

P(three brothers are selected) $= \dfrac{_3C_3 \cdot {}_{21}C_3}{_{24}C_6} = \dfrac{(1)(1330)}{134596} = 0.00988$

41. $_7C_5 = \dfrac{7!}{2!5!} = \dfrac{7\cdot 6}{2\cdot 1} = 21$ and from problem 9, $_{52}C_5 = 2{,}598{,}960$

a) P(royal spade flush) $= \dfrac{21}{2598960} = \dfrac{1}{123760}$

b) P(any royal flush) $= \dfrac{4}{123760} = \dfrac{1}{30940}$

For problems 42 – 45 use the fact that, total combinations = $18 \cdot 18 \cdot 18 = 5832$.

43. $_4C_1 \cdot _5C_1 \cdot _2C_1 = 4 \cdot 5 \cdot 2 = 40$

P(3 cherries) = $\dfrac{40}{5832} = \dfrac{5}{729}$

45. $_{14}C_1 \cdot _{13}C_1 \cdot _{14}C_1 = 14 \cdot 13 \cdot 14 = 2548$

P(no cherries) = $\dfrac{2548}{5832} = \dfrac{637}{1458}$

P(at least 1 cherry) = $1 - \dfrac{637}{1458} = \dfrac{821}{1458}$

47. A slate of 3 officers can be selected from 15 people in $15 \cdot 14 \cdot 13 = 2730$ ways. From the remaining 12 people, committees of 5 can be selected in

$$_{12}C_5 = \dfrac{12!}{7!5!} = \dfrac{12 \cdot 11 \cdot 10 \cdot 9 \cdot 8}{5 \cdot 4 \cdot 3 \cdot 2 \cdot 1} = 792 \text{ ways}$$

Thus, the number of ways to select the officers and committee is $2730 \cdot 792 = 2{,}162{,}160$.

a) P(specific slate, specific committee) = $\dfrac{1}{2162160}$

b) P(any 3 of the 8 for officers) = $\dfrac{8 \cdot 7 \cdot 6}{2162160} = \dfrac{1}{6435}$

Exercise Set 12.11

1. A probability distribution shows the probability associated with each specific outcome of an experiment. In a probability distribution every possible outcome must be listed and the sum of all the probabilities must be 1.

3. $P(x) = {_nC_x}\, p^x q^{n-x}$

5. $P(1) = {_4C_1}(0.1)^1 (0.9)^{4-1}$
   $= 4 \cdot (0.1)^1 (0.9)^3$
   $= 0.2916$

7. $P(2) = {_5C_2}(0.4)^2 (0.6)^{5-2}$
   $= 10 \cdot (0.4)^2 (0.6)^3$
   $= 0.3456$

9. $P(0) = {_4C_0}(0.5)^0 (0.5)^{4-0}$
   $= 1 \cdot (0.5)^0 (0.5)^4$
   $= 1 \cdot 1 \cdot (0.5)^4 = 0.0625$

11. $p = 0.15$, $q = 1 - p = 1 - 0.15 = 0.85$
    a) $P(x) = {_nC_x}(0.15)^x (0.85)^{n-x}$
    b) $n = 12$, $x = 2$, $p = 0.15$, $q = 0.85$
    $P(2) = {_{12}C_2}(0.15)^2 (0.85)^{12-2}$

13. $P(1) = {_5C_1}(0.2)^1 (0.8)^{5-1}$
    $= 5 \cdot (0.2)^1 (0.8)^4$
    $= 0.4096$

15. $P(2) = {_3C_2}(0.96)^2 (0.04)^{3-2}$
    $= 3 \cdot (0.96)^2 (0.04)^1$
    $= 0.1106$

17. $P(4) = {_6C_4}(0.92)^4 (0.08)^{6-4}$
    $= 15 \cdot (0.92)^4 (0.08)^2$
    $= 0.0688$

19. $P(3) = {_4C_3}\left(\frac{2}{3}\right)^3 \left(\frac{1}{3}\right)^{4-3}$
    $= 4 \cdot \left(\frac{2}{3}\right)^3 \left(\frac{1}{3}\right)^1$
    $= \dfrac{32}{81} = 0.3951$

21. a) $P(0) = {}_5C_0 (0.6)^0 (0.4)^{5-0}$

$= 1 \cdot 1 \cdot (0.4)^5$

$= 0.0102$

b) $P(\text{at least } 1) = 1 - P(0) = 0.9898$

23. a) $P(3) = {}_6C_3 \left(\frac{12}{52}\right)^3 \left(\frac{40}{52}\right)^3$

$= 20 \cdot \left(\frac{3}{13}\right)^3 \left(\frac{10}{13}\right)^3$

$= 0.1119$

b) $P(2) = {}_6C_2 \left(\frac{13}{52}\right)^2 \left(\frac{39}{52}\right)^4$

$= 15 \cdot \left(\frac{1}{4}\right)^2 \left(\frac{3}{4}\right)^4$

$= 0.2966$

Review Exercises

1. Relative frequency over the long run can accurately be predicted, not individual events or totals.

2. Roll the die many times then compute the relative frequency of each outcome and compare with the expected probability 1/6.

3. $P(\text{heads}) = \frac{55}{60} = \frac{11}{12} = 0.92$

4. Your answer should be close to 0.25.

5. $P(\text{male}) = \frac{58}{100} = \frac{29}{50} = 0.58$

6. $P(\text{odd}) = \frac{5}{10} = \frac{1}{2}$

7. $P(\text{even or greater than } 4) = \frac{8}{10} = \frac{4}{5}$

8. $P(\text{greater than 2 or less than 5}) = \frac{10}{10} = 1$

9. $P(\text{even and greater than } 4) = \frac{2}{10} = \frac{1}{5}$

10. $P(\text{coke}) = \frac{17}{50}$

11. $P(\text{Pepsi}) = \frac{15}{50} = \frac{3}{10}$

12. $P(\text{Dr. Pepper or 7-up}) = \frac{10+8}{50} = \frac{18}{50} = \frac{9}{25}$

13. $P(\text{coke or pepsi or 7-up}) = \frac{17+15+8}{50} = \frac{40}{50} = \frac{4}{5}$

14. $P(\text{gold star}) = \frac{1}{10}$, $P(\text{not gold star}) = \frac{9}{10}$

   a) odds against gold star $= \dfrac{P(\text{not gold star})}{P(\text{gold star})}$

   $= \dfrac{9/10}{1/10} = \dfrac{9}{10} \cdot \dfrac{10}{1} = \dfrac{9}{1}$ or 9:1

   b) odds in favor of gold star are 1:9

15. odds against corn $= \dfrac{P(\text{not corn})}{P(\text{corn})} = \dfrac{5/8}{3/8} = \dfrac{5}{8} \cdot \dfrac{8}{3} = \dfrac{5}{3}$ or 5:3

16. $P(\text{winning}) = \dfrac{3}{2+3} = \dfrac{3}{5}$

17. odds in favor of restaurant succeeding $= \dfrac{P(\text{succeeds})}{P(\text{ not succeed})} = \dfrac{0.6}{0.4} = \dfrac{6/10}{4/10} = \dfrac{6}{10} \cdot \dfrac{10}{4} = \dfrac{6}{4} = \dfrac{3}{2}$ or 3:2

18. a) E = P(win $200) · $198 + P(win $100) · $98 + P(lose) · (–$2)

$$= \frac{3}{1000} \cdot 198 + \frac{2}{1000} \cdot 98 - \frac{995}{1000} \cdot 2 = \frac{594}{1000} + \frac{196}{1000} - \frac{1990}{1000} = \frac{1200}{1000} = -\$1.20$$

   b) The expectation of a person who purchases three tickets would be 3(–1.20) = –$3.60.

   c) Expected value = Fair price – Cost
$$-1.20 = \text{Fair price} - 2.00$$
$$80¢ = \text{Fair price}$$

19. a) E_{Cameron} = P(picture card)($9) + P(not a picture card)(–$3) = $\frac{12}{52}(9) - \frac{40}{52}(3) = \frac{27}{13} - \frac{30}{13} = \frac{-3}{13} \approx -\$0.23$

   b) E_{Lindsey} = P(picture card)(–$9) + P(not a picture card)($3) = $\frac{-27}{13} + \frac{30}{13} = \frac{3}{13} \approx \$0.23$

   c) Cameron can expect to lose $100 \cdot \left(\frac{3}{13}\right) \approx \$23.08$

20. E = P(sunny)(1000) + P(cloudy)(500) + P(rain)(100)
$$= 0.4(1000) + 0.5(500) + 0.1(100) = 400 + 250 + 10 = 660 \text{ people}$$

21. a)

b) Sample Space

President	Vice Pres.	Sample Space
T	J	T, J
	G	T, G
	C	T, C
J	T	J, T
	G	J, G
	C	J, C
G	T	G, T
	J	G, J
	C	G, C
C	T	C, T
	J	C, J
	G	C, G

   c) P(Gina is Pres. and Jake V.P.) = $\frac{1}{12}$

22. a)

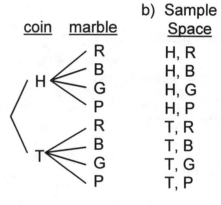

b) Sample Space

coin	marble	Sample Space
H	R	H, R
	B	H, B
	G	H, G
	P	H, P
T	R	T, R
	B	T, B
	G	T, G
	P	T, P

   c) P(heads, and red or purple) = $\frac{2}{8} = \frac{1}{4}$

23. P(outer is odd and inner is odd) = P(outer is odd) · P(inner is odd) = $\frac{4}{8} \cdot \frac{4}{8} = \frac{1}{2} \cdot \frac{1}{2} = \frac{1}{4}$

24. P(outer is greater than 5 and inner is greater than 5)

   = P(outer is greater than 5) · P(inner is greater than 5) = $\frac{3}{8} \cdot \frac{3}{8} = \frac{9}{64}$

25. P(outer odd and inner less than 6) = P(outer odd) · P(inner less than 6) = $\frac{4}{8} \cdot \frac{5}{8} = \frac{1}{2} \cdot \frac{5}{8} = \frac{5}{16}$

26. P(outer is even or less than 6) = P(even) + P(less than 6) – P(even and less than 6) = $\frac{4}{8} + \frac{5}{8} - \frac{2}{8} = \frac{7}{8}$

27. P(inner is not blue or is even) = P(not blue) + P(even) − P(not blue and even) = $\dfrac{6}{8} + \dfrac{4}{8} - \dfrac{2}{8} = \dfrac{8}{8} = 1$

28. P(outer is blue and inner is not blue) = P(outer blue) · P(inner not blue) = $\dfrac{2}{8} \cdot \dfrac{6}{8} = \dfrac{1}{4} \cdot \dfrac{3}{4} = \dfrac{3}{16}$

29. P(all 3 are Hersheys) = $\dfrac{5}{12} \cdot \dfrac{4}{11} \cdot \dfrac{3}{10} = \dfrac{60}{1320} = \dfrac{1}{22}$

30. P(none are Nestle) = $\dfrac{8}{12} \cdot \dfrac{7}{11} \cdot \dfrac{6}{10} = \dfrac{336}{1320} = \dfrac{14}{55}$

31. P(at least one is Nestle) = 1 − P(none are Nestle) = $1 - \dfrac{14}{55} = \dfrac{55}{55} - \dfrac{14}{55} = \dfrac{41}{55}$

32. P(Hershey and Hershey and Reese) = $\dfrac{5}{12} \cdot \dfrac{4}{11} \cdot \dfrac{3}{10} = \dfrac{60}{1320} = \dfrac{1}{22}$

33. P(red) = $\dfrac{1}{4}$

34. odds against red = $\dfrac{P(\text{not red})}{P(\text{red})} = \dfrac{3/4}{1/4} = \dfrac{3}{4} \cdot \dfrac{4}{1} = \dfrac{3}{1}$ or 3:1

    The odds in favor of red are then 1:3.

35. fair price = P(red)($5) = $\dfrac{1}{4}(5) = \dfrac{5}{4}$ = $1.25

36. P(red and then gray) = P(red) · P(gray) = $\dfrac{1}{4} \cdot \dfrac{1}{2} = \dfrac{1}{8}$

37. P(not gray) = $\dfrac{1}{4} + \dfrac{1}{4} + \dfrac{1}{8} = \dfrac{5}{8}$

38. odds in favor of gray = $\dfrac{P(\text{gray})}{P(\text{not gray})} = \dfrac{3/8}{5/8} = \dfrac{3}{8} \cdot \dfrac{8}{5} = \dfrac{3}{5}$ or 3:5

    The odds against gray are then 5:3.

39. E = P(gray)($10) + P(red)($5) + P(yellow)(−$20)= $\dfrac{3}{8}(10) + \dfrac{1}{2}(5) - \dfrac{1}{8}(20) = \dfrac{15}{4} + \dfrac{10}{4} - \dfrac{10}{4} = \dfrac{15}{4}$ = $3.75

40. P(at least one red) = 1 − P(none are red) = $1 - \left(\dfrac{1}{2} \cdot \dfrac{1}{2} \cdot \dfrac{1}{2}\right) = 1 - \dfrac{1}{8} = \dfrac{7}{8}$

41. P(fewer than 6 defects | American built) = $\dfrac{89}{106} = 0.84$

42. P(fewer than 6 defects | foreign built) = $\dfrac{55}{74} = 0.74$

43. P(six or more defects | foreign built) = $\dfrac{19}{74} = 0.26$

44. P(six or more defects | American built) = $\dfrac{17}{106} = 0.16$

45. P(right handed) = $\dfrac{230}{400} = \dfrac{23}{40}$

46. P(left brained | left handed) = $\dfrac{30}{170} = \dfrac{3}{17}$

47. P(right handed | no predominance) = $\dfrac{60}{80} = \dfrac{3}{4}$

48. P(right brained | left handed) = $\dfrac{120}{170} = \dfrac{12}{17}$

49. a) $_4P_4 = \dfrac{4!}{(4-4)!} = \dfrac{4!}{0!} = 4! = 4\cdot 3\cdot 2\cdot 1 = 24$ ways

   b) $E = \dfrac{1}{4}(10,000) + \dfrac{1}{4}(1,000) + \dfrac{1}{4}(500) + \dfrac{1}{4}(100) = \$2,900$

50. number of possible arrangements = $_5C_2 \cdot {}_3C_2 \cdot {}_1C_1 = \dfrac{5!}{3!2!} \cdot \dfrac{3!}{1!2!} \cdot \dfrac{1!}{0!1!} = 10 \cdot 3 \cdot 1 = 30$

51. $_8P_3 = \dfrac{8!}{(8-3)!} = \dfrac{8!}{5!} = \dfrac{8\cdot 7\cdot 6\cdot 5!}{5!} = 336$

52. $_9P_3 = \dfrac{9!}{(93)!} = \dfrac{9!}{6!} = 9\cdot 8\cdot 7 = 504$

53. $_6C_3 = \dfrac{6!}{3!3!} = \dfrac{6\cdot 5\cdot 4}{3\cdot 2\cdot 1} = 20$

54. a) $_{15}C_{10} = \dfrac{15!}{5!10!} = \dfrac{15\cdot 14\cdot 13\cdot 12\cdot 11}{5\cdot 4\cdot 3\cdot 2\cdot 1} = 3,003$

   b) number of arrangements = $10! = 3,628,800$

55. a) P(match 5 numbers) = $\dfrac{1}{_{50}C_5} = \dfrac{1}{\dfrac{50!}{45!5!}} = \dfrac{45!5!}{50!} = \dfrac{1}{2118760}$

   b) P(Big game win) = P(match 5 numbers and match Big number)

   = P(match 5 numbers) • P(match Big number) = $\dfrac{1}{2118760} \cdot \dfrac{1}{36} = \dfrac{1}{76275360}$

56. $_4C_2 \cdot {}_6C_3 = \dfrac{4!}{2!2!} \cdot \dfrac{6!}{3!3!} = 6 \cdot 20 = 120$ combinations

57. $_8C_3 \cdot {}_5C_2 = \dfrac{8!}{5!3!} \cdot \dfrac{5!}{3!2!} = \dfrac{8\cdot 7\cdot 6}{3\cdot 2\cdot 1} \cdot \dfrac{5\cdot 4}{2\cdot 1} = 560$

58. P(two aces) = $\dfrac{_4C_2}{_{52}C_2} = \dfrac{\dfrac{4!}{2!2!}}{\dfrac{52!}{50!2!}} = \dfrac{4!}{2!2!} \cdot \dfrac{50!2!}{52!} = \dfrac{1}{221}$

59. P(all three are red) = $\dfrac{5}{10} \cdot \dfrac{4}{9} \cdot \dfrac{3}{8} = \dfrac{1}{12}$

60. P(first two are red and 3rd is blue) = $\dfrac{5}{10} \cdot \dfrac{4}{9} \cdot \dfrac{2}{8} = \dfrac{1}{18}$

61. P(1st red, 2nd white, 3rd blue) = $\dfrac{5}{10} \cdot \dfrac{3}{9} \cdot \dfrac{2}{8} = \dfrac{1}{24}$

62. P(at least one red) = 1 – P(none are red) = $1 - \left(\dfrac{5}{10} \cdot \dfrac{4}{9} \cdot \dfrac{3}{8}\right) = 1 - \dfrac{1}{12} = \dfrac{11}{12}$

63. P(3 maples) = $\dfrac{6}{14} \cdot \dfrac{5}{13} \cdot \dfrac{4}{12} = \dfrac{5}{91}$

64. P(two pines and one maple) = $\dfrac{_5C_2 \cdot {}_6C_1}{_{14}C_3} = \dfrac{\dfrac{5!}{3!2!} \cdot \dfrac{6!}{5!1!}}{\dfrac{14!}{11!3!}} = \dfrac{15}{91}$

65. P(no pines) = $\dfrac{9}{14} \cdot \dfrac{8}{13} \cdot \dfrac{7}{12} = \dfrac{3}{13}$

66. P(at least one pine) = 1 − P(no pines) = $1 - \dfrac{3}{13} = \dfrac{10}{13}$

67. a) $P(x) = {}_nC_x (0.6)^x (0.4)^{n-x}$

     b) $P(75) = {}_{100}C_{75} (0.6)^{75} (0.4)^{25}$

68. n = 5, x = 3, p = 1/5, q = 4/5

$$P(3) = {}_5C_3 \left(\frac{1}{5}\right)^3 \left(\frac{4}{5}\right)^2$$

$$= 10 \cdot \left(\frac{1}{5}\right)^3 \left(\frac{4}{5}\right)^2 = 0.0512$$

69. a) n = 4, p = 0.6, q = 0.4

$$P(0) = {}_4C_0 (0.6)^0 (0.4)^4$$

$$= 1 \cdot 1 \cdot (0.4)^4 = 0.0256$$

     b) P(at least 1) = 1 − P(0)

$$= 1 - 0.0256$$

$$= 0.9744$$

Chapter Test

1. P(fishing for bass) = $\dfrac{14}{20} = \dfrac{7}{10} = 0.7$

2. P(greater than 7) = $\dfrac{2}{9} \approx 0.22$

3. P(odd) = $\dfrac{5}{9} \approx 0.55$

4. P(even or greater than 4) = $\dfrac{7}{9} \approx 0.78$

5. P(odd and greater than 4) = $\dfrac{3}{9} = \dfrac{1}{3} \approx 0.33$

6. P(both greater than 5) = $\dfrac{4}{9} \cdot \dfrac{3}{8} = \dfrac{12}{72} = \dfrac{1}{6}$

7. P(both even) = $\dfrac{4}{9} \cdot \dfrac{3}{8} = \dfrac{1 \cdot 1}{3 \cdot 2} = \dfrac{1}{6}$

8. P(1st odd, 2nd even) = $\dfrac{5}{9} \cdot \dfrac{4}{8} = \dfrac{5}{9} \cdot \dfrac{1}{2} = \dfrac{5}{18}$

9. P(neither greater than 6) = $\dfrac{6}{9} \cdot \dfrac{5}{8} = \dfrac{1 \cdot 5}{3 \cdot 4} = \dfrac{5}{12}$

10. P(red or picture)

     = P(red) + P(picture) − P(red and picture)

     $= \dfrac{26}{52} + \dfrac{12}{52} - \dfrac{6}{52} = \dfrac{32}{52} = \dfrac{8}{13}$

11. 6 • 3 = 18

12.

die	letter	Sample Space
1	a	1, a
	b	1, b
	c	1, c
2	a	2, a
	b	2, b
	c	2, c
3	a	3, a
	b	3, b
	c	3, c
4	a	4, a
	b	4, b
	c	4, c
5	a	5, a
	b	5, b
	c	5, c
6	a	6, a
	b	6, b
	c	6, c

13. $P(4 \text{ and a}) = \dfrac{1}{18}$

14. $P(4 \text{ or a}) = \dfrac{8}{18} = \dfrac{4}{9}$

15. $P(\text{even number or b}) = \dfrac{12}{18} = \dfrac{2}{3}$

16. Number of codes $= 9 \cdot 26 \cdot 26 \cdot 10 \cdot 10 = 608{,}400$

17. odds against male $= \dfrac{P(\text{not male})}{P(\text{male})}$

$= \dfrac{3/8}{5/8} = \dfrac{3}{8} \cdot \dfrac{8}{5} = \dfrac{3}{5}$ or 3:5

18. odds against Aimee winning are 5:2 or

$\dfrac{5}{2} = \dfrac{5/7}{2/7} = \dfrac{P(\text{not winning})}{P(\text{winning})}$

Therefore, $P(\text{Aimee wins}) = 2/7$

19. $E = P(\text{club})(\$8) + P(\text{heart})(\$4) + P(\text{spade or diamond})(-\$6)$

$= \dfrac{1}{4}(10) + \dfrac{1}{4}(4) + \dfrac{2}{4}(-6) = \dfrac{8}{4} + \dfrac{4}{4} - \dfrac{12}{4} = \dfrac{0}{4} = \$0$

20. $P(\text{gray squirrel} \mid \text{Yosemite}) = \dfrac{60}{105} = \dfrac{4}{7}$

21. ${}_6P_3 = \dfrac{6!}{(6-3)!} = \dfrac{6!}{3!} = 6 \cdot 5 \cdot 4 = 120$

22. $P(\text{neither is good}) = \dfrac{8}{20} \cdot \dfrac{7}{19} = \dfrac{2}{5} \cdot \dfrac{7}{19} = \dfrac{14}{95}$

23. $P(\text{at least 1 good})$

$= 1 - P(\text{neither is good}) = 1 - \dfrac{14}{95} = \dfrac{81}{95}$

24. ${}_7C_3 = \dfrac{7!}{4!3!} = \dfrac{7 \cdot 6 \cdot 5}{3 \cdot 2 \cdot 1} = 35$

${}_5C_2 = \dfrac{5!}{3!2!} = \dfrac{5 \cdot 4}{2 \cdot 1} = 10$

${}_{10}C_5 = \dfrac{12!}{7!5!} = \dfrac{12 \cdot 11 \cdot 10 \cdot 9 \cdot 8}{5 \cdot 4 \cdot 3 \cdot 2 \cdot 1} = 792$

$P(3 \text{ red and 2 green}) = \dfrac{35 \cdot 10}{792} = \dfrac{175}{396}$

25. $n = 4$, $x = 3$, $p = 3/5$, $q = 2/5$

$P(3) = {}_4C_3 \left(\dfrac{3}{5}\right)^3 \left(\dfrac{2}{5}\right)^{4-3} = 4 \cdot \left(\dfrac{3}{5}\right)^3 \left(\dfrac{2}{5}\right)^1 = 0.3456$

CHAPTER THIRTEEN

STATISTICS

Exercise Set 13.1

1. **Descriptive statistics** is concerned with the collection, organization, and analysis of data.
   Inferential statistics is concerned with making generalizations or predictions from the data collected.
3. Answers will vary.
5. Answers will vary.
7. a) A **population** consists of all items or people of interest.
   b) A **sample** is a subset of the population.
9. a) A **systematic sample** is a sample obtained by selecting every n^{th} item on a list or production line.
   b) Use a random number table to select the first item, then select every n^{th} item after that.
11. a) A **stratified sample** is obtained when the population is divided into parts, called strata.
    b) Selection can be made by dividing the population into strata and then taking a random sample from each strata.
13. a) An **unbiased sample** is one that is a small replica of the entire population with regard to income, education, sex, race, religion, political affiliation, age, etc.

15. Random sample
17. Cluster sample
19. Systematic sample
21. Convenience sample
23. Cluster sample
25. Answers will vary.

Exercise Set 13.2

1. Answers will vary.
3. Every employee may not make the average salary. Some may have a salary far below the average or far above the average.
5. The fact that Morgan's is the largest department store does not imply it is inexpensive.
7. Most driving is done close to home. Thus, one might expect more accidents close to home.
9. Averages apply to a set of data. Thus, although the female average score may be greater, some males have higher scores than some females.
11. There may be deep sections in the pond, so it may not be safe to go wading.
13. Half the students in a population are expected to be below average.
15. Just because some prefer it does not mean they buy it. Other factors, such as cost, must be considered.

17. a)

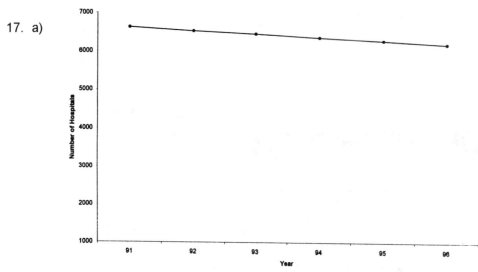

b)

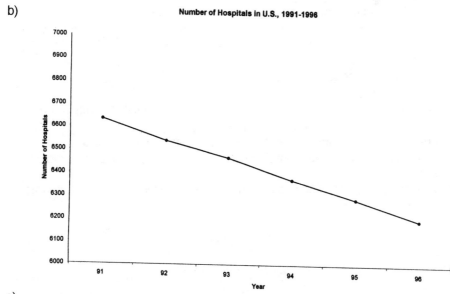

19. a)

Median Age at First Marriage for Males

19. b)
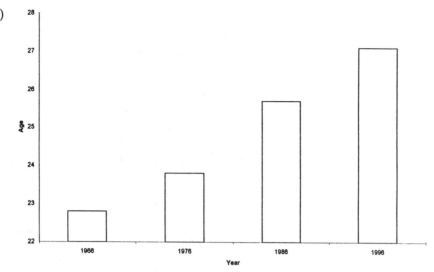

Gateway Computer Sales

21. a)
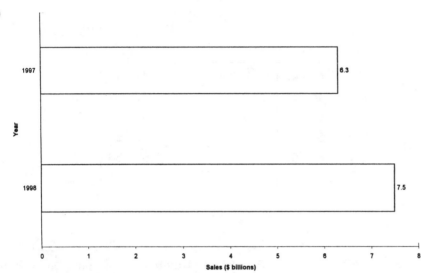

b) Yes, the new graph suggests less growth.

Exercise Set 13.3

1. A **frequency distribution** is a listing of observed values and the corresponding frequency of occurrence of each value.

3. a) 7   b) 16-22   c) 16   d) 22

5. The **modal class** is the class with the greatest frequency.

7. a) Number of observations = sum of frequencies = 17
    b) Width = 14 - 9 = 5
    c) $\dfrac{14+18}{2} = \dfrac{32}{2} = 16$

    d) The modal class is the class with the greatest frequency. Thus, the modal class is 14 - 18.
    e) Since the class widths are 5, the next class would be 39 - 43.

9.

Number Sold	Number of Days
0	3
1	8
2	3
3	5
4	2
5	7
6	2
7	3
8	4
9	1
10	2

11.

I.Q.	Number of Students
78 - 86	2
87 - 95	15
96 - 104	18
105 - 113	7
114 - 122	6
123 - 131	1
132 - 140	1

13.

I.Q.	Number of Students
80 - 90	8
91 - 101	22
102 - 112	11
113 - 123	7
124 - 134	1
135 - 145	1

15.

Age	Number of Pres.
40 - 45	2
46 - 51	12
52 - 57	16
58 - 63	6
64 - 69	5

17.

Age	Number of Pres.
42 - 46	4
47 - 51	10
52 - 56	12
57 - 61	9
62 - 66	4
67 - 71	2

19.

Cost (Millions)	# of Comp.
90 - 199	18
200 - 309	15
310 - 419	5
420 - 529	2
530 - 639	8
640 - 749	0
750 - 859	1
860 - 969	1

21.

Cost (Millions)	# of Comp.
50 - 149	12
150 - 249	14
250 - 349	7
350 - 449	5
450 - 549	3
550 - 649	7
650 - 749	0
750 - 849	1
850 - 949	0
950 - 1049	1

23.

Population (To nearest 100,000)	Number of Cities
5.4 - 7.4	10
7.5 - 9.5	5
9.6 - 11.6	10
11.7 - 13.7	4
13.8 - 15.8	1
15.9 - 17.9	4
18.0 - 20.0	0
20.1 - 22.1	0
22.2 - 24.2	0
24.3 - 26.3	0
26.4 - 28.4	1

25.

Population (To nearest 100,000)	Number of Cities
5.1 - 7.6	11
7.7 - 10.2	8
10.3 - 12.8	10
12.9 - 15.4	1
15.5 - 18.0	4
18.1 - 20.6	0
20.7 - 23.2	0
23.3 - 25.8	0
25.9 - 28.4	1

27.	Percent with Bachelor's Degree	Number of States
	14.6 - 18.5	6
	18.6 - 22.5	20
	22.6 - 26.5	11
	26.6 - 30.5	11
	30.6 - 34.5	3

29.	Percent with Bachelor's Degree	Number of States
	14.6 - 18.0	5
	18.1 - 21.5	14
	21.6 - 25.0	14
	25.1 - 28.5	13
	28.6 - 32.0	2
	32.1 - 35.5	3

Exercise Set 13.4

1. Answers will vary.

3. Answers will vary.

5. a) Answers will vary.

    b)

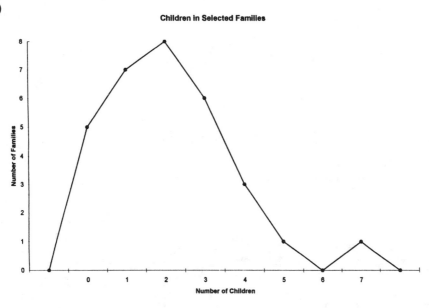

7. a) Answers will vary.

    b)

Class	Frequency
45	3
46	0
47	1
48	0
49	1
50	1
51	2

9. None: 0.29(500) = 145
   One: 0.31(500) = 155
   Two: 0.14(500) = 70
   Three: 0.10(500) = 50
   Four or more: 0.16(500) = 80

11.

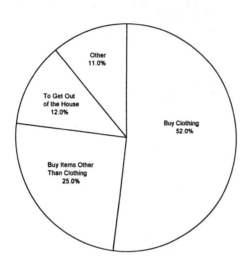

Reasons for Going to the Mall

13. a) and b)

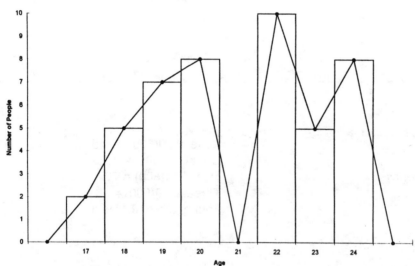

Age of People Attending a Jazz Concert

15. a) and b)

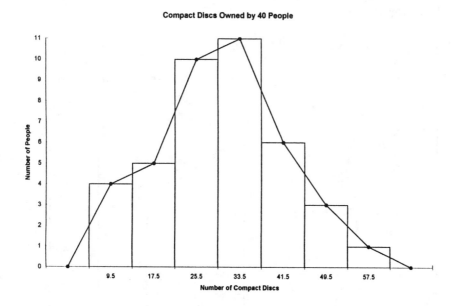

Compact Discs Owned by 40 People

17. a) The total number of people surveyed:
    2 + 5 + 8 + 7 + 4 + 3 + 1 = 30
    b) Four people purchased four books.
    c) The modal class is 2 because more people
    purchased 2 books than any other number of books.
    d) Two people bought 0 books   0
       Five people bought 1 book   5
       Eight people bought 2 books   16
       Seven people bought 3 books   21
       Four people bought 4 books   16
       Three people bought 5 books   15
       One person bought 6 books   6
    Total number of books purchased: 79

    e)

Number of Books	Number of People
0	2
1	5
2	8
3	7
4	4
5	3
6	1

19. a) 7 calls

   b) Adding the number of calls responded to in 6, 5, 4, or 3 minutes gives: 4 + 7 + 3 + 2 = 16 calls

   c) The total number of calls surveyed: 2 + 3 + 7 + 4 + 3 + 8 + 6 + 3 = 36

   d)
Response Time (Min.)	Number of Calls
3	2
4	3
5	7
6	4
7	3
8	8
9	6
10	3

   e)

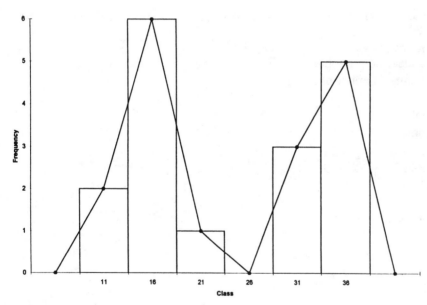

21.

23. 1 | 5 represents 15

   1 | 0 5 7
   2 | 4 4
   3 | 6 0 3
   4 | 8 5 2 5 8
   5 | 3 4
   6 | 0 2 0

25. a)

Salaries (in $1000)	Number of Companies
25	1
26	7
27	4
28	3
29	2
30	3
31	3
32	2

b) and c)

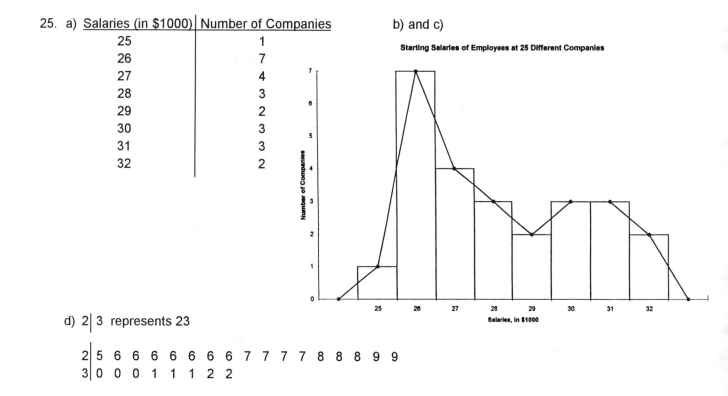

d) 2│3 represents 23

```
2│5  6  6  6  6  6  6  6  7  7  7  7  8  8  8  9  9
3│0  0  0  1  1  1  2  2
```

27. a)

Sales (Millions)	Number of Magazines
63 - 122	29
123 - 182	4
183 - 242	8
243 - 302	1
303 - 362	2
363 - 422	2
423 - 482	1
483 - 542	1
543 - 602	2

b) and c)

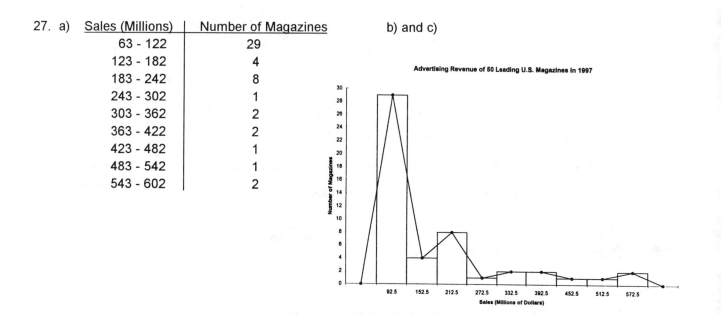

Exercise Set 13. 5

1. The **mean** is the balancing point of a set of data. It is the sum of the data divided by the number of pieces of data.

3. The **median** is the value in the middle of a set of ranked data. To find the median, rank the data and select the value in the middle.

5. The **mode** is the most common piece of data. The piece of data that occurs most frequently is the mode.

7. The median should be used when there are some values that differ greatly from the rest of the values in the set, for example, salaries.

9. The mean is used when each piece of data is to be considered and "weighed" equally, for example, weights of adult males.

	mean	median	mode	midrange
11.	$\dfrac{90}{9} = 10$	8	11	$\dfrac{2+36}{2} = 19$
13.	$\dfrac{523}{7} \approx 74.7$	80	none	$\dfrac{45+96}{2} = 70.5$
15.	$\dfrac{64}{8} = 8$	$\dfrac{7+9}{2} = 8$	none	$\dfrac{1+15}{2} = 8$
17.	$\dfrac{510}{7} \approx 72.9$	60	none	$\dfrac{30+140}{2} = 85$
19.	$\dfrac{95}{8} \approx 11.9$	$\dfrac{12+13}{2} = 12.5$	13	$\dfrac{6+17}{2} = 11.5$
21.	$\dfrac{232}{7} \approx 33.1$	31	none	$\dfrac{17+51}{2} = 34$

23. a) $\dfrac{34}{7} \approx 4.9$ 5   5 $\dfrac{1+11}{2} = 6$

     b) $\dfrac{37}{7} \approx 5.3$ 5   5 $\dfrac{1+11}{2} = 6$

     c) Only the mean

     d) $\dfrac{33}{7} \approx 4.7$ 5   5 $\dfrac{1+10}{2} = 5.5$

        The mean and the midrange

25. A 79 average on 10 exams gives a total of 790 points. An 80 average on 10 exams requires a total of 800 points. Thus, Jim missed a B by 10 points not 1 point.

27. a) Mean: $\dfrac{2677}{15} \approx 178.5\, ft.$ b) Median: $190\, ft.$

     c) Mode: none

                                d) Midrange: $\dfrac{95+284}{2} = 189.5\, ft.$

     e) Median, when there are a few "extreme" values, the median is the best measure of central tendency.

29. a) Mean: $\dfrac{82.2}{10} = 8.22 \approx 8.2$ million   b) Median: $\dfrac{6.0+8.9}{2} = 7.45$ million

     c) Mode: none

                                d) Midrange: $\dfrac{3.7+15.6}{2} = 9.65$ million

31. Let $x =$ the sum of his scores

$$\frac{x}{6} = 78$$

$$x = 78(6) = 468$$

33. One example is 72, 73, 74, 76, 77, 78.

35. a) Yes
    b) Cannot be found since we do not know the middle two numbers in the ranked list
    c) Cannot be found without knowing all of the numbers
    d) Yes
    e) Mean: $\dfrac{24,000}{120} = 200$, Midrange: $\dfrac{20+500}{2} = 260$

37. a) For a mean average of 60 on 7 exams, she must have a total of $60 \times 7 = 420$ points. Sheryl presently has 49 + 72 + 80 + 60 + 57 + 69 = 387 points. Thus, to pass the course, her last exam must be 420 - 387 = 33 or greater.
    b) A C average requires a total of $70 \times 7 = 490$ points. Sheryl has 387. Therefore, she would need 490 - 387 = 103 on her last exam. If the maximum score she can receive is 100, she cannot obtain a C.
    c) For a mean average of 60 on 6 exams, she must have a total of $60 \times 6 = 360$ points. If the lowest score on an exam she has already taken is dropped, she will have a total of 72 + 80 + 60 + 57 + 69 = 338 points. Thus, to pass the course, her last exam must be 360 - 338 = 22 or greater.
    d) For a mean average of 70 on 6 exams, she must have a total of $70 \times 6 = 420$ points. If the lowest score on an exam she has already taken is dropped, she will have a total of 338 points. Thus, to obtain a C, her last exam must be 420 - 338 = 82 or greater.

39. One example is 1, 2, 3, 3, 4, 5 changed to 1, 2, 3, 4, 4, 5.

41. No, by changing only one piece of data you cannot alter both the median and the midrange.

43. The data must be arranged in either ascending or descending order.
45. Kevin was taller than approximately 35% of all kindergarten children.
47. Second quartile, median

49. a) $490   b) $500   c) 25%   d) 25%   e) 17%   f) 100 x $510 = $51,000

51. a) Ruth: $\approx$ 0.290, 0.359, 0.301, 0.272, 0.315
       Mantle: $\approx$ 0.300, 0.365, 0.304, 0.275, 0.321
    b) Mantle's is greater in every case.
    c) Ruth: $\dfrac{593}{1878} \approx 0.316$, Mantle: $\dfrac{760}{2440} \approx 0.311$, Ruth's is greater.
    d) Answers will vary.
    e) Ruth: $\dfrac{1.537}{5} \approx 0.307$, Mantle: $\dfrac{1.565}{5} = 0.313$, Mantle's is greater.
    f) and g) Answers will vary.

Exercise Set 13.6

1. To find the **range**, subtract the lowest value in the set of data from the highest value.

3. Answers will vary.

5. It may be important to determine the consistency of the data.

7. Where one expects to find a large variability such as test scores

9. The first set of data will have the greater standard deviation because the scores have a greater spread about the mean.

11. The sum of the values in the (Data – Mean)^2 column will always be greater than or equal to 0.

13. Range = 11 – 0 = 11

$$\bar{x} = \frac{25}{5} = 5$$

x	$x - \bar{x}$	$(x - \bar{x})^2$
5	0	0
3	-2	4
0	-5	25
6	1	1
11	6	36
	0	66

$$\frac{66}{4} = 16.5, s = \sqrt{16.5} \approx 4.06$$

15. Range = 156 – 150 = 6

$$\bar{x} = \frac{1071}{7} = 153$$

x	$x - \bar{x}$	$(x - \bar{x})^2$
150	-3	9
151	-2	4
152	-1	1
153	0	0
154	1	1
155	2	4
156	3	9
	0	28

$$\frac{28}{6} \approx 4.67, s = \sqrt{4.67} \approx 2.16$$

17. Range = 9 – 4 = 5

$$\bar{x} = \frac{21}{3} = 7$$

x	$x - \bar{x}$	$(x - \bar{x})^2$
4	-3	9
8	1	1
9	2	4
	0	14

$$\frac{14}{2} = 7, s = \sqrt{7} \approx 2.65$$

19. Range = 12 – 7 = 5

$$\bar{x} = \frac{63}{7} = 9$$

x	$x - \bar{x}$	$(x - \bar{x})^2$
7	-2	4
9	0	0
7	-2	4
9	0	0
9	0	0
10	1	1
12	3	9
	0	18

$$\frac{18}{6} = 3, s = \sqrt{3} \approx 1.73$$

21. Range = 9 − 2 = 7

$\bar{x} = \dfrac{50}{10} = 5$

x	$x-\bar{x}$	$(x-\bar{x})^2$
3	-2	4
4	-1	1
5	0	0
9	4	16
3	-2	4
7	2	4
4	-1	1
4	-1	1
9	4	16
2	-3	9
	0	56

$\dfrac{56}{9} \approx 6.22, s = \sqrt{6.22} \approx 2.49$

23. Range = 50 − 18 = $32

$\bar{x} = \dfrac{360}{10} = \$36$

x	$x-\bar{x}$	$(x-\bar{x})^2$
28	-8	64
28	-8	64
50	14	196
45	9	81
30	-6	36
45	9	81
48	12	144
18	-18	324
45	9	81
23	-13	169
	0	1240

$\dfrac{1240}{9} \approx 137.78, s = \sqrt{137.78} \approx \$11.74$

25. a) Range = 68 - 5 = $63

$\bar{x} = \dfrac{204}{6} = 34$

x	$x-\bar{x}$	$(x-\bar{x})^2$
32	-2	4
60	26	676
14	-20	400
25	-9	81
5	-29	841
68	34	1156
	0	3158

$\dfrac{3158}{5} = 631.6, s = \sqrt{631.6} \approx \$25.13$

b) New data: 42, 70, 24, 35, 15, 78

The range and standard deviation will be the same. If each piece of data is increased by the same number, the range and standard deviation will remain the same.

c) Range = 78 - 15 = $63

$\bar{x} = \dfrac{264}{6} = 44$

x	$x-\bar{x}$	$(x-\bar{x})^2$
42	-2	4
70	26	676
24	-20	400
35	-9	81
15	-29	841
78	34	1156
	0	3158

$\dfrac{3158}{5} = 631.6, s = \sqrt{631.6} \approx \$25.13$

d) Yes

27. a) - c) Answers will vary.

    d) If each number in a distribution is multiplied by n, both the mean and standard deviation of the new distribution will be n times that of the original distribution.

    e) The mean of the second set is $5 \times 4 = 20$, and the standard deviation of the second set is $5 \times 2 = 10$.

29. a) The standard deviation increases. There is a greater spread from the mean as they get older.

    b) $\approx 133\,lb.$

    c) $\dfrac{175 - 90}{4} = 21.25 \approx 21\,lb.$

    d) The mean weight is about 100 pounds and the normal range is about 60 to 140 pounds.

    e) The mean height is about 62 inches and the normal range is about 53 to 68 inches.

    f) 100% - 95% = 5%

31. a)

East		West	
Number of Footware Sold	Number of Weeks	Number of Footware Sold	Number of Weeks
15-20	2	15-20	0
21-26	2	21-26	0
27-32	5	27-32	6
33-38	4	33-38	9
39-44	7	39-44	4
45-50	1	45-50	6
51-56	1	51-56	0
57-62	2	57-62	0
63-68	1	63-68	0

b)

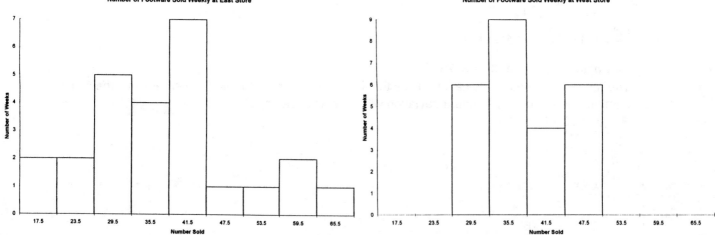

c) They appear to have about the same mean since they are both centered around 38.

d) The distribution for East is more spread out. Therefore, East has a greater standard deviation.

e) East: $\dfrac{950}{25} = 38$, West: $\dfrac{950}{25} = 38$

31. f)

East				West		
x	$x-\bar{x}$	$(x-\bar{x})^2$		x	$x-\bar{x}$	$(x-\bar{x})^2$
33	-5	25		38	0	0
30	-8	64		38	0	0
25	-13	169		37	-1	1
27	-11	121		36	-2	4
40	2	4		30	-8	64
44	6	36		45	7	49
49	11	121		28	-10	100
52	14	196		47	9	81
42	4	16		30	-8	64
59	21	441		46	8	64
19	-19	361		38	0	0
22	-16	256		39	1	1
57	19	361		40	2	4
67	29	841		34	-4	16
15	-23	529		31	-7	49
41	3	9		45	7	49
43	5	25		29	-9	81
27	-11	121		38	0	0
42	4	16		38	0	0
43	5	25		39	1	1
37	-1	1		37	-1	1
38	0	0		42	4	16
31	-7	49		46	8	64
32	-6	36		31	-7	49
35	-3	9		48	10	100
	0	3832			0	858

$$\frac{3832}{24} \approx 159.67, s = \sqrt{159.67} \approx \$12.64 \qquad \frac{858}{24} = 35.75, s = \sqrt{35.75} \approx \$5.98$$

Exercise Set 13.7

1. A **rectangular distribution** is one where all the values have the same frequency.
3. A **bimodal distribution** is one where two nonadjacent values occur more frequently than any other value in a set of data.
5. A **distribution skewed to the left** is one that has "a tail" on its left.
7. The distribution of outcomes from the roll of a die
9. Skewed left - a listing of test scores where most of the students did well and a few did poorly; Skewed right - number of cans of soda consumed in a day where most people consumed a few cans and a few people consumed many cans
11. Rectangular
13. Normal
15. The mode is the lowest value, the median is greater than the mode, and the mean is greater than the median. The greatest frequency appears on the left side of the curve. Since the mode is the value with the greatest frequency, the mode would appear on the left side of the curve (where the lowest values are). Every value in the set of data is considered in determining the mean. The values on the far right of the curve would increase the value of the mean. Thus, the value of the mean would be farther to the right than the mode. The median would be between the mode and the mean.
17. Answers will vary.
19. In a normal distribution the mean, median, and the mode all have the same value.
21. A z-score will be negative when the data is less than the mean.
23. 0

25. 0.500

27. 0.477 + 0.341 = 0.818

29. 0.500 − 0.458 = 0.042

31. 0.500 − 0.463 = 0.037

33. 0.500 − 0.481 = 0.019

35. 0.500 − 0.447 = 0.053

37. 0.282 = 28.2%

39. 0.410 + 0.488 = 0.898 = 89.8%

41. 0.500 + 0.471 = 0.971 = 97.1%

43. 0.500 + 0.475 = 0.975 = 97.5%

45. 0.466 − 0.437 = 0.029 = 2.9%

47. a) Jake, Sarah, and Carol scored above the mean because their z-scores are positive.
    b) Marie and Kevin scored at the mean because their z-scores are zero
    c) Omar, Justin, and Kim scored below the mean because their z-scores are negative.

49. $z_{75} = \dfrac{75-69}{6} = \dfrac{6}{6} = 1.00; \ 0.341 = 34.1\%$

51. $z_{63} = \dfrac{63-69}{6} = \dfrac{-6}{6} = -1.00$

    $0.341 + 0.341 = 0.682 = 68.2\%$

53. $z_{50} = \dfrac{50-48}{4} = \dfrac{2}{4} = .50$

    $0.500 + 0.192 = 0.692 = 69.2\%$

55. $z_{54} = \dfrac{54-48}{4} = \dfrac{6}{4} = 1.50$

    $0.433 - 0.192 = 0.241 = 24.1\%$

57. $z_{44} = \dfrac{44-48}{4} = \dfrac{-4}{4} = -1.00$

    $z_{49} = \dfrac{49-48}{4} = \dfrac{1}{4} = 0.25$

    $0.099 + 0.341 = 0.44 = 44.0\%$

59. $z_{30,000} = \dfrac{30,000-35,000}{2500} = \dfrac{-5000}{2500} = -2.00$

    $z_{37,500} = \dfrac{37,500-35,000}{2500} = \dfrac{2500}{2500} = 1.00$

    $0.477 + 0.341 = 0.818 = 81.8\%$

61. The tires that last less than 30,000 miles will fail to live up to the guarantee.

    0.500 − 0.477 = 0.023 = 2.3%

63. 50%

65. $z_{70} = \dfrac{70-80}{8} = \dfrac{-10}{8} = -1.25$

    $0.500 - 0.394 = 0.106 = 10.6\%$

67. 0.106(200) = 21.2 ≈ 21 students

69. $z_{7.4} = \dfrac{7.4-7.6}{0.4} = \dfrac{-0.2}{0.4} = -.50$

    $z_{7.7} = \dfrac{7.7-7.6}{0.4} = \dfrac{0.1}{0.4} = .25$

    $0.192 + 0.099 = 0.291 = 29.1\%$

71. 0.500 + 0.099 = 0.599 = 59.9%

73. $z_{1450} = \dfrac{1450-1500}{100} = \dfrac{-50}{100} = -.50$

    $0.192 + 0.500 = 0.692 = 69.2\%$

75. $z_{1480} = \dfrac{1480-1500}{100} = \dfrac{-20}{100} = -.20$

    $0.500 - 0.079 = 0.421 = 42.1\%$

77. $z_{1400} = \dfrac{1400 - 1500}{100} = \dfrac{-100}{100} = -1.00$

$z_{1600} = \dfrac{1600 - 1500}{100} = \dfrac{100}{100} = 1.00$

0.341 + 0.341 = 0.682 = 68.2%

0.682(80,000) = 54,560 light bulbs

79. A motor will require repair or replacement if it breaks down in less than 8 years.

$z_8 = \dfrac{8 - 10.2}{1.8} = \dfrac{-2.2}{1.8} \approx -1.22$

0.500 − 0.389 = 0.111 = 11.1%

81. A z-score of 1.8 or higher is required for an A. The area from the mean to 1.8 is 0.464.
Thus, 0.500 − 0.464 = 0.036 = 3.6% will receive an A.
A z-score between 1.8 and 1.1 is required for a B. The areas from the mean to these z-scores are 0.464 and 0.364, respectively. Thus, 0.464 − 0.364 = 0.100 = 10.0% will receive a B.
A z-score between 1.1 and -1.2 is required for a C. The areas from the mean to these z-scores are 0.364 and 0.385, respectively. Thus, 0.364 + 0.385 = 0.749 = 74.9% will receive a C.
A z-score between -1.2 and -1.9 is required for a D. The areas from the mean to these z-scores are 0.385 and 0.471, respectively. Thus, 0.471 − 0.385 = 0.086 = 8.6% will receive a D.
A z-score of -1.9 or lower is required for an F. The area from the mean to -1.9 is 0.471.
Thus, 0.500 − 0.471 = 0.029 = 2.9% will receive an F.

83. a) Katie: $z_{28,408} = \dfrac{28,408 - 23,200}{2170} = \dfrac{5208}{2170} = 2.4$

Stella: $z_{29,510} = \dfrac{29,510 - 25,600}{2300} = \dfrac{3910}{2300} = 1.7$

b) Katie. Her z-score is higher than Stella's z-score. This means her sales are further above the mean than Stella's sales.

Exercise Set 13.8

1. The **correlation coefficient** measures the strength of the relationship between the quantities.

3. 1   5. 0

7. A negative correlation indicates as one quantity increases, the other quantity decreases.

9. The **level of significance** is used to identify the cutoff between results attributed to chance and results attributed to an actual relationship between the two variables.

11. No correlation   13. Strong positive

15. Yes, $|0.73| > 0.684$ 17. No, $|-0.63| < 0.707$

19. No, $|-0.23| < 0.254$ 21. No, $|0.82| < 0.917$

Note: The answers in the remainder of this section may differ slightly from your answers depending upon how your answers are rounded and which calculator you used.

23. a)

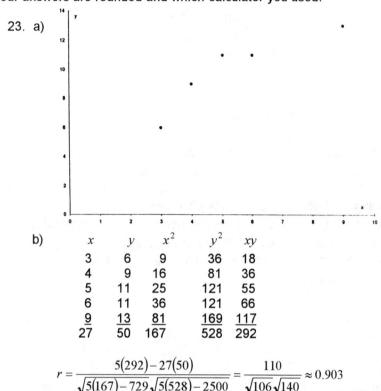

b)

x	y	x^2	y^2	xy
3	6	9	36	18
4	9	16	81	36
5	11	25	121	55
6	11	36	121	66
9	13	81	169	117
27	50	167	528	292

$$r = \frac{5(292) - 27(50)}{\sqrt{5(167) - 729}\sqrt{5(528) - 2500}} = \frac{110}{\sqrt{106}\sqrt{140}} \approx 0.903$$

c) Yes, $\left|0.903\right| > 0.878$ d) No, $\left|0.903\right| < 0.959$

25. a)

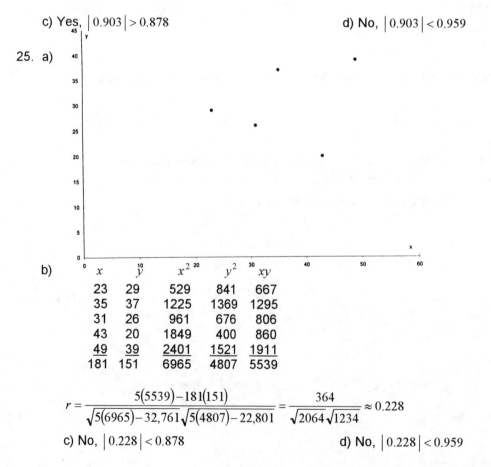

b)

x	y	x^2	y^2	xy
23	29	529	841	667
35	37	1225	1369	1295
31	26	961	676	806
43	20	1849	400	860
49	39	2401	1521	1911
181	151	6965	4807	5539

$$r = \frac{5(5539) - 181(151)}{\sqrt{5(6965) - 32,761}\sqrt{5(4807) - 22,801}} = \frac{364}{\sqrt{2064}\sqrt{1234}} \approx 0.228$$

c) No, $\left|0.228\right| < 0.878$ d) No, $\left|0.228\right| < 0.959$

27. a)

b)

x	y	x^2	y^2	xy
5.3	10.3	28.09	106.09	54.59
4.7	9.6	22.09	92.16	45.12
8.4	12.5	70.56	156.25	105
12.7	16.2	161.29	262.44	205.74
4.9	9.8	24.01	96.04	48.02
36	58.4	306.04	712.98	458.47

$$r = \frac{5(458.47) - 36(58.4)}{\sqrt{5(306.04) - 1296}\sqrt{5(712.98) - 3410.56}} = \frac{189.95}{\sqrt{234.2}\sqrt{154.34}} \approx 0.999$$

c) Yes, $|0.999| > 0.878$ 　　　　　　　　 d) Yes, $|0.999| > 0.959$

29. a)

b)

x	y	x^2	y^2	xy
100	2	10,000	4	200
80	3	6400	9	240
60	5	3600	25	300
60	6	3600	36	360
40	6	1600	36	240
20	8	400	64	160
360	30	25,600	174	1500

$$r = \frac{6(1500) - 360(30)}{\sqrt{6(25,600) - 129,600}\sqrt{6(174) - 900}} = \frac{-1800}{\sqrt{24,000}\sqrt{144}} \approx -0.968$$

c) Yes, $|-0.968| > 0.811$ 　　　　　　　　 d) Yes, $|-0.968| > 0.917$

31. From # 23: $m = \dfrac{5(292) - 27(50)}{5(167) - 729} = \dfrac{110}{106} \approx 1.0$

    $b = \dfrac{50 - \dfrac{110}{106}(27)}{5} \approx 4.4, \quad y = 1.0x + 4.4$

33. From # 25: $m = \dfrac{5(5539) - 181(151)}{5(6965) - 32{,}761} = \dfrac{364}{2064} \approx 0.2$

    $b = \dfrac{151 - \dfrac{364}{2064}(181)}{5} \approx 23.8, \quad y = 0.2x + 23.8$

35. From # 27: $m = \dfrac{5(458.47) - 36(58.4)}{5(306.04) - 1296} = \dfrac{189.95}{234.2} \approx 0.8$

    $b = \dfrac{58.4 - \dfrac{189.95}{234.2}(36)}{5} \approx 5.8, \quad y = 0.8x + 5.8$

37. From # 29: $m = \dfrac{6(1500) - 360(30)}{6(25{,}600) - 129{,}600} = \dfrac{-1800}{24{,}000} \approx -0.1$

    $b = \dfrac{30 - \dfrac{-1800}{24{,}000}(360)}{6} \approx 9.5, \quad y = -0.1x + 9.5$

39. a)

x	y	x^2	y^2	xy
10	37	100	1369	370
15	43	225	1849	645
12	37	144	1369	444
20	49	400	2401	980
25	54	625	2916	1350
17	45	289	2025	765
99	265	1783	11,929	4554

$$r = \frac{6(4554) - 99(265)}{\sqrt{6(1783) - 9801}\sqrt{6(11{,}929) - 70{,}225}} = \frac{1089}{\sqrt{897}\sqrt{1349}} \approx 0.990$$

b) Yes, $|0.990| > 0.811$

c) $m = \dfrac{6(4554) - 99(265)}{6(1783) - 9801} = \dfrac{1089}{897} \approx 1.2$, $b = \dfrac{265 - \dfrac{1089}{897}(99)}{6} \approx 24.1$, $y = 1.2x + 24.1$

41. a)

x	y	x^2	y^2	xy
1	690	1	476,100	690
4	780	16	608,400	3120
7	460	49	211,600	3220
10	280	100	78,400	2800
13	200	169	40,000	2600
16	330	256	108,900	5280
51	2740	591	1,523,400	17,710

$$r = \frac{6(17,710) - 51(2740)}{\sqrt{6(591) - 2601}\sqrt{6(1,523,400) - 7,507,600}} = \frac{-33,480}{\sqrt{945}\sqrt{1,632,800}} \approx -0.852$$

b) Yes, $|-0.852| > 0.811$

c) $m = \dfrac{6(17,710) - 51(2740)}{6(591) - 2601} = \dfrac{-33,480}{945} \approx -35.4$, $\quad b = \dfrac{2740 - \dfrac{-33,480}{945}(51)}{6} \approx 757.8$, $\quad y = -35.4x + 757.8$

d) $y = -35.4(9) + 757.8 = \$439.20$

43. a)

x	y	x^2	y^2	xy
20	8	400	64	160
12	10	144	100	120
18	12	324	144	216
15	9	225	81	135
22	6	484	36	132
10	15	100	225	150
20	7	400	49	140
12	18	144	324	216
129	85	2221	1023	1269

$$r = \frac{8(1269) - 129(85)}{\sqrt{8(2221) - 16,641}\sqrt{8(1023) - 7225}} = \frac{-813}{\sqrt{1127}\sqrt{959}} \approx -0.782$$

b) Yes, $|-0.782| > 0.707$

c) $m = \dfrac{8(1269) - 129(85)}{8(2221) - 16,641} = \dfrac{-813}{1127} \approx -0.7$, $\quad b = \dfrac{85 - \dfrac{-813}{1127}(129)}{8} \approx 22.3$, $\quad y = -0.7x + 22.3$

d) $y = -0.7(14) + 22.3 = 12.5$ muggings

45. a)

x	y	x^2	y^2	xy
89	22	7921	484	1958
110	28	12,100	784	3080
125	30	15,625	900	3750
92	26	8464	676	2392
100	22	10,000	484	2200
95	21	9025	441	1995
108	28	11,664	784	3024
97	25	9409	625	2425
816	202	84,208	5178	20,824

$$r = \frac{8(20{,}824) - 816(202)}{\sqrt{8(84{,}208) - 665{,}856}\sqrt{8(5178) - 40{,}804}} = \frac{1760}{\sqrt{7808}\sqrt{620}} \approx 0.800$$

b) Yes, $|0.800| > 0.707$

c) $m = \dfrac{8(20{,}824) - 816(202)}{8(84{,}208) - 665{,}856} = \dfrac{1760}{7808} \approx 0.2$, $\quad b = \dfrac{202 - \dfrac{1760}{7808}(816)}{8} \approx 2.3$, $\quad y = 0.2x + 2.3$

d) $y = 0.2(115) + 2.3 = 25.3 \approx 25$ units

47. a)

x	y	x^2	y^2	xy
1	80.0	1	6400.0	80.0
2	76.2	4	5806.4	152.4
3	68.7	9	4719.7	206.1
4	50.1	16	2510.0	200.4
5	30.2	25	912.0	151.0
6	20.8	36	432.6	124.8
21	326	91	20,780.7	914.7

$$r = \frac{6(914.7) - 21(326)}{\sqrt{6(91) - 441}\sqrt{6(20{,}780.7) - 106{,}276}} = \frac{-1357.8}{\sqrt{105}\sqrt{18{,}408.2}} \approx -0.977$$

b) Yes, $|-0.977| > 0.917$

c) $m = \dfrac{6(914.7) - 21(326)}{6(91) - 441} = \dfrac{-1357.8}{105} \approx -12.9$, $\quad b = \dfrac{326 - \dfrac{-1357.8}{105}(21)}{6} \approx 99.6$, $\quad y = -12.9x + 99.6$

d) $y = -12.9(4.5) + 99.6 = 41.55 \approx 41.6\%$

49. a) and b) Answers will vary.

c)

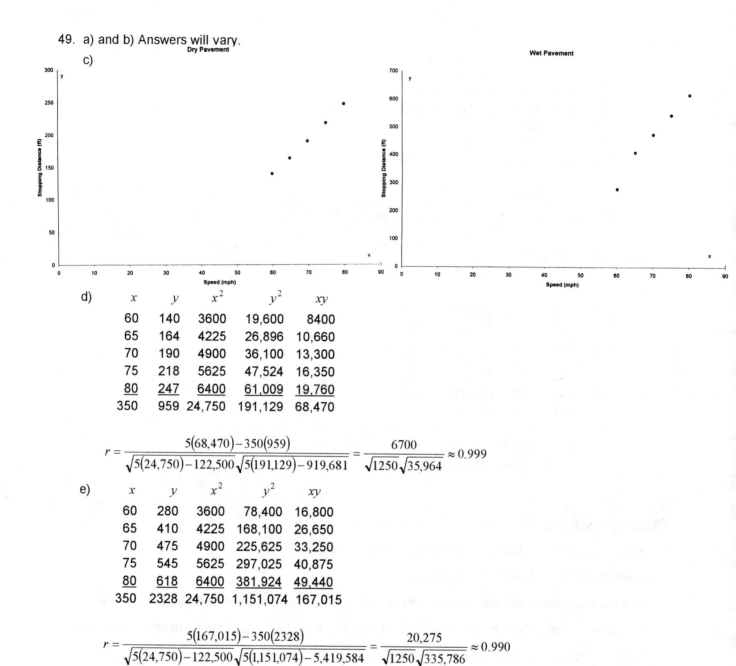

d)

x	y	x^2	y^2	xy
60	140	3600	19,600	8400
65	164	4225	26,896	10,660
70	190	4900	36,100	13,300
75	218	5625	47,524	16,350
80	247	6400	61,009	19,760
350	959	24,750	191,129	68,470

$$r = \frac{5(68,470) - 350(959)}{\sqrt{5(24,750) - 122,500}\sqrt{5(191,129) - 919,681}} = \frac{6700}{\sqrt{1250}\sqrt{35,964}} \approx 0.999$$

e)

x	y	x^2	y^2	xy
60	280	3600	78,400	16,800
65	410	4225	168,100	26,650
70	475	4900	225,625	33,250
75	545	5625	297,025	40,875
80	618	6400	381,924	49,440
350	2328	24,750	1,151,074	167,015

$$r = \frac{5(167,015) - 350(2328)}{\sqrt{5(24,750) - 122,500}\sqrt{5(1,151,074) - 5,419,584}} = \frac{20,275}{\sqrt{1250}\sqrt{335,786}} \approx 0.990$$

f) Answers will vary.

g) $m = \dfrac{5(68,470) - 350(959)}{5(24,750) - 122,500} = \dfrac{6700}{1250} \approx 5.4$, $\quad b = \dfrac{959 - \dfrac{6700}{1250}(350)}{5} = -183.4$, $\quad y = 5.4x - 183.4$

h) $m = \dfrac{5(167,015) - 350(2328)}{5(24,750) - 122,500} = \dfrac{20,275}{1250} \approx 16.2$, $\quad b = \dfrac{2328 - \dfrac{20,275}{1250}(350)}{5} = -669.8$, $\quad y = 16.2x - 669.8$

i) Dry: $y = 5.4(77) - 183.4 = 232.4$ ft.

   Wet: $y = 16.2(77) - 669.8 = 577.6$ ft.

51. Answers will vary.

53. a)

x	y	x^2	y^2	xy
90	130	8100	16,900	11,700
91	136	8281	18,496	12,376
92	140	8464	19,600	12,880
93	144	8649	20,736	13,392
94	148	8836	21,904	13,912
95	153	9025	23,409	14,535
555	851	51,355	121,045	78,795

$$r = \frac{6(78,795) - 555(851)}{\sqrt{6(51,355) - 308,025}\sqrt{6(121,045) - 724,201}} = \frac{465}{\sqrt{105}\sqrt{2069}} \approx 0.998$$

b) Should be the same

c)

x	y	x^2	y^2	xy
0	130	0	16,900	0
1	136	1	18,496	136
2	140	4	19,600	280
3	144	9	20,736	432
4	148	16	21,904	592
5	153	25	23,409	765
15	851	55	121,045	2205

$$r = \frac{6(2205) - 15(851)}{\sqrt{6(55) - 225}\sqrt{6(121,045) - 724,201}} = \frac{465}{\sqrt{105}\sqrt{2069}} \approx 0.998$$

Review Exercises

1. a) A **population** consists of all items or people of interest.

   b) A **sample** is a subset of the population.

2. A **random sample** is one where every item in the population has the same chance of being selected.

3. The candy bars may have lots of calories, or fat, or salt. Therefore, it may not be healthy to eat them.

4. Sales may not necessarily be a good indicator of profit. Expenses must also be considered.

5. a)

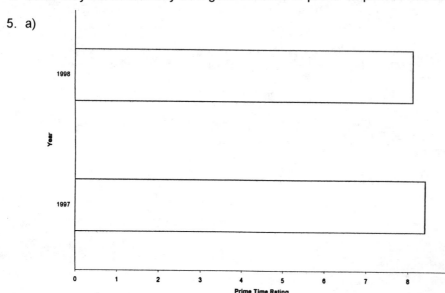

5. b)

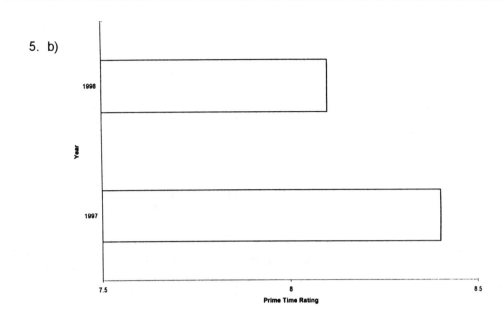

6. a)

Class	Frequency
35	1
36	3
37	6
38	2
39	3
40	0
41	4
42	1
43	3
44	1
45	1

b) and c)

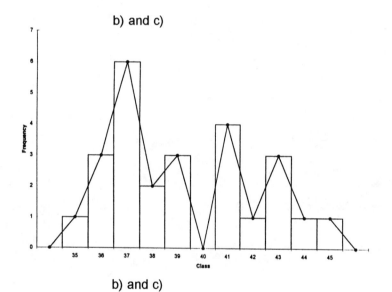

7. a)

High Temps.	Number of Cities
40 - 49	4
50 - 59	11
60 - 69	11
70 - 79	10
80 - 89	4

b) and c)

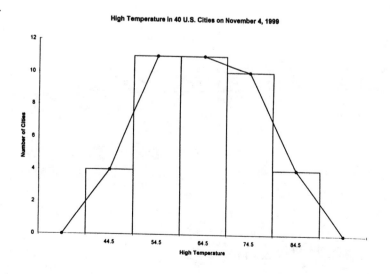

7. d)   4|6 represents 46

```
4| 0  6  6  8
5| 0  1  2  3  3  4  4  4  5  6  7
6| 1  4  5  6  6  6  7  8  8  9  9
7| 0  0  1  2  2  2  5  5  5  6
8| 0  1  1  7
```

8. $\bar{x} = \dfrac{480}{6} = 80$

9. $\dfrac{79+83}{2} = 81$

10. None

11. $\dfrac{63+93}{2} = 78$

12. $93 - 63 = 30$

13.

x	$x-\bar{x}$	$(x-\bar{x})^2$
63	-17	289
76	-4	16
79	-1	1
83	3	9
86	6	36
93	13	169
	0	520

$$\frac{520}{5} = 104, \; s = \sqrt{104} \approx 10.20$$

14. $\bar{x} = \dfrac{156}{12} = 13$

15. $\dfrac{12+14}{2} = 13$

16. None

17. $\dfrac{4+23}{2} = 13.5$

18. $23 - 4 = 19$

19.

x	$x-\bar{x}$	$(x-\bar{x})^2$
4	-9	81
5	-8	64
7	-6	36
7	-6	36
12	-1	1
12	-1	1
14	1	1
15	2	4
17	4	16
19	6	36
21	8	64
23	10	100
	0	440

$$\frac{440}{11} = 40, \; s = \sqrt{40} \approx 6.32$$

20. $z_{37} = \dfrac{37-42}{5} = \dfrac{-5}{5} = -1.00$

   $z_{47} = \dfrac{47-42}{5} = \dfrac{5}{5} = 1.00$

   $0.341 + 0.341 = 0.682 = 68.2\%$

21. $z_{32} = \dfrac{32-42}{5} = \dfrac{-10}{5} = -2.00$

   $z_{52} = \dfrac{52-42}{5} = \dfrac{10}{5} = 2.00$

   $0.477 + 0.477 = 0.954 = 95.4\%$

22. $z_{50} = \dfrac{50-42}{5} = \dfrac{8}{5} = 1.60$

$0.500 + 0.445 = 0.945 = 94.5\%$

23. $z_{50} = \dfrac{50-42}{5} = \dfrac{8}{5} = 1.60$

$0.500 - 0.445 = 0.055 = 5.5\%$

24. $z_{39} = \dfrac{39-42}{5} = \dfrac{-3}{5} = -.60$

$0.500 + 0.226 = 0.726 = 72.6\%$

25. $z_{4.7} = \dfrac{4.7-4.2}{0.5} = \dfrac{0.5}{0.5} = 1.00$

$0.341 = 34.1\%$

26. $z_4 = \dfrac{4-4.2}{0.5} = \dfrac{-0.2}{0.5} = -.40$

$0.500 - 0.155 = 0.345 = 34.5\%$

27. $z_{4.4} = \dfrac{4.4-4.2}{0.5} = \dfrac{0.2}{0.5} = .40$

$z_{5.4} = \dfrac{5.4-4.2}{0.5} = \dfrac{1.2}{0.5} = 2.40$

$0.492 - 0.155 = 0.337 = 33.7\%$

28. If a CD player lasts less than 3 years, it will need to be replaced.

$z_3 = \dfrac{3-4.2}{0.5} = \dfrac{-1.2}{0.5} = -2.40$

$0.500 - 0.492 = 0.008 = 0.8\%$

29. a)

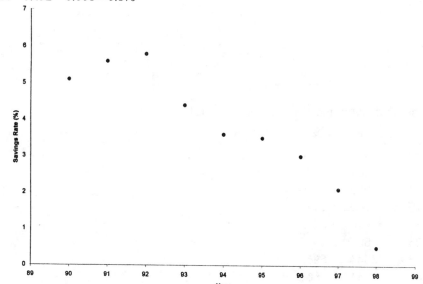

b) Yes, negative because generally as the year increases, the savings rate decreases.

c)

x	y	x^2	y^2	xy
90	5.1	8100	26.01	459.0
91	5.6	8281	31.36	509.6
92	5.8	8464	33.64	533.6
93	4.4	8649	19.36	409.2
94	3.6	8836	12.96	338.4
95	3.5	9025	12.25	332.5
96	3.0	9216	9.00	288.0
97	2.1	9409	4.41	203.7
98	0.5	9604	0.25	49.0
846	33.6	79,584	149.24	3123

$$r = \frac{9(3123) - 846(33.6)}{\sqrt{9(79,584)-715,716}\sqrt{9(149.24)-1128.96}} = \frac{-318.6}{\sqrt{540}\sqrt{214.2}} \approx -0.94$$

29. d) Yes, $|-0.94| > 0.666$

  e) $m = \dfrac{9(3123) - 846(33.6)}{9(79,584) - 715,716} = \dfrac{-318.6}{540} \approx -0.6$

  $b = \dfrac{33.6 - \dfrac{-318.6}{540}(846)}{9} \approx 59.2, \ y = -0.6x + 59.2$

30. a)

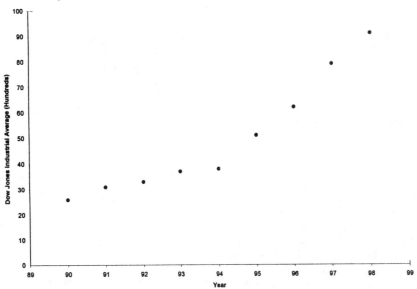

  b) Yes, positive because as the year increases the savings rate increases.

  c)

x	y	x^2	y^2	xy
90	26	8100	676	2340
91	31	8281	961	2821
92	33	8464	1089	3036
93	37	8649	1369	3441
94	38	8836	1444	3572
95	51	9025	2601	4845
96	62	9216	3844	5952
97	79	9409	6241	7663
98	91	9604	8281	8918
846	448	79,584	26,506	42,588

  $r = \dfrac{9(42,588) - 846(448)}{\sqrt{9(79,584) - 715,716}\sqrt{9(26,506) - 200,704}} = \dfrac{4284}{\sqrt{540}\sqrt{37,850}} \approx 0.95$

  d) Yes, $|0.95| > 0.798$

  e) $m = \dfrac{9(42,588) - 846(448)}{9(79,584) - 715,716} = \dfrac{4284}{540} \approx 7.9$

  $b = \dfrac{448 - \dfrac{4284}{540}(846)}{9} \approx -696.0, \ y = 7.9x - 696.0$

31. a)

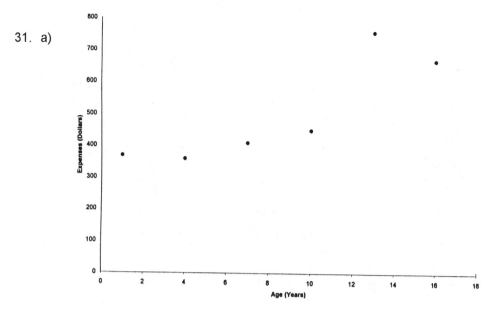

b) Yes, positive because generally as the age increases the expense increases.

c)

x	y	x^2	y^2	xy
1	370	1	136,900	370
4	360	16	129,600	1440
7	410	49	168,100	2870
10	450	100	202,500	4500
13	760	169	577,600	9880
16	670	256	448,900	10,720
51	3020	591	1,663,600	29,780

$$r = \frac{6(29,780) - 51(3020)}{\sqrt{6(591) - 2601}\sqrt{6(1,663,600) - 9,120,400}} = \frac{24,660}{\sqrt{945}\sqrt{861,200}} \approx 0.86$$

d) Yes, $|0.86| > 0.811$

e) $m = \dfrac{6(29,780) - 51(3020)}{6(591) - 2601} = \dfrac{24,660}{945} \approx 26.1$

$b = \dfrac{3020 - \dfrac{24,660}{945}(51)}{6} \approx 281.5, \ y = 26.1x + 281.5$

f) $y = 26.1(12) + 281.5 = \$594.70$

32. Mode = 175 lb.
34. 25%
36. 100% - 86% = 14%
38. 187 + 2(23) = 233 lb.
40. $\bar{x} = \dfrac{148}{41} \approx 3.610$

42. 3

44. 14 - 0 = 14

33. Median = 180 lb.
35. 25%
37. 100(187) = 18,700 lb.
39. 187 - 1.8(23) = 145.6 lb.
41. 2

43. $\dfrac{0+14}{2} = 7$

45.

x	$x-\bar{x}$	$(x-\bar{x})^2$	x	$x-\bar{x}$	$(x-\bar{x})^2$	x	$x-\bar{x}$	$(x-\bar{x})^2$
0	-3.6	12.96	2	-1.6	2.56	4	0.4	0.16
0	-3.6	12.96	2	-1.6	2.56	5	1.4	1.96
0	-3.6	12.96	3	-0.6	0.36	5	1.4	1.96
0	-3.6	12.96	3	-0.6	0.36	5	1.4	1.96
0	-3.6	12.96	3	-0.6	0.36	6	2.4	5.76
0	-3.6	12.96	3	-0.6	0.36	6	2.4	5.76
1	-2.6	6.76	3	-0.6	0.36	6	2.4	5.76
1	-2.6	6.76	3	-0.6	0.36	6	2.4	5.76
2	-1.6	2.56	4	0.4	0.16	6	2.4	5.76
2	-1.6	2.56	4	0.4	0.16	7	3.4	11.56
2	-1.6	2.56	4	0.4	0.16	8	4.4	19.36
2	-1.6	2.56	4	0.4	0.16	10	6.4	40.96
2	-1.6	2.56	4	0.4	0.16	14	10.4	108.16
2	-1.6	2.56	4	0.4	0.16			329.76

$$\frac{329.76}{40} = 8.244, \; s = \sqrt{8.244} \approx 2.87$$

46.

# of Child.	# of Presidents
0 - 1	8
2 - 3	14
4 - 5	10
6 - 7	6
8 - 9	1
10 - 11	1
12 - 13	0
14 - 15	1

47. and 48.

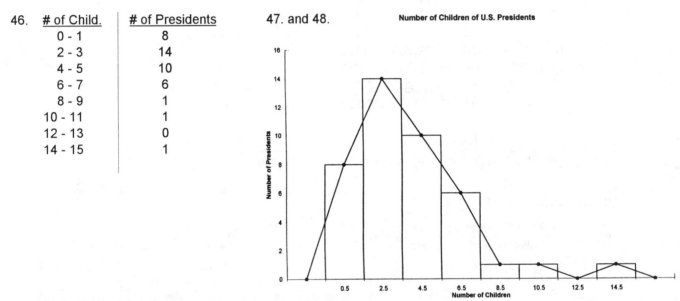

Number of Children of U.S. Presidents

49. No, the distribution is not symmetrical about the mean.

50. No, some families have no children, more have one child, the greatest percent may have two children, fewer have three children, etc.

51. No, the number of children per family has decreased over the years.

Chapter Test

1. $\bar{x} = \dfrac{150}{5} = 30$

2. 31

3. 31

4. $\dfrac{15+40}{2} = 27.5$

5. 40 - 15 = 25

6.

x	$x - \bar{x}$	$(x - \bar{x})^2$
15	-15	225
31	1	1
31	1	1
33	3	9
40	10	100
	0	336

$$\frac{336}{4} = 84, \; s = \sqrt{84} \approx 9.17$$

7.

Class	Frequency
25 - 30	7
31 - 36	5
37 - 42	1
43 - 48	7
49 - 54	5
55 - 60	3
61 - 66	2

8. and 9.

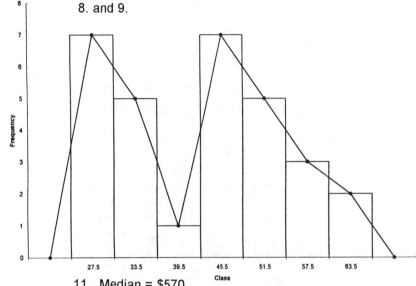

10. Mode = $595

11. Median = $570

12. 100% - 25% = 75%

13. 79%

14. 100(600) = $60,000

15. 600 + 1(40) = $640

16. 600 - 1.5(40) = $540

17. $z_{50,000} = \dfrac{50,000 - 75,000}{12,000} = \dfrac{-25,000}{12,000} \approx -2.08$

$z_{70,000} = \dfrac{70,000 - 75,000}{12,000} = \dfrac{-5000}{12,000} = -.42$

$0.481 - 0.163 = 0.318 = 31.8\%$

18. $z_{60,000} = \dfrac{60,000 - 75,000}{12,000} = \dfrac{-15,000}{12,000} = -1.25$

$0.500 + 0.394 = 0.894 = 89.4\%$

19. $z_{90,000} = \dfrac{90,000 - 75,000}{12,000} = \dfrac{15,000}{12,000} = 1.25$

$0.500 - 0.394 = 0.106 = 10.6\%$

20. From #17 and #18,

$z_{60,000} = -1.25$ and $z_{70,000} \approx -.42$

$0.394 - 0.163 = 0.231 = 23.1\%$

$0.231(300) = 69.3 \approx 69$ cars

21. a)

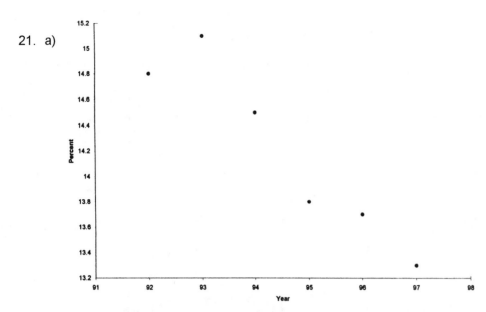

b) Yes, negative because generally as the year increases the percent decreases.

c)

x	y	x^2	y^2	xy
92	14.8	8464	219.04	1361.6
93	15.1	8649	228.01	1404.3
94	14.5	8836	210.25	1363
95	13.8	9025	190.44	1311
96	13.7	9216	187.69	1315.2
97	13.3	9409	176.89	1290.1
567	85.2	53,599	1212.32	8045.2

$$r = \frac{6(8045.2) - 567(85.2)}{\sqrt{6(53,599) - 321,489}\sqrt{6(1212.32) - 7259.04}} = \frac{-37.2}{\sqrt{105}\sqrt{14.88}} \approx -0.94$$

d) Yes, $|-0.94| > 0.811$

e) $m = \dfrac{6(8045.2) - 567(85.2)}{6(53,599) - 321,489} = \dfrac{-37.2}{105} \approx -0.4$

$b = \dfrac{85.2 - \dfrac{-37.2}{105}(567)}{6} = 47.7, \; y = -0.4x + 47.7$

f) $y = -0.4(98) + 47.7 = 8.5\%$

CHAPTER FOURTEEN

GRAPH THEORY

Exercise Set 14.1

1. A **graph** is a finite set of points, called **vertices**, that are connected with a set of line segments, called **edges**.

3.

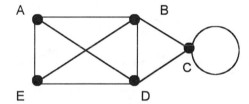

5. If the number of edges connected to the vertex is even, the vertex is **even**. If the number of edges connected to the vertex is odd, the vertex is **odd**.

7. In the graphs below, the second graph is disconnected since no path connects vertices A, D, and E to vertices B and C.

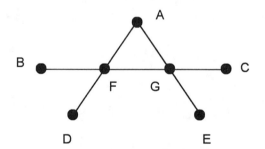

Connected Graph

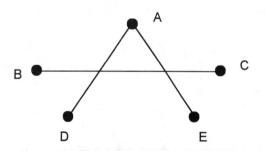

Disconnected Graph

9.

A, B, C, and D are all even.

11.

B and C are even. A and D are odd.

13.

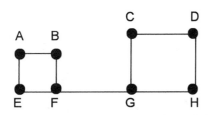

FG is a bridge.

15. No. There is no edge connecting vertices C and D. Therefore, A, B, C, D, E is not a path.

17. No. One attempt would be A, E, D, B, which does not contain C. A second attempt would be A, E, C, B, which does not contain D.

19. Yes. One example is B, D, E, A, B, C, E.

21.

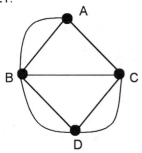

23.

25.

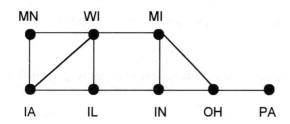

27.

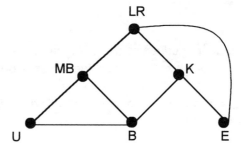

29.

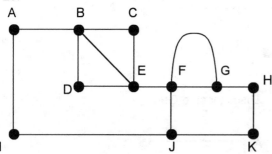

31. Connected

33. Disconnected. There is no path that connects A to B.

35. Edge AB

37. Edge EF

39.

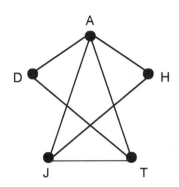

Other answers are possible.

41. It is impossible to have a graph with an odd number of odd vertices.

Exercise Set 14.2

1. a) An **Euler path** is a path that must include each edge of a graph exactly one time.
   b) and c)

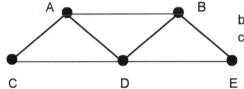

b) The path A, B, E, D, C is a path that is not an Euler path.
c) The path A, B, E, D, C, A, D, B is an Euler path.

3. a) Yes, according to Euler's Theorem.
   b) Yes, according to Euler's Theorem.
   c) No, according to Euler's Theorem.

5. If all of the vertices are even, the graph has an Euler circuit.
7. D, E, C, B, A, D, B, E; other answers are possible.
9. B, C, E, D, B, A, E; other answers are possible.
11. A, B, C, B, F, E, B, D, A; other answers are possible.
13. C, B, A, D, B, E, F, B, C; other answers are possible.
15. E, F, B, C, B, A, D, B, E; other answers are possible.

17. a) Yes. There are zero odd vertices.   19.   a) No. There are more than two odd vertices.
    b) Yes. There are zero odd vertices.   b) No. There are more than zero odd vertices.

21. a) Yes. The land at the top and the island on the left would each correspond to an odd vertex. According to item 2 of Euler's Theorem, a graph with exactly two odd vertices has at least one Euler path, but no Euler circuits.
    b) They could start either on the land at the top of the picture or on the island on the left. If they started on the island, then they would end on the land at the top, and vice versa.

23. a) Yes. The graph representing the map:

They are seeking an Euler path or an Euler circuit. Note that vertices WA and AZ are both odd. According to item 2 of Euler's Theorem, since there are exactly two odd vertices, at least one Euler path, but no Euler circuits exist.
b) One path is WA, OR, CA, AZ.
c) No. According to Euler's Theorem, each Euler path must begin at one odd vertex and end at the other.

25. a) Yes. The graph representing the map:

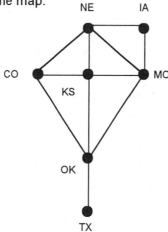

They are seeking an Euler path or an Euler circuit. Note that vertices CO and TX are both odd. According to item 2 of Euler's Theorem, since there are exactly two odd vertices, at least one Euler path, but no Euler circuits exist.
b) One path is TX, OK, MO, IA, NE, MO, KS, NE, CO, KS, OK, CO.
c) No. According to Euler's Theorem, each Euler path must begin at one odd vertex and end at the other.

27. a) Yes. The graph representing the floor plan:

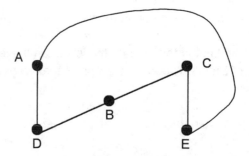

The wood carver is seeking an Euler path or an Euler circuit. Note that there are no odd vertices. According to item 1 of Euler's Theorem, since there are no odd vertices, at least one Euler path (which is also an Euler circuit) must exist.
b) One path (which is also a circuit) is A, D, B, C, E, A.

29. a) Yes. The graph representing the floor plan:

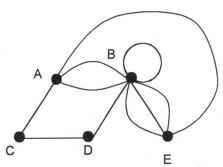

The wood carver is seeking an Euler path or an Euler circuit. Note that there are no odd vertices. According to item 1 of Euler's Theorem, since there are no odd vertices, at least one Euler path (which is also an Euler circuit) must exist.
b) One path (which is also a circuit) is A, C, D, B, E, B, A.

31. a) Yes. The graph representing the map:

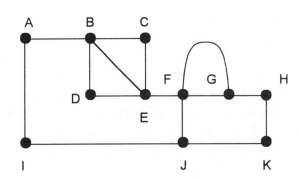

They are seeking an Euler path or an Euler circuit. Note that vertices G and J are both odd. According to item 2 of Euler's Theorem, since there are exactly two odd vertices, at least one Euler path, but no Euler circuits exist.
b) The residents would need to start at one of the two odd vertices.

33. H, I, F, C, B, D, G, H, E, D, A, B, E, F; other answers are possible.
35. A, B, C, E, F, D, E, B, D, A; other answers are possible.
37. A, B, C, D, F, C, B, E, F, H, G, E, A; other answers are possible.
39. A, B, C, E, B, D, E, F, D, A, C, A; other answers are possible.
41. F, C, J, M, P, H, F, M, P; other answers are possible.
43. B, E, I, F, B, C, F, J, G, G, C, D, K, J, I, H, E, A, B; other answers are possibe.
45. J, F, C, B, F, I, E, B, A, E, H, I, J, G, G, C, D, K, J; other answers are possible.

47. It is impossible to draw a graph with an Euler circuit that has a bridge. Therefore, a graph with an Euler circuit has no bridge.

Exercise Set 14.3
1. A **Hamilton path** is a path that passes through each vertex exactly one time.
3. A **Hamilton circuit** is a path that begins and ends at the same vertex and passes through all other vertices exactly one time.
5. A **weighted graph** is a graph with a number, or weight, assigned to each edge.

7. a) The **factorial** is computed by multiplying the given number by each natural number less than the given number.
    b) 8! = 8(7)(6)(5)(4)(3)(2)(1) = 40,320

9. To find the number of unique Hamilton circuits, take the factorial of the number which is one less than the number of vertices.

11. To find the optimal solution using the **Brute Force method**, write down all possible Hamilton circuits and then compute the cost or distance associated with each Hamilton circuit. The one with the lowest cost or shortest distance is the optimal solution to the traveling salesman problem.

13. F, B, C, A, D, E, G and E, G, D, A, C, F, B; other answers are possible.
15. A, B, C, D, H, G, F, E, I, J, K, L and A, E, I, J, F, B, C, G, K, L, H, D; other answers are possible.
17. A, B, C, D, H, L, K, G, F, J, I, E, A and A, E, I, J, K, L, H, D, C, G, F, B, A; other answers are possible.
19. A, B, C, F, I, E, H, G, D, A and A, E, B, C, F, I, H, G, D, A; other answers are possible.

21.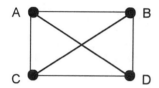

23. The number of unique Hamilton circuits within the complete graph with eight vertices representing this situation is (8 - 1)! = 7! = 7(6)(5)(4)(3)(2)(1) = 5040 ways
25. The number of unique Hamilton circuits within the complete graph with twelve vertices representing this situation is (12 - 1)! = 11! = 11(10)(9)(8)(7)(6)(5)(4)(3)(2)(1) = 39,916,800 ways

27.   a)

Other graphs are possible.

b)

Hamilton Circuit	First Leg/Cost	Second Leg/Cost	Third Leg/Cost	Fourth Leg/Cost	Total Cost
S, R, B, T, S	113	337	393	803	$1646
S, R, T, B, S	113	841	393	855	$2202
S, T, B, R, S	803	393	337	113	$1646
S, T, R, B, S	803	841	337	855	$2836
S, B, R, T, S	855	337	841	803	$2836
S, B, T, R, S	855	393	841	113	$2202

The least expensive route is S, R, B, T, S or S, T, B, R, S

c) $1646

29.   a)

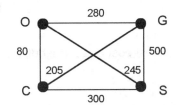

Other graphs are possible.

b)

Hamilton Circuit	First Leg/Distance	Second Leg/Distance	Third Leg/Distance	Fourth Leg/Distance	Total Distance
C, O, G, S, C	80	280	500	300	1160 miles
C, O, S, G, C	80	245	500	205	1030 miles
C, G, O, S, C	205	280	245	300	1030 miles
C, G, S, O, C	205	500	245	80	1030 miles
C, S, G, O, C	300	500	280	80	1160 miles
C, S, O, G, C	300	245	280	205	1030 miles

The shortest route is C, O, S, G, C or C, G, O, S, C or C, G, S, O, C or C, S, O, G, C

c) 1030 miles

31. a)

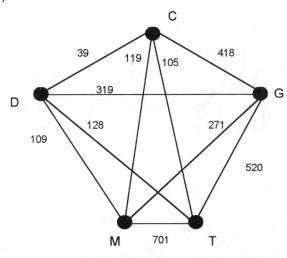

Other graphs are possible.

b) C, D, M, G, T, C for 39 + 109 + 271 + 520 + 105 = $1044
c) Answers will vary.

33. Answers will vary.

Exercise Set 14.4

1. A **tree** is a connected graph in which each edge is a bridge.

3. Yes, because removing the edge would create a disconnected graph.

5. A **minimum-cost spanning tree** is a spanning tree that has the lowest cost or shortest distance of all spanning trees for a given graph.

7.

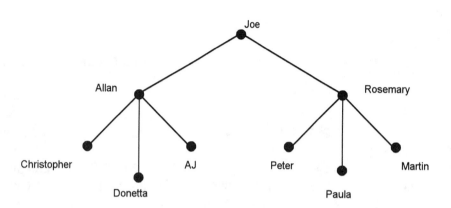

9.

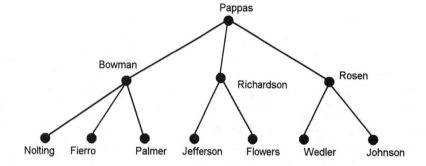

11.

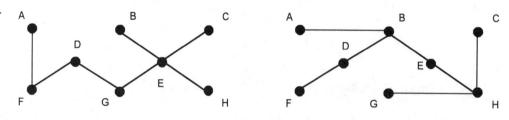

Other answers are possible.

13.

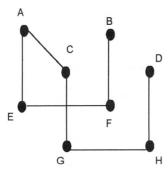   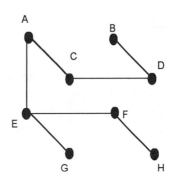

Other answers are possible.

15.

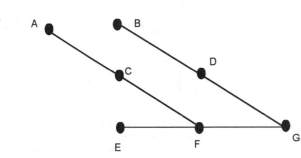   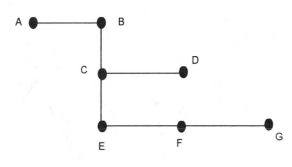

Other answers are possible.

17.

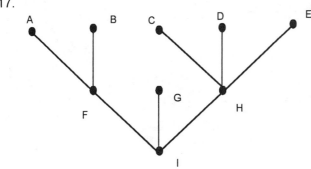   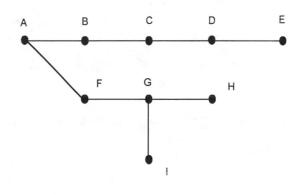

Other answers are possible.

19.

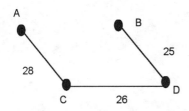

Choose edges in the following order:
BD, CD, AC

21.

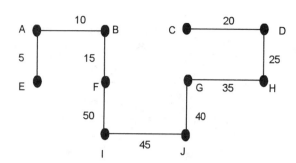

Choose edges in the following order:
AE, AB, BF, CD, DH, GH, GJ, IJ, FI

23.

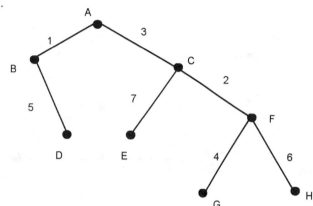

Choose edges in the following order:
AB, CF, AC, FG, BD, FH, EC

25.

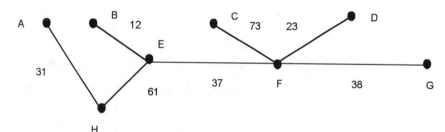

Choose edges in the following order: BE, FD, AH, EF, FG, HE, CF

27. a)

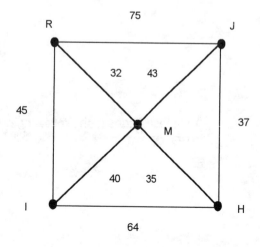

27. b)

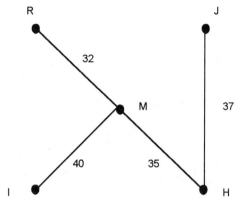

Choose edges in the following order:
RM, MH, JH, IM

c) 15(32 + 35 + 37 + 40) = 15(144) = $2160

29. a)

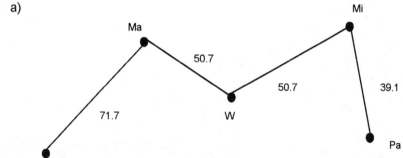

Choose edges in the following order: Mi Pa, W Mi, Ma W, Ma Pl

b) 895(39.1 + 50.7 + 50.7 + 71.7) = 895(212.2) = $189,919

31. a)

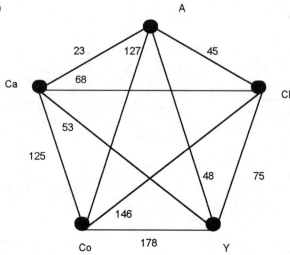

Other graphs are possible.

31. b)

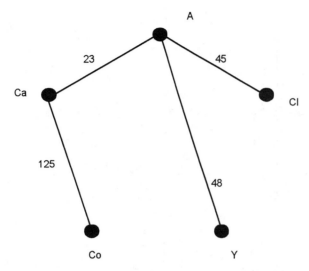

Choose edges in the following order: ACa, AC, AY, CaCo

c) 2300(23 + 45 + 48 + 125) = 2300(241) = $554,300

33. a)

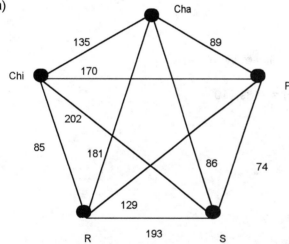

Other graphs are possible.

33. b)

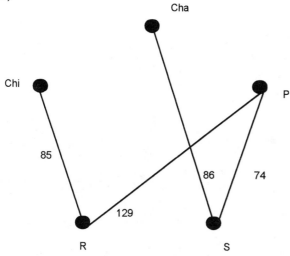

Choose edges in the following order: PS, Chi R, Cha S, RP

c) 74 + 85 + 86 + 129 = 374 miles

Review Exercises

1.

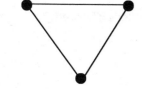

2.

3. One example is D, A, B, D, E, B, C, E.
4. No. To trace each edge in the graph with a path would require you to trace at least one edge twice.

5.

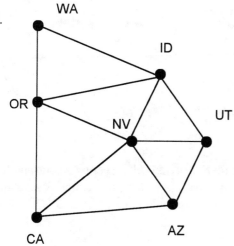

6.

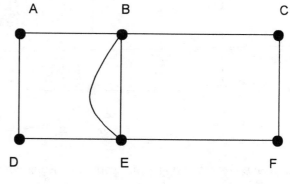

7. Connected

8. Disconnected. There is no path that connects A to C.

9. Edge CD

10. B, A, E, B, C, D, F, C, E, F; Other answers are possible.

11. F, E, A, B, C, D, F, C, E, B; Other answers are possible.

12. B, C, A, D, F, E, C, D, E, B; Other answers are possible.

13. E, F, D, E, C, D, A, C, B, E; Other answers are possible.

14. No. The graph representing the map:

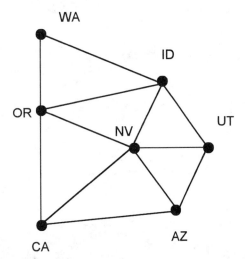

Note that vertices CA, NV, UT, and AZ are all odd. According to item 3 of Euler's Theorem, since there are more than two odd vertices, no Euler path or Euler circuit can exist.

15. a) Yes. The graph representing the floor plan:

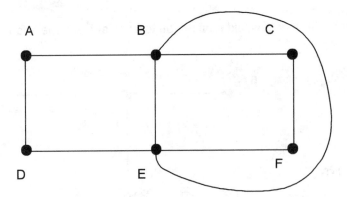

We are seeking an Euler path or an Euler circuit. Note that there are no odd vertices. According to item 1 of Euler's Theorem, since there are no odd vertices, at least one Euler path (which is also an Euler circuit) must exist.

b) You may start in any room and you will end where you started.

16. a) Yes. The graph representing the map:

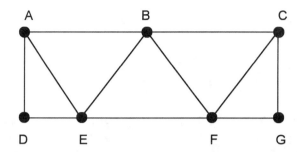

The officer is seeking an Euler path or an Euler circuit. Note that vertices A and C are both odd. According to item 2 of Euler's Theorem, since there are exactly two odd vertices, at least one Euler path but no Euler circuits exist.

b) The officer would have to start at either the upper left-hand corner or the upper right-hand corner and end at the other one.

17. F, B, A, E, F, G, C, D, H, G; Other answers are possible.
18. A, B, C, D, H, G, C, F, G, B, F, E, A; Other answers are possible.
19. A, C, B, F, E, D, G and A, C, D, G, F, B, E; Other answers are possible.
20. A, B, C, D, F, E, A and A, E, F, B, C, D, A; Other answers are possible.

21.

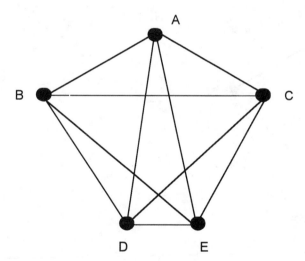

22. The number of unique Hamilton circuits within the complete graph with 5 vertices representing this situation is (5 - 1)! = 4! = 4(3)(2)(1) = 24 ways

23. a)

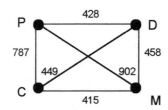

b)

Hamilton Circuit	First Leg/Cost	Second Leg/Cost	Third Leg/Cost	Fourth Leg/Cost	Total Cost
P, D, C, M, P	428	449	415	902	$2194
P, D, M, C, P	428	458	415	787	$2088
P, C, M, D, P	787	415	458	428	$2088
P, C, D, M, P	787	449	458	902	$2596
P, M, D, C, P	902	458	449	787	$2596
P, M, C, D, P	902	415	449	428	$2194

The least expensive route is P, D, M, C, P or P, C, M, D, P

c) $2088

24. a)

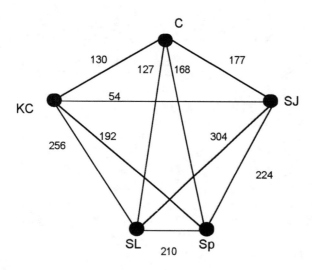

b) SJ, KC, C, SL, Sp, SJ traveling a total of 54 + 130 + 127 + 210 + 224 = 745 miles

c) Sp, C, SL, KC, SJ, Sp traveling a total of 168 + 127 + 256 + 54 + 224 = 829 miles

25.

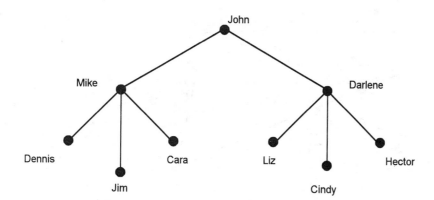

26.

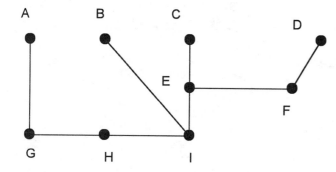

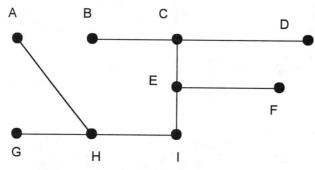

Other answers are possible.

27.

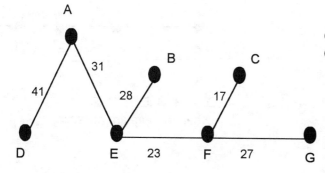

Choose edges in the following order:
CF, EF, FG, BE, AE, AD

28. a)

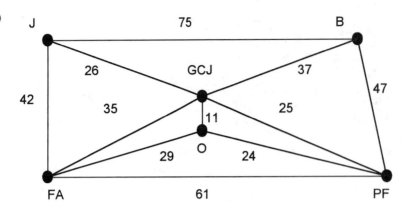

b)

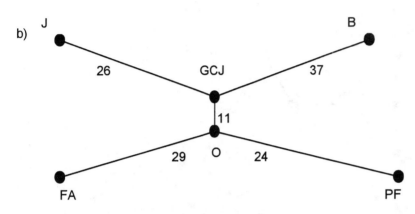

Choose edges in the following order:
O GCJ, O PF, J GCJ, FA O, GCJ B

c) 2.50(11 + 24 + 26 + 29 + 37) = 2.50(127) = $317.50

Chapter Test

1.

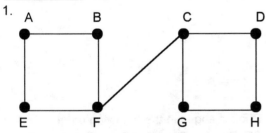

Other answers are possible.

2.

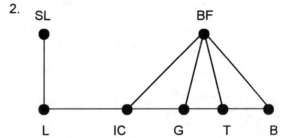

3. One example:

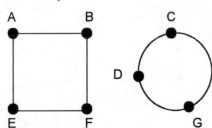

4. D, A, B, C, E, B, D, E;
Other answers are possible.

5. Yes. The graph representing the floor plan:

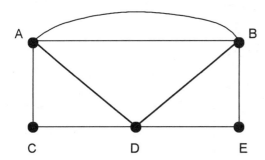

You are seeking an Euler path or an Euler circuit. Note that there are no odd vertices. According to item 1 of Euler's Theorem, since there are no odd vertices, at least one Euler path (which is also an Euler circuit) must exist.
You may start in any room and you will end where you started.

6. A, D, E, A, F, E, H, F, I, G, F, B, G, C, B, A; Other answers are possible.
7. A, B, C, D, H, L, K, G, F, J, I, E, A; Other answers are possible.
8. The number of unique Hamilton circuits within the complete graph with 8 vertices representing this situation is (8 - 1)! = 7! = 7(6)(5)(4)(3)(2)(1) = 5040 ways

9. a)

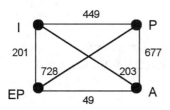

b)

Hamilton Circuit	First Leg/Cost	Second Leg/Cost	Third Leg/Cost	Fourth Leg/Cost	Total Cost
I, P, EP, A, I	449	728	49	203	$1429
I, P, A, EP, I	449	677	49	201	$1376
I, A, P, EP, I	203	677	728	201	$1809
I, A, EP, P, I	203	49	728	449	$1429
I, EP, A, P, I	201	49	677	449	$1376
I, EP, P, A, I	201	728	677	203	$1809

The least expensive route is I, P, A, EP, I or I, EP, A, P, I for $1376.

c) I, EP, A, P, I for $1376.

10.

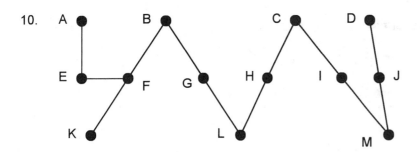

11.

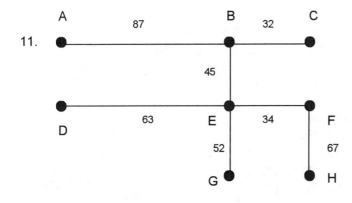

Choose edges in the following order:
BC, EF, BE, EG, DE, FH, AB

12. a)

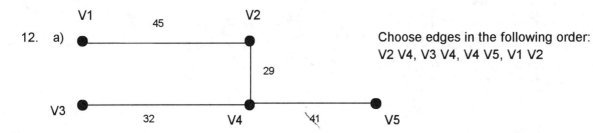

Choose edges in the following order:
V2 V4, V3 V4, V4 V5, V1 V2

b) 1.25(29 + 32 + 41 + 45) = 1.25(147) = $183.75

CHAPTER FIFTEEN

VOTING AND APPORTIONMENT

Exercise Set 15.1

1. When a candidate receives more than 50% of the votes.

3. Voters rank candidates from most favorable to least favorable. Each last place vote is awarded one point, each next to last place vote is awarded two points, each third from last place vote is awarded three points, etc. The candidate receiving the most points is the winner.

5. Voters rank the candidates. A series of comparisons in which each candidate is compared to each of the other candidates follows. If candidate A is preferred to candidate B, then A receives one point. If candidate B is preferred to candidate A, then B receives one point. If the candidates tie, each receives ½ point. The candidate receiving the most points is declared the winner.

7. a) Felicia is the winner. Felicia received the most votes.

   b) No. $\dfrac{2863}{2192 + 2562 + 1671 + 2863 + 1959} = \dfrac{2863}{11247} \approx 0.25$ is not a majority.

9.
Number of votes	3	1	2	2	1
First	B	A	C	C	A
Second	A	B	B	A	C
Third	C	C	A	B	B

11. $8 + 4 + 3 + 2 = 17$

13. Votes – (J): 8, (P): 4 + 3 = 7, (C): 2. Jones wins with the most votes.

15. A majority out of 17 votes is 9 or more votes.
    First choice votes:
    (C): 2, (J):8, (P): 4 + 3 = 7 None receives a majority, thus Choi with the least votes is eliminated.

Number of votes	8	4	3	2
First	J	P	P	P
Second	P	J	J	J

First Choice Votes: (J): 8, (P): 4 + 3 + 2 = 9 Patterson is the winner with 9 votes – a majority.

17. Grand Canyon
    2 first place votes producing $2 \times 3 = 6$ points
    $3 + 1 = 4$ second place votes producing $4 \times 2 = 8$ points
    $2 + 1 = 3$ third place votes producing $3 \times 1 = 3$ points
    Grand Canyon receives $6 + 8 + 3 = 17$ points

    Disney World
    $2 + 1 = 3$ first place votes producing $3 \times 3 = 9$ points
    $1 + 2 = 3$ second place votes producing $3 \times 2 = 6$ points
    3 third place votes producing $3 \times 1 = 3$ points
    Disney World receives $9 + 6 + 3 = 18$ points

    Beach
    $3 + 1 = 4$ first place votes producing $4 \times 3 = 12$ points
    2 second place votes producing $2 \times 2 = 4$ points
    $2 + 1 = 3$ third place votes producing $3 \times 1 = 3$ points
    The Beach receives $12 + 4 + 3 = 19$ points

    The beach wins with the most points.

19. Grand Canyon vs. Disney World
    (G): $3 + 2 = 5$, (B): $2 + 1 + 1 = 4$
    Grand Canyon is awarded 1 point.

    Grand Canyon vs. The Beach
    (G): $2 + 1 = 3$, (B): $3 + 2 + 1 = 6$
    The beach is awarded 1 point.

    The Beach vs. Disney World
    (B): $3 + 1 = 4$, (D): $2 + 2 + 1 = 5$
    Disney World receives 1 point.

    Since (G) received 1 point, (D) received 1 point, and (B) received 1 point, There is no winner.

21. Votes: (S): $7 + 3 + 2 = 12$, (L): $5 + 3 = 8$, (H): $4 + 3 + 2 = 9$, (T): 1
    San Antonio wins with the most votes.

23. Majority out of 30 voters is 16 or more votes.
    First choice votes:
    (S): $7 + 3 + 2 = 12$, (L): $5 + 3 = 8$, (H): $4 + 3 + 2 = 9$, (T): 1
    None receives a majority. Thus (T) with the least is eliminated.

Number of votes	7	5	3	4	3	3	2	1	2
First	S	L	L	H	S	H	S	H	H
Second	L	H	S	L	L	L	H	S	S
Third	H	S	H	S	H	S	L	L	L

    First choice votes: (S): $7 + 3 + 2 = 12$, (L): $5 + 3 = 8$, (H): $4 + 3 + 1 + 2 = 10$
    None receives a majority. Thus (L) with the least is eliminated.

Number of votes	7	5	3	4	3	3	2	1	2
First	S	H	S	H	S	H	S	H	H
Second	H	S	H	S	H	S	H	S	S

    First choice votes: (S): $7 + 3 + 3 + 2 = 15$, (H): $5 + 4 + 3 + 1 + 2 = 15$
    Since neither has a majority, there is no winner.

25. Williams:

     5 first place votes producing $5 \times 3 = 15$ points
     4 second place votes producing $4 \times 2 = 8$ points
     $1 + 2 = 3$ third place votes producing $3 \times 1 = 3$ points
     Williams receives $15 + 8 + 3 = 26$ points

    Diaz:

     1 first place votes producing $1 \times 3 = 3$ points
     $5 + 2 = 7$ second place votes producing $7 \times 2 = 14$ points
     4 third place votes producing $4 \times 1 = 4$ points
     Diaz receives $3 + 14 + 4 = 21$ points

    Johnson:

     $4 + 2 = 6$ first place votes producing $6 \times 3 = 18$ points
     1 second place votes producing $1 \times 2 = 2$ points
     5 third place votes producing $5 \times 1 = 5$ points
     Johnson receives $18 + 2 + 5 = 25$ points

    Williams wins with the most points.

27. (W) vs. (D)   (W) vs. (J)   (J) vs. (D)
    (W): $5 + 4 = 9$, (D): $1 + 2 = 3$ (W): 5, (J): $1 + 4 + 2 = 7$ (J): $4 + 2 = 6$, (D): $5 + 1 = 6$
    (W) is awarded 1 point   (J) is awarded 1 point   Each is awarded ½ point

    Johnson is the winner with the most points.

29. A majority out of 12 voters is 7 or more votes. First choice votes: (W): 5, (D): 1, (J): $4 + 2 = 6$
    None receives a majority. Thus eliminate Johnson with the most last place votes.

Number of votes	5	1	4	2
First	W	D	W	D
Second	D	W	D	W

    First choice votes: (W): $5 + 4 = 9$, (D): $1 + 2 = 3$. Williams wins with a majority of the votes.

31. Lehigh Road:

     5 first place votes producing $5 \times 3 = 15$ points
     0 second place votes producing $0 \times 2 = 0$ points
     $2 + 4 = 6$ third place votes producing $6 \times 1 = 6$ points
     Lehigh Road receives $15 + 6 = 21$ points

    Erie Road:

     2 first place votes producing $2 \times 3 = 6$ points
     $5 + 4 = 9$ second place votes producing $9 \times 2 = 18$ points
     0 third place votes producing $0 \times 1 = 0$ points
     Erie Road receives $6 + 18 = 24$ points

    Ontario Road:

     4 first place votes producing $4 \times 3 = 12$ points
     2 second place votes producing $2 \times 2 = 4$ points
     5 third place votes producing $5 \times 1 = 5$ points
     Ontario Road receives $12 + 4 + 5 = 21$ points

    Erie Road wins with the most points.

33. (L) vs. (E)   (L) vs. (O)   (E) vs. (O)

    (L): 5, (E): 2 + 4 = 6   (L): 5, (O): 2 + 4 = 6   (E): 5 + 2 = 7, (O): 4

    (E) is awarded 1 point   (O) is awarded 1 point   (E) is awarded 1 point

    Erie Road wins with the most points.

35. a) Votes: (TI): 6 + 4 = 10, (C): 3, (HP): 2, (S): 0

       TI wins with the most votes

   b) TI:

      6 + 4 = 10 first place votes producing $10 \times 4 = 40$ points

      3 + 2 = 5 second place votes producing $5 \times 3 = 15$ points

      0 third place votes producing $0 \times 2 = 0$ points

      0 fourth place votes producing $0 \times 1 = 0$ points

      TI receives 40 + 15 = 55 points

      (C):

      3 first place votes producing $3 \times 4 = 12$ points

      6 second place votes producing $6 \times 3 = 18$ points

      4 + 2 = 6 third place votes producing $6 \times 2 = 12$ points

      0 fourth place votes producing $0 \times 1 = 0$ points

      (C) receives 12 + 18 + 12 = 42 points

      (HP):

      2 first place votes producing $2 \times 4 = 8$ points

      4 second place votes producing $4 \times 3 = 12$ points

      0 third place votes producing $0 \times 2 = 0$ points

      6 + 3 = 9 fourth place votes producing $9 \times 1 = 9$ points

      (HP) receives 8 + 12 + 9 = 29 points

      (S):

      0 first place votes producing $0 \times 4 = 0$ points

      0 second place votes producing $0 \times 3 = 0$ points

      6 + 3 = 9 third place votes producing $9 \times 2 = 18$ points

      4 + 2 = 6 fourth place votes producing $6 \times 1 = 6$ points

      (S) receives 18 + 6 = 24 points

      TI is the winner with the most points.

   c) A majority out of 15 voters is 8 or more votes.

      First choice votes: (TI): 6 + 4 = 10, (C): 3, (HP): 2. (S): 0

      TI wins with a majority of the votes.

d) (TI) vs. (C)
(TI): 6 + 4 + 2 = 12, (C): 3
(TI) is awarded 1 point

(TI) vs. (HP)
(TI): 6 + 4 + 3 = 13, (HP): 2
(TI) is awarded 1 point

(TI) vs. (S)
(TI): 6 + 4 + 3 + 2 = 15, (S): 0
(TI) is awarded 1 point

(C) vs. (HP)
(C): 6 + 3 = 9, (HP): 2 + 4 = 6
(C) is awarded 1 point

(C) vs. (S)
(C): 6 + 4 + 3 + 2 = 15, (S): 0
(C) is awarded 1 point

(S) vs. (HP)
(S): 6 + 3 = 9, (HP): 4 + 2 = 6
(S) is awarded 1 point

TI wins with the most points.

37. a) (ND) vs. (YS)
(ND): 7 + 2 = 9, (YS): 3 + 1 = 4
(ND) is awarded 1 point

(ND) vs. (GK)
(ND): 7 + 3 + 1 = 11, (GK): 2
(ND) is awarded 1 point

(ND) vs. (MR)
(ND): 7 + 2 + 1 = 10, (MR): 3
(ND) is awarded 1 point

(YS) vs. (GK)
(YS): 7 + 3 + 1 = 11, (GK): 2
(YS) is awarded 1 point

(YS) vs. (MR)
(YS): 3 + 1 = 4, (MR): 7 + 2 = 9
(MR) is awarded 1 point

(GK) vs. (MR)
(GK): 2 + 1 = 3, (MR): 7 + 3 = 10
(MR) is awarded 1 point

(ND): 3 points, (YS): 1 point, (GK): 0, (MR): 2 points
(ND) wins with the most points.

b) A majority out of 13 voters is 7 or more votes.
First choice votes: (ND): 7, (YS): 3 + 1 = 4, (GK): 2, (MR): 0
None has a majority, thus eliminate (MR) with the least votes.

Number of votes	7	3	2	1
First	ND	YS	GK	YS
Second	YS	ND	ND	ND
Third	GK	GK	YS	GK

First choice votes: (ND): 7, (YS): 3 + 1 = 4, (GK): 2
None has the majority, thus eliminate (GK) with the least votes.

Number of votes	7	3	2	1
First	ND	YS	ND	YS
Second	YS	ND	YS	ND

First choice votes: (ND): 7 + 2 = 9, (YS): 3 + 1 = 4
(ND) wins with a majority of the votes.

c) (ND):

7 first place votes producing $7 \times 4 = 28$ points

$2 + 1 = 3$ second place votes producing $3 \times 3 = 9$ points

3 third place votes producing $3 \times 2 = 6$ points

0 fourth place votes producing $0 \times 1 = 0$ points

(ND) receives $28 + 9 + 6 = 43$ points

(YS):

$3 + 1 = 4$ first place votes producing $4 \times 4 = 16$ points

0 second place votes producing $0 \times 3 = 0$ points

7 third place votes producing $7 \times 2 = 14$ points

2 fourth place votes producing $2 \times 1 = 2$ points

(YS) receives $16 + 14 + 2 = 32$ points

(GK):

2 first place votes producing $2 \times 4 = 8$ points

0 second place votes producing $0 \times 3 = 0$ points

1 third place votes producing $1 \times 2 = 2$ points

$7 + 3 = 10$ fourth place votes producing $10 \times 1 = 10$ points

(GK) receives $8 + 2 + 10 = 20$ points

(MR):

0 first place votes producing $0 \times 4 = 0$ points

$7 + 3 = 10$ second place votes producing $10 \times 3 = 30$ points

2 third place votes producing $2 \times 2 = 4$ points

1 fourth place votes producing $1 \times 1 = 1$ points

(MR) receives $30 + 4 + 1 = 35$ points

(ND) wins with the most points.

d) Votes: (ND): 7, (YS): $3 + 1 = 4$, (GK): 2, (MR): 0

(ND) wins with the most votes.

39. a) If there were only two columns then only two of the candidates were the first choice of the voters. If each of the 15 voters cast a ballot, then one of the voters must have received a majority of votes because 15 cannot be split evenly.

b) An odd number cannot be divided evenly so one of the two first choice candidates must receive more than half of the votes.

41. a) Comets:
　　　　1 first place votes producing 1 × 4 = 4 points
　　　　0 second place votes producing 0 × 3 = 0 points
　　　　0 third place votes producing 0 × 2 = 0 points
　　　　2 fourth place votes producing 2 × 1 = 2 points
　　　　Comets receives 4 + 2 = 6 points

　　　　Rams:
　　　　2 first place votes producing 2 × 4 = 8 points
　　　　1 second place votes producing 1 × 3 = 3 points
　　　　0 third place votes producing 0 × 2 = 0 points
　　　　0 fourth place votes producing 0 × 1 = 0 points
　　　　Rams receives 8 + 3 = 11 points

　　　　Warriors:
　　　　0 first place votes producing 0 × 4 = 0 points
　　　　2 second place votes producing 2 × 3 = 6 points
　　　　2 third place votes producing 2 × 2 = 4 points
　　　　2 fourth place votes producing 2 × 1 = 2 points
　　　　Warriors receives 6 + 4 + 2 = 12 points

　　　　Tigers:
　　　　1 first place votes producing 1 × 4 = 4 points
　　　　1 second place votes producing 1 × 3 = 3 points
　　　　2 third place votes producing 2 × 2 = 4 points
　　　　0 fourth place votes producing 0 × 1 = 0 points
　　　　Tigers receives 4 + 3 + 4 = 11 points

　　　　Warriors are first, Rams and Tigers are tied and Comets are last.

　　b) Comets would receive 5 points.
　　　　Rams would receive 13 points.
　　　　Warriors would receive 8 points.
　　　　Tigers would receive 10 points.
　　　　The new rank would be Rams first, Tigers second, Warriors third, and Comets fourth.

43. Votes: (A): 10, (B): 7, (C): 5, (D): 9
　　　A and D would win since they received the most votes.

Exercise Set 15.2

1. If a candidate receives a majority of first place votes, then that candidate should be declared the winner.

3. A candidate who wins a first election and then gains additional support without losing any of the original support should also win a second election.

5. A candidate that is preferred to all others will win each pairwise comparison and be selected with the pairwise comparison method.

7. (F) receives 25 points, (S) receives 23 points and (M) receives 18 points
   (F) wins with the Borda count method but S has 6 votes which is a majority out of the 11 voters.

9. Votes: A:4, B:2, C:5; C wins with the plurality method.
   However, A is favored over the others using a head-to-head comparison.
   Thus, the head-to-head criterion is <u>not</u> satisfied.

11. A receives 19 points, B receives 15 points, C receives 20 points; C wins with the Borda count method.
    However, A is favored over B and C in a head-to-head comparison.
    Thus, the head-to-head criterion is <u>not</u> satisfied.

13. A majority out of 25 voters is 13 or more votes.
    B wins with a majority of the votes.
    B also wins in a head-to-head comparison with the others.
    Thus, the head-to-head criterion is satisfied.

15. Votes: A:8, B:4, C:5; thus A wins
    If B drops out we get the following:
    Votes: A:8, B:4 + 5 = 9, thus B would win.
    The irrelevant alternatives criterion is <u>not</u> satisfied.

17. A receives 38 points, B receives 35 points, C receives 35 points
    Thus, A wins using the Borda count method.
    If B drops out we get the following:
    A receives 25 points, C receives 29 points
    Thus, C wins the second vote.
    The irrelevant alternatives criterion is <u>not</u> satisfied.

19. A majority out of 21 voters is 11 or more votes.
    Votes: A:5 + 3 = 8, B:6, C:7; none has a majority, thus eliminate B.
    Votes: A:5 + 3 = 8, C: 6 + 7 = 13, thus C wins.
    If the three voters who voted for A,C,B change to C,A,B the table become:

Number of votes	5	6	10
First	A	B	C
Second	B	C	A
Third	C	A	B

    The new set of votes is
    Votes: A:5, B:6, C:10; none has a majority, thus eliminate A.
    Votes: B:5 + 6 = 11, D:10, thus B wins this time.
    Thus, the monotonicity criterion is <u>not</u> satisfied.

21. A majority out of 23 voters is 12 votes.
    Votes: A:10, B:8, C:5; none has a majority, thus eliminate C.
    Votes: B:10, B:8 + 5 = 13; thus B wins.
    After A drops out the new table is:

Number of votes	10	8	5
First	C	B	C
Second	B	C	B

    Votes: B:8, C:10 + 5 = 15; thus C wins this time.
    The irrelevant alternatives criterion is <u>not</u> satisfied.

23. A receives 2 points
    B receives 3 points
    C receives 2 points
    D receives 1 point
    E receives 2 points
    Thus, B wins.

    After A, C and E drop out the new table is

Number of votes	1	1	1	1	1
First	B	B	D	D	D
Second	D	D	B	B	B

    (B) vs. (D)
    Votes: (B):2, (D):3; thus D wins this time.
    The irrelevant alternatives criterion is <u>not</u> satisfied.

25. a) A majority out of 23 votes is 12 votes.
       First place votes: C:8, G:0, H:3, S:12
       (S) holds a majority of first place votes.

    b) Votes: C:8, G:0, H:3, S:12. Thus, (S) wins.

    c) C receives 62 points, G receives 63 points, H receives 40 points, S receives 65 points. Thus, (S) wins.

    d) A majority out of 23 votes is 12 votes. In part (a) we find that (S) holds a majority. Thus, (S) wins.

    e) C receives 1 point, G receives 2 points, H receives 0 points, S receives 3 points. Thus, (S) wins.

    f) None, since (S) wins in every case.

27. a) A majority out of 82 votes is 42 votes or more.
       Votes: A:28, B:24, C:20 + 10 = 30; none has a majority, thus, eliminate B
       Votes: A:28 + 24 = 52, G:20 + 10 = 30; A has a majority; thus A wins

    b) Votes: A:36, B:24, C:20 + 2 = 22; none has a majority; thus eliminate C
       Votes: A:35 + 2 = 38, B:24 + 20 = 44; thus B wins

    c) Yes. There is a new winner.

29. If a candidate receives a majority of votes, that candidate will also have the most votes.

31. If there is a candidate that is the first choice of a majority of voters, that candidate will be declared the winner in the first round of the plurality with elimination method.

Exercise Set 15.3

1. If we divide the total population by the number of items to be apportioned we obtain a number called the standard divisor.

3. The standard quota rounded up to the nearest whole number.

5. An apportionment should always be either the upper quota or the lower quota.

7. Jefferson's method, Webster's method, Adams's method

9. a) Standard divisor = $\dfrac{7500000}{150} = 50{,}000$

b & c)

State	A	B	C	D	Total
Population	1,222,000	2,730,000	857,000	2,693,000	7,500,000
Standard Quota	24.40	54.60	17.14	53.86	
Lower Quota	24	54	17	53	148
Hamilton's Apportionment	24	55	17	54	150

11. a & b)

State	A	B	C	D	Total
Population	1,222,000	2,730,000	857,000	2,693,000	7,500,000
Modified Quota	24.70	55.26	17.35	54.51	
Jefferson's Apportionment (round down)	24	55	17	54	150

13. a & b)

State	A	B	C	D	Total
Population	1,222,000	2,730,000	857,000	2,693,000	7,500,000
Modified Quota	24.06	53.85	16.90	53.12	
Adams' Apportionment (round up)	25	54	17	54	150

15. a & b)

State	A	B	C	D	Total
Population	1,222,000	2,730,000	857,000	2,693,000	7,500,000
Modified Quota	24.38	54.55	17.12	53.81	
Webster's Apportionment	24	55	17	54	150

17. a & b)

Person	Al	Bob	Charlie	Total
Amount	350	530	470	1350
Modified Quota	8.05	12.18	10.84	
Jefferson's Apportionment (rounded down)	8	12	10	30

19. a & b)

Person	Al	Bob	Charlie	Total
Amount	350	530	470	1350
Modified Quota	7.45	11.28	10.00	
Adam's Apportionment (rounded up)	8	12	10	30

21. a & b)

Person	Al	Bob	Charlie	Total
Amount	350	530	470	1350
Standard Quota	7.78	11.78	10.44	
Webster's Apportionment (standard rounding)	8	12	10	30

23. a) A standard divisor = $\dfrac{\text{total}}{60} = \dfrac{1260}{60} = 21$

b)

State	A	B	C	D	Total
Population	123	484	382	271	1260
Standard Quota	5.86	23.05	18.19	12.90	

25. A divisor of 20.5 was used.

State	A	B	C	D	Total
Population	123	484	382	271	1260
Modified Quota	6.00	23.61	18.63	13.22	
Jefferson's Apportionment (round down)	6	23	18	13	60

27.

State	A	B	C	D	Total
Population	123	484	382	271	1260
Standard Quota	5.86	23.05	18.19	12.90	
Webster's Apportionment	6	23	18	13	60

29.

School	LA	Sci.	Eng.	Bus.	Hum	Total
Enrollment	1746	7095	2131	937	1091	13000
Standard Quota	33.58	136.44	40.98	18.02	20.98	
Lower Quota	33	136	40	18	20	247
Hamilton's Apportionment	34	136	41	18	21	250

31. A divisor of 52.5 was used.

School	LA	Sci.	Eng.	Bus.	Hum	Total
Enrollment	1746	7095	2131	937	1091	13000
Modified Quota	33.26	135.14	40.59	17.85	20.78	
Adam's Apportionment (round up)	34	136	41	18	21	250

33. a) Standard divisor = $\dfrac{\text{total}}{50} = \dfrac{400}{50} = 8$

b)

Division	LA	Sci.	Bus.	Hum	Total
Faculty	130	175	46	49	
Standard Quota	16.25	21.88	5.75	6.13	

35. The divisor of 7.65 was used.

Division	LA	Sci.	Bus.	Hum	Total
Faculty	130	175	46	49	
Modified Quota	16.99	22.88	6.01	6.41	
Jefferson's Apportionment (round down)	16	22	6	6	50

37.

Division	LA	Sci.	Bus.	Hum	Total
Faculty	130	175	46	49	
Standard Quota	15.76	21.21	5.58	5.94	
Webster's Apportionment (standard rounding)	16	22	6	6	50

39.

Precinct	A	B	C	D	E	F	Total
Crimes	743	367	432	491	519	388	2940
Standard Quota	53.07	26.21	30.86	35.07	37.07	27.71	
Lower Quota	53	26	30	35	37	27	208
Hamilton's Apportionment	53	26	31	35	37	28	210

41. The divisor 14.2 as used.

Precinct	A	B	C	D	E	F	Total
Crimes	743	367	432	491	519	388	2940
Modified Quota	52.32	22.85	30.42	34.58	36.55	27.32	
Adam's Apportionment (round up)	53	26	31	35	37	28	210

43. a) Standard divisor = $\dfrac{\text{total}}{200} = \dfrac{2400}{200} = 12$

b)

Shift	A	B	C	D	Total
Room calls	751	980	503	166	2400
Standard Quota	62.58	81.67	41.92	13.83	

45. The divisor 11.9 was used.

Shift	A	B	C	D	Total
Room calls	751	980	503	166	2400
Modified Quota	63.11	82.35	42.27	13.95	
Jefferson's Apportionment (round down)	63	82	42	13	200

47. The divisor 12.02 was used.

Shift	A	B	C	D	Total
Room calls	751	980	503	166	2400
Modified Quota	62.48	81.53	41.85	13.81	
Webster's Apportionment (standard rounding)	62	82	42	14	200

Exercise set 15.4

1. The Alabama paradox occurs when an increase in the total number of items results in a loss of items for a group.

3. The new-sates paradox occurs when the addition of a new group changes the apportionment of another group.

5. New divisor = $\dfrac{900}{51} = 17.65$

School	A	B	C	D	E	Total
Standard Quota	11.90	9.35	9.07	9.92	10.76	
Lower Quota	11	9	9	9	10	48
Hamilton's Apportionment	12	9	9	10	11	51

No. No school suffers a loss so the Alabama paradox does not occur.

7. a) Standard divisor = $\dfrac{900}{30} = 30$

State	A	B	C	Total
Population	161	250	489	900
Standard Quota	5.37	8.33	16.30	
Lower Quota	5	8	16	29
Hamilton's Apportionment	6	8	16	30

b) new divisor = $\dfrac{900}{31} = 29.03$

State	A	B	C	Total
Population	161	250	489	900
Standard Quota	5.55	8.61	16.84	
Lower Quota	5	8	16	29
Hamilton's Apportionment	5	9	17	31

Yes. State A loses a seat while states B and C each gain a seat.

9. a) Standard divisor = $\dfrac{20000}{200} = 100$

City	A	B	C	Total
Population	7130	2030	10,840	20,000
Standard Quota	71.3	20.3	108.4	
Lower Quota	71	20	108	199
Hamilton's Apportionment	71	20	109	200

b) New divisor = $\dfrac{20010}{200} = 100.05$

City	A	B	C	Total
New Population	7135	2030	10,845	20,010
Standard Quota	71.31	20.29	108.40	
Lower Quota	71	20	108	199
Hamilton's Apportionment	71	20	109	200

No. None of the Cities loses a bonus.

11. a) Standard divisor $= \dfrac{5400}{54} = 100$

Division	A	B	C	D	E	Total
Population	733	1538	933	1133	1063	5400
Standard Quota	7.33	15.38	9.33	11.33	10.63	
Lower Quota	7	15	9	11	10	52
Hamilton's Apportionment	7	16	9	11	11	54

b) New divisor $= \dfrac{5454}{54} = 101$

Division	A	B	C	D	E	Total
Population	733	1539	933	1133	1116	
Standard Quota	7.26	15.238	9.238	11.22	11.05	
Lower Quota	7	15	9	11	11	53
Hamilton's Apportionment	8	15	9	11	11	54

Yes. Division B loses a seat to division A even though the population of division B grew faster than the population of division A.

13. a) Standard divisor $= \dfrac{4800}{48} = 100$

Tech. Data	A	B	Total
Employees	844	3956	4800
Standard Quota	8.44	39.56	
Lower Quota	8	39	47
Hamilton's Apportionment	8	40	48

b) New divisor $= \dfrac{5524}{55} = 100.44$

Tech. Data	A	B	C	Total
Employees	844	3956	724	5524
Standard Quota	8.40	39.39	7.21	
Lower Quota	8	39	7	54
Hamilton's Apportionment	9	39	7	55

Yes. The US lost an employee to Europe.

15. a) Standard divisor $= \dfrac{10000}{100} = 100$

State	A	B	Total
Population	11.35	8865	10,000
Standard Quota	11.35	88.65	
Lower Quota	11	88	99
Hamilton's Apportionment	11	89	100

b) New divisor $= \dfrac{10625}{106} = 100.24$

State	A	B	C	Total
Population	11.35	8865	625	5524
Standard Quota	11.32	88.44	6.24	
Lower Quota	11	88	6	105
Hamilton's Apportionment	11	89	6	106

No. The apportionment is the same.

Review Exercises

1. a) Robert Rivera wins with the most votes (12).

    b) A majority out of 24 voters is 13 or more votes. Robert Rivera does not have a majority.

2. a) Michelle MacDougal wins with the most votes (224).

    b) Yes. A majority out of 421 voters is 211 or more votes.

3.

Number of votes	3	2	1	3	1
First	B	A	D	C	D
Second	A	C	C	B	A
Third	C	D	A	A	B
Fourth	D	B	B	D	C

4.

Number of votes	2	2	2	1
First	C	A	B	C
Second	A	B	C	B
Third	B	C	A	A

5. Number of votes = 6 + 4 + 3 + 2 + 1 + 1 = 17

6. Votes: P:6 + 1 = 7, D:4, M:3 + 2 = 5, B:1.   Pizza Hut wins.

7. P:50 points, D:47 points, M:35 points, B:38 points. Pizza Hut wins.

8. A majority out 17 voters is 9 or more votes.

    Votes: P:6 + 1 = 7, D:4, M: 3 + 2 = 5, B:1.   None has a majority, thus eliminate B.

    Votes: P:6 + 1 = 7, D:4, M: 3 + 2 + 1 = 6. None has a majority, thus eliminate D.

    Votes: P:6 + 4 + 1 = 11, M: 3 + 2 + 1 = 6. Pizza Hut wins.

9. P:3 points, D:2 points, M:0 points, B:1 point; Pizza Hut wins.

10. Votes: P:7, D:4, M:5, B:1

    None has a majority, thus eliminate M with most last place votes.

    Votes: P:10, D:4, B:3; Pizza Hut wins.

11. Voters: 38 + 30 + 25 + 7 + 10 = 110

12. Votes: S:38, V:30 + 10 = 40, B:25 + 7 = 32; Volleyball wins.

13. S:223 points, V:215 points, B:222 points; Soccer wins.

14. A majority out of 110 voters is 56 or more votes.

    Votes: S:38, V:40, B:32; None has a majority, thus eliminate B

    Votes: S:45, V:65; Volleyball wins.

15. S:1 point, V:1 point, B:1 point; A 3-way tie.

16. Votes: S:38, V:40, B:32; none has a majority, thus eliminate V with the most last place votes.

    Votes: S:68, B:42; Soccer wins.

17. a) Votes: A:150 + 123 = 273, F:45, M:3, P:0; A wins.

    b) Yes. A majority out of 321 voters is 161 or more votes. A receives a majority.

    c) A:1230 points, F:609 points, M:621 points, P:750 points. A wins.

    d) 161 or more votes is needed for a majority. Votes: A:273, F:45, M:3, P::0; A wins.

    e) A:3 points, F:1 point, M:1 point, P:1 point; A wins.

18. a) Votes – (C):30, (D):45, (I):60 + 10 = 70, (M):55. Indianapolis wins.

    b) A majority out of 200 voters is 101 or more votes. None of the cities has a majority.

    c) (C):495 points, (D):495 pints, (I):410 points, (M):600 points. Milwaukee wins.

    d) Votes: C:30, D:45, I:70, M:55; None has a majority, thus eliminate C.

      Votes: D:45, I:70, M:55 + 30 = 85; None has a majority, thus eliminate D.

      Votes: I:70, M:130; Milwaukee wins.

    e) C:1 point, D:2 points, I:0 points, M:3 points; Milwaukee wins.

19. a) A majority out of 16 voters is 9 or more votes.
     Votes: (EB):4 + 3+ = 7, (FW): 1 + 1 – 2, (G):0, (WB): 6 + 1 = 7;
     None has a majority, thus eliminate G.
     Votes: (EB):4 + 3 = 7, (FW):1 + 1 = 2, (WB): 6 + 1 = 7;
     None has a majority, thus eliminate FW
     Votes: (EB): 4 + 3 + 1 = 8, (WB): 6 + 1 + 1 = 8. Thus, EB and WB tie.

   b) Use the Borda count method to break the tie.
     (EB) has 46 points, (WB) has 50 points; World Book wins.

   c) (EB) vs. (WB)
     EB:4 + 3 + 1 = 8 points, (WB):6 + 1 + 1 = 8 points.   EB and WB tie again.

20. A:23 points, B:26 points, C:18 points, D:13 points.   Using the Borda count method B wins.
   However, B only has 2 first place votes, thus the majority criterion is <u>not</u> satisfied.

21. In a head-to-head comparison B must win over all the others. For (B vs. A) A wins. The head-to-head
   criterion is <u>not</u> satisfied.

22. a) A majority out of 42 voters is 22 or more votes.
     Votes: A:12, B:10 + 6 = 16, C:14; None has the majority, thus eliminate A.
     Votes: B:10 + 6 = 16, C:14 + 12 = 26; C wins.

   b) The new preference table is

Number of votes	10	20	12
First	B	C	A
Second	A	B	C
Third	C	A	B

   Votes: A:12, B:10, C:20; None has a majority, thus eliminate B.
   Votes: A:22, C:20; A wins.
   When the order is changed A wins. Therefore, the monotonicity criterion is <u>not</u> satisfied.

   c) If B drops out the new table is

Number of votes	10	14	6	12
First	A	C	C	A
Second	C	A	A	C

   Votes: A:10 + 12 = 22, C:14 + 6 = 20; A wins.
   Since C won the first election and then after B dropped out A won, the irrelevant criterion is not
   satisfied.

23. a) Yes. (C) Rene Descartes is favored when compared to each of the other candidates.

   b) Votes: (A):29, (B)43, (C):26 + 14 = 40, (D):30. (B) Bernhard Bolzano wins.

   c) A:422, B:297, C:380, D:361; (A) Maria Agnesi wins.

   d) A majority out of 142 voters is 72 or more votes.
     Votes: A:29, B:43, C:26 + 14 = 40, D:30; None has a majority, thus eliminate A.
     Votes: B:432, C:29 + 26 + 14 = 69, D:30; None has a majority, thus eliminate D.
     Votes: B:43, C:69 + 30 = 99; (C) Marquis deCondorcet wins.

   e) A received 2 points, B receive 0 points, C receives 1 point, D receives 3 points; D wins.

   f) From part (a) we see that Rene Descartes is favored over each of the others when compared
     head-to-head. However, Renee Descartes does not win when the <u>plurality method</u>, <u>Borda count
     method</u> and <u>plurality with elimination method</u> are used. Thus, these methods violate the head-to-head
     criterion.

24. a) Yes. (D) Dire Straits is favored when compared to each of the other bands.

   b) Votes: A:15, B:34, C:9 + 4 = 13, D:25; (B) Boston wins.

   c) A:217 points, B:198 points, C:206 points, D:249 points; (D) Dire Straits wins.

   d) A majority out of 87 voters is 44 or more votes.
      Votes: A:15, B:34, C:13, D:25; None has a majority, thus eliminate C.
      Votes: A:15 + 9 +4 = 28, B:34, D:25; None has a majority, thus eliminate D.
      Votes: A:28 + 25 = 53, B:34; (A) Abba wins.

   e) A receives 2 points, B receives 0 points, C receives 1 point, D receives 3 points; thus (D) Dire Straits wins.

   f) The plurality method and the plurality with elimination method.

25. A majority out of 70 voters is 36 or more votes. Candidate A has a majority of the votes.
    Using plurality A wins. Using Borda count B wins. Using plurality with elimination A wins, Using Pairwise A wins. The only method to violate the majority criterion is the Borda count method.

26. The only methods that violate the monotonicity criterion are the plurality method and the plurality with elimination method.

27. Using the plurality method, B wins with D included and B wins after D drops out.
    Using the Borda count method, A wins with D included but E wins after D drops out.
    Using plurality with elimination, B wins with D included and B wins after D drops out.
    Using the pairwise method, B wins with D include but E wins after D drops out.
    The Borda count and pairwise comparison methods violate the irrelevant alternatives criterion.

28. Standard divisor = $\dfrac{6000}{10}$ = 600

Region	A	B	C	Total
Number of Houses	2592	1428	1980	6000
Standard Quota	4.32	2.38	3.30	
Lower Quota	4	2	3	9
Hamilton's Apportionment	4	3	3	10

29. Using the modified divisor 500.

Region	A	B	C	Total
Number of Houses	2592	1428	1980	6000
Modified Quota	5.18	2.86	3.96	
Jefferson's Apportionment (rounded down)	5	2	3	10

30. Using the modified divisor 700.

Region	A	B	C	Total
Number of Houses	2592	1428	1980	6000
Modified Quota	3.70	2.04	2.83	
Adam's Apportionment (rounded up)	4	3	3	10

31. Using the modified divisor 575.

Region	A	B	C	Total
Number of Houses	2592	1428	1980	6000
Modified Quota	4.51	2.48	3.4	
Webster's Apportionment (normal rounding)	5	2	3	10

32. Yes. Hamilton's Apportionment becomes 5, 2, 4.
    Region B loses one truck.

33. Standard divisor = $\dfrac{690}{23} = 30$

Course	A	B	C	Total
Number of Students	311	219	160	690
Standard Quota	10.37	7.30	5.33	
Lower Quota	10	7	5	22
Hamilton's Apportionment	11	7	5	23

34. Use the modified divisor 28

Course	A	B	C	Total
Number of Students	311	219	160	690
Modified Quota	11.12	7.82	5.71	
Jefferson's Apportionment (round down)	11	7	5	23

35. Use the modified divisor 31.5

Course	A	B	C	Total
Number of Students	311	219	160	690
Modified Quota	9.87	6.95	5.08	
Adam's Apportionment (round up)	10	7	6	23

36. Use the modified divisor 29.5

Course	A	B	C	Total
Number of Students	311	219	160	690
Modified Quota	10.54	7.42	5.42	
Webster's Apportionment (standard rounding)	11	7	5	23

37. The new divisor is $\dfrac{698}{23} = 30.35$

Course	A	B	C	Total
Number of Students	317	219	162	698
Standard Quota	10.44	7.22	5.34	
Lower Quota	10	7	5	22
Hamilton's Apportionment	11	7	5	23

No. The apportionment remains the same.

38. The Standard divisor = $\dfrac{50000}{50} = 1000$

State	A	B	Total
Population	4420	45580	50,000
Standard Quota	4.42	45.58	
Lower Quota	4	45	49
Hamilton's Apportionment	4	46	50

39. Use the modified divisor 975

State	A	B	Total
Population	4420	45580	50,000
Modified Quota	4.53	46.75	
Jefferson's Apportionment (round down)	4	46	50

40. Use the modified divisor 1025

State	A	B	Total
Population	4420	45580	50,000
Modified Quota	4.31	44.47	
Adam's Apportionment (round up)	5	45	50

41. Use the standard divisor 1000

State	A	B	Total
Population	4420	45580	50,000
Standard Quota	4.42	45.58	
Webster's Apportionment (standard rounding)	4	46	50

42. The new divisor is $\dfrac{55400}{55} = 1007.27$

State	A	B	C	Total
Population	4420	45580	5400	55,400
Standard Quota	4.39	45.25	5.36	
Lower Quota	4	45	5	54
Hamilton's Apportionment	5	45	5	55

Yes. State A. gains a seat while State B loses a seat.

Chapter Test
1. Number of voters = 4 + 3 + 3 + 2 = 12.
2. A majority out of 12 voters is 7 or more votes.
   Votes: D:4, C: 3 + 2 = 5, S:3; None of them has a majority.
3. Chris wins with the most votes.

4. Chris (C)-   First: $5 \times 3 = 15$ points
                Second: $4 \times 2 = 8$ points
                Third: $3 \times 1 = 3$ points

C receives 26 points.

Donyall (D) -   First: $4 \times 3 = 12$ points
                Second: $5 \times 2 = 10$ points
                Third: $3 \times 1 = 3$ points

D receives 25 points.

Sam (S) -   First: $3 \times 3 = 9$ points
            Second: $3 \times 2 = 6$ points
            Third: $6 \times 1 = 6$ points

S receives 21 points.

Chris is the winner with 26 points.

5.   A majority of 7 or more votes is required to win.
     Votes: D:4, C:3 + 2 = 5, S:3; None has a majority, thus eliminate (S) with the lease votes.

Number of votes	4	3	3	2
First	D	C	D	C
Second	C	D	C	D

Votes: D:4 + 3 = 7, C = 3 + 2 = 5; Donyall (D) wins.

6. D vs. C, D:7, C:5; D is awarded 1 point.
   D vs. S, D:6, S:6; D and S are awarded ½ point each.
   C vs. S, C:9, S:3; C is awarded 1 point.
   Donyall (D) has the most points, thus D wins.

7. a) Votes: H:26 + 14 = 40, I:29, L:30, S:43; thus hamster (H) wins.

   b) Hamster (H) - First: $40 \times 4 = 160$ points
                    Second: $59 \times 3 = 177$ points
                    Third: $0 \times 2 = 0$ points
                    Fourth: $43 \times 1 = 43$ points

   H receives 380 points.

   Iguana (I) -   First: $29 \times 4 = 116$ points
                  Second: $40 \times 3 = 120$ points
                  Third: $73 \times 2 = 146$ points
                  Fourth: $0 \times 1 = 0$ points

   I receives 382 points.

   Ladybug (L) - First: $30 \times 4 = 120$ points
                 Second: $43 \times 3 = 129$ points
                 Third: $43 \times 2 = 86$ points
                 Fourth: $26 \times 1 = 26$ points

   L receives 361 points

   Snail (S) -   First: $43 \times 4 = 172$ points
                 Second: $0 \times 3 = 0$ points
                 Third: $26 \times 2 = 52$ points
                 Fourth: $73 \times 1 = 73$ points

   S receives 297 points.
   The iguana (I) wins with the most points.

    c) A majority out of 142 voters is 72 or more votes.
       Votes: H:40, I:29, L:30, S:43; None has a majority, thus eliminate I.
       Votes: H:40 + 29 = 69, L:30, S:43; None has a majority, thus eliminate L.
       Votes: H:69 + 30 = 99, S:43; hamster (H) wins.

    d) H vs. I: I is awarded 1 point
       H vs. L: L is awarded 1 point
       H vs. S: H is awarded 1 point
       I vs. L: L is awarded 1 point
       I vs. S: I is awarded 1 point
       L vs. S: L is awarded 1 point

       H: 1 point, I:2 points, L:3 points, S: 0 points; ladybug (L) wins.

8. Plurality:
   Votes: W: 86, X:52 + 28 = 80, Y:60, Z:58; W wins.

   Borda count:
   W receives 594 points, X receives 760 points, Y receives 722 points, Z receives 764 points; Z wins

   Plurality with elimination:
   A majority out of 284 voters is 143 or more votes.
   Votes: W:86, X:80, Y:60, Z:58; None has a majority, thus eliminate Z.
   Votes: W:86, X:80 + 58 = 138, Y:60; None has a majority, thus eliminate Y.
   Votes: W:86, S:1328 + 60 = 198; X wins.

   Head-to-Head:
   When Y is compared to each of the others, Y is favored. Thus Y wins the head-to-head comparison.

   Plurality, Borda count and Plurality with elimination each violate the head-to-head criterion. The pairwise Method never violates the head-to-head criterion.

9. A majority out of 35 voters is 18 or more votes. Louisiana (L) has a majority.
   However, Mississippi (M) wins using the Borda count method. Thus the majority criterion is violated.

10. a) The standard divisor = $\dfrac{30000}{30} = 1000$

State	A	B	C	Total
Population	6,100	8,700	15,200	30,000
Standard Quota	6.10	8.70	15.20	
Lower Quota	6	8	15	29
Hamilton's Apportionment	6	9	15	30

    b) Use the modified divisor 960.

State	A	B	C	Total
Population	6,100	8,700	15,200	30,000
Modified Quota	6.35	9.06	15.83	
Jefferson's Apportionment (round down)	6	9	15	30

c) The new divisor 967.74.

State	A	B	C	Total
Population	6,100	8,700	15,200	30,000
Standard Quota	6.30	8.99	15.71	
Lower Quota	6	8	15	29
Hamilton's Apportionment	6	9	16	31

The Alabama paradox does not occur, sine none of the states loses a seat.

APPENDIX

GRAPH THEORY

<u>Exercise Set</u>

1. A **vertex** is a designated point.
3. To determine whether a vertex is odd or even, count the number of edges attached to the vertex.
   If the number of edges is odd, the vertex is **odd**. If the number of edges is even, the vertex is **even**.

5. 5 vertices, 7 edges
9. Each graph has the same number of edges from the corresponding vertices

7. 7 vertices, 11 edges
11. Odd vertices: C, D
    Even vertices: A, B

13. Yes. The figure has exactly two odd vertices, namely C and D. Therefore, the figure is traversable. You may start at C and end at D, or start at D and end at C.
15. Yes. The figure has no odd vertices. Therefore, the figure is traversable. You may start at any point and end where you started.
17. No. The figure has four odd vertices, namely A, B, E, and F. There are more than two odd vertices. Therefore, the figure is not traversable.
19. Yes. The figure has exactly two odd vertices, namely A and C. Therefore, the figure is traversable. You may start at A and end at C, or start at C and end at A.

21. a) 0 rooms have an odd number of doors.
    5 rooms have an even number of doors.
    b) Yes because the figure would have no odd vertices.
    c) Start in any room and end where you began. For example: A to D to B to C to E to A.
23. a) 2 rooms have an odd number of doors.
    4 rooms have an even number of doors.
    b) Yes because the figure would have exactly two odd vertices.
    c) Start at B and end at F, or start at F and end at B.
    For example: B to C to F to E to D to A to B to E to F
25. a) 4 rooms have an odd number of doors.
    1 room has an even number of doors.
    b) No because the figure would have more than two odd vertices.
27. a) 3 rooms have an odd number of doors.
    2 rooms have an even number of doors.
    b) No because the figure would have more than two odd vertices.
29. The door must be placed in room D. Adding a door to any other room would create two rooms with an odd number of vertices. You would then be unable to enter the building through the door marked "enter" and exit through the new door without going through a door at least twice.

31. Yes because the figure would have exactly two odd vertices. Begin at either the island on the left or on the right and end at the other island.

33.

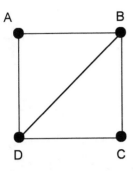

35. a) Kentucky, Virginia, North Carolina, Georgia, Alabama, Mississippi, Arkansas, Missouri
    b) Illinois, Arkansas, Tennessee

37. a) 4
    b) 4
    c) 11

39.

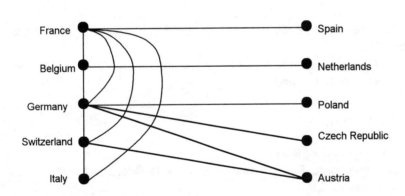

41. a) Yes, the graph has exactly two odd vertices, namely C and G.
    b) C, A, B, E, F, D, G, C